**FORECASTING
ECONOMIC TIME SERIES**

SECOND EDITION

BOX 7

Rebecca

D1003388

Rebecca

This is a volume in
ECONOMIC THEORY, ECONOMETRICS, AND MATHEMATICAL
  ECONOMICS

A Series of Monographs and Textbooks
Consulting Editor: KARL SHELL

A complete list of titles in this series is available from the Publisher upon request.

FORECASTING
ECONOMIC TIME SERIES
SECOND EDITION

C. W. J. GRANGER

Department of Economics
University of California, San Diego
La Jolla, California

PAUL NEWBOLD

Department of Economics
University of Illinois
Urbana-Champaign, Illinois

Academic Press
San Diego New York Boston
London Sydney Tokyo Toronto

Find Us on the Web!   http://www.apnet.com

COPYRIGHT © 1986 BY ACADEMIC PRESS
ALL RIGHTS RESERVED
NO PART OF THIS PUBLICATION MAY BE REPRODUCED OR
TRANSMITTED IN ANY FORM OR BY ANY MEANS. ELECTRONIC
OR MECHANICAL. INCLUDING PHOTOCOPY. RECORDING. OR
ANY INFORMATION STORAGE AND RETRIEVAL SYSTEM. WITHOUT
PERMISSION IN WRITING FROM THE PUBLISHER.

Academic Press
A Division of Harcourt Brace & Company
525 B Street, Suite 1900, San Diego, California 92101-4495

United Kingdom Edition published by
ACADEMIC PRESS LIMITED
24-28 Oval Road, London NW1 7DX

Library of Congress Cataloging in Publication Data

Granger, C. W. J. (Clive William John), Date
    Forecasting economic time series.

    (Economic theory, econometrics, and mathematical
economics)
    Bibliography: p.
    Includes indexes.
    1. Economic forecasting.   2. Time-series analysis.
I. Newbold, Paul. II. Title. III. Series.
HB3730.G67 1986   338.5'442   86-8071
ISBN 0–12–295183–2 (hardcover) (alk. paper)
ISBN 0–12–295184–0 (paperback) (alk. paper)

PRINTED IN THE UNITED STATES OF AMERICA
        97 98 IBT 9 8 7 6 5

To Alice and Pat

CONTENTS

CHAPTER THREE
BUILDING LINEAR TIME SERIES MODELS

CHAPTER FOUR
THE THEORY OF FORECASTING

CHAPTER FIVE
PRACTICAL METHODS FOR UNIVARIATE TIME SERIES FORECASTING

CHAPTER SIX
FORECASTING FROM REGRESSION MODELS

CHAPTER SEVEN
MULTIPLE SERIES MODELING AND FORECASTING

The decade since the first edition of this book was prepared has seen many developments in time series analysis and forecasting theory and practice, particularly as applied to economics. One of the most significant developments has been the acceptance of time series procedures in mainstream economic theory and econometric model building, as can be seen, for example, from the interest in rational expectations theory and in causality testing.

This new edition attempts to reflect some of these developments. The major changes are in the theory and application of multiple series modeling procedures. Chapter 7 of the first edition has been expanded to two chapters, Chapters 7 and 8, in this edition. The final chapter has also been rewritten since many of the original topics have been superseded. The aim in this final chapter is to survey briefly some more recent or advanced topics which we believe are either currently or potentially important. We have naturally tried to use our own judgment as to what was most appropriate to include and what to omit. We feel sure that some topics that deserve inclusion have not been mentioned, but space, time, and relevance to the question of economic forecasting have provided severe constraints.

We should like to acknowledge the advice and assistance of Rob Engle and Steve Hotopp. However, since neither has read the complete revision it would be particularly unfair to blame them for any remaining errors.

The academic literature on forecasting is very extensive, but in reality it is not a single body of literature, being rather two virtually nonoverlapping sets concerned with the theoretical aspects of forecasting and the applied aspects. A typical member of one set is very unlikely to mention any member of the other set. It was this realization that motivated the sequence of research projects that eventually resulted in this book. One of the few exceptions to the above statement about nonoverlapping sets is the well-known book by Box and Jenkins, and our own approach owes a lot to their book. However, we have tried to take the state of the art further by introducing new multivariate techniques, by considering questions such as forecast evaluation, and by examining a wider range of forecasting methods, particularly those which have been applied to economic data, on which this present book concentrates. It is one of our aims to further bridge the gap between the theoretical and applied aspects of forecasting.

The analysis of economic data has also been approached from two different philosophies, that proposed by time series analysts and the more classical econometric approach. Although we favor the former, it is quite clear that both approaches have a great deal to contribute and that they need to be brought together to a much greater extent. In the past couple of years, a number of steps have been taken in this direction, and we have tried to encourage the merger movement in this book by showing how a combined approach to data analysis can lead to potential benefits.

We have many individuals and organizations to warmly thank for their help and encouragement in the preparation of this book and in the research projects that led up to it. Gareth Janacek, John Payne, and Harold Nelson gave considerable help with various aspects of the research; Rick Ashley and Allan Andersen have read and corrected large sections of the manuscript, as have many of our graduate students who had parts of the text inflicted on them for course reading; Alice Newbold prepared all the diagrams for us; Elizabeth Burford and Linda Sykes prepared the final version of the manuscript with great ability and patience; and Robert Young proofread it for us. The Social Science Research Council of the United Kingdom provided the funds to start our research on forecasting in 1970 at the University of Nottingham, and the National Science Foundation of the United States gave us a grant to finally complete the task at the University of California, San Diego. Both universities provided us with excellent facilities, as well as delightful surroundings. Finally, we would like to thank Mike Godfrey, Herman Karreman, and Marc Nerlove for permission to use parts of their own work for illustrations in ours. Of course, we shall have to assume the usual responsibility for those errors that undoubtedly still lurk somewhere in the book.

CHAPTER ONE

INTRODUCTION TO THE THEORY OF TIME SERIES

> *If we could first know where we are and whither we are tending, we could better judge what to do and how to do it.*
>
> A. LINCOLN

1.1 Introducing Time Series

The majority of statistical procedures are designed to be used with data originating from a series of independent experiments or survey interviews. The resulting data, or sample, x_i, $i = 1, \ldots, n$, are taken to be representative of some population. The statistical analysis that follows is largely concerned with making inferences about the properties of the population from the sample. With this type of data, the *order* in which the sample is presented to the statistician is irrelevant. With time series data this is by no means the case. A time series is a sequence of values or readings ordered by a time parameter, such as hourly temperature readings. Since the order of the data is now of considerable importance, most of the classical statistical techniques are no longer relevant and so new techniques have to be devised. Time series are found in many fields, such as economics (e.g., monthly employment figures), sociology (crime figures), meteorology (rainfall, temperature, wind speed), medicine (electrocardiograms and electroencephalograms), vibrating physical systems (such as the rise of a car traveling over a rough surface), seismology, oceanography, and geomorphology. They also occur in astronomy (star brightness, solar activity), as outputs of certain electronic devices, and in industrial processes, for example, the thickness of steel plate from a continuous rolling mill. The methods devised to deal with such data can also frequently be applied to data not gathered through time but ordered along a line, for example, height above sea level along a line of latitude. Although the methods of time series analysis work perfectly well in such situations, interpretation of the results is more difficult when time is not involved.

1

For some series it is possible to take measurements at every moment of time, so that a trace results. Such data, which may be denoted by $x(t)$, are said to form a *continuous* time series. However, most available series, particularly in the social sciences, consist of readings taken at predetermined, equal-interval time points, so that one might get hourly, daily, monthly, or quarterly readings. Such data form a *discrete* time series, denoted by x_t. In this work we shall deal exclusively with discrete equal-interval time series since so much actual data are of this form and becuase a continuous series can always be well approximated by a discrete series by suitable choice of the sampling interval.

A further classification of series is occasionally needed. A discrete series is said to be *instantaneously recorded* if it *could* have been measured at every moment of time even though it is in fact only recorded at the sampling points, examples being temperature, prices, and interest rates. Some series cannot be measured at every moment of time because they are accumulations of values. Examples of *accumulated* series are rainfall, production figures, and volume of sales. (These two types of series are called respectively stock and flow variables by economists.) For most purposes it is not necessary to distinguish between these two types since the methods and theory to be introduced will usually apply equally well to either, but there is the occasional circumstance where this is not so.

An actual observed series x_t, $t = 1, \ldots, n$, may be considered as a realization of some theoretical process which will be called the stochastic process.[1] In classical statistics one has the vital concepts of population and sample, and the equivalent concepts with time series are the (theoretical) stochastic process and the realization or observed series. The initial objective of time series analysis is to make inferences about the properties or basic features of the stochastic process from the information contained in the observed series. The first step in the analysis is usually to form certain summary statistics, but the eventual aim is to construct a *model* from the data, a model that it is hoped has similar properties to those of the generating mechanism of the stochastic process. A simple example of a stochastic process would be a sequence of random variables generated by the iterative scheme $X_t = 0.5X_{t-1} + \epsilon_t$ where ϵ_t is a sequence of purely independent and identically distributed random variables. The process is seen to be the output of a generating mechanism. Many other examples are possible and two of the essential stages in model building are to determine the class of models that seem appropriate and then to estimate the parameter values of the model.

Once a model has been obtained it can be used either to test some hypothesis or theory about the generating mechanism of the process, it can be used to forecast future values of the series, and it may be used to decide

---

[1] *Stochastic* simply means *random*. For simplicity, the word *stochastic* may sometimes be dropped in subsequent exposition.

on a system to control future values. The last use, although very important, will not be discussed in this book. We shall concentrate only on forecasting problems and will introduce those parts of time series theory and analysis that will be needed for the subsequent chapters dealing with forecasting.

In this chapter only univariate time series theory will be discussed. The generalization to multivariate series will be considered in Chapter 7.

1.2 Covariances and Stationarity

Consider a process X_t, defined for all integer values of t. In general, the process will be generated by some scheme involving random inputs, and so X_t will be a random variable for each t and $(X_{t_1}, X_{t_2}, \ldots, X_{t_N})'$ will be an $N \times 1$ vector random variable. To fully characterize such random variables, one needs to specify distribution functions; but, for reasons that will soon become apparent, it will usually be too ambitious to attempt to specify fully or to estimate these functions. Nevertheless, theoretically such distribution functions will exist; and so one can use the usual expectation notation without ambiguity. The mean of X_t will be defined by

$$\mu_t = E[X_t] \tag{1.2.1}$$

and the covariance between X_t and X_s will be

$$\lambda_{t,s} = \text{cov}(X_t, X_s) = E[(X_t - \mu_t)(X_s - \mu_s)] \tag{1.2.2}$$

so that $\lambda_{t,t}$ is the variance of X_t. The *linear* properties of the process can be described in terms of just these quantities. If it is assumed that the process is Gaussian, by which is meant that $(X_{t_1}, X_{t_2}, \ldots, X_{t_N})$ is an N-dimensional normal distribution for every set $t_1, \ldots, t_N$ and every finite integer N, then the values of $\mu_t, \lambda_{t,s}$ will be sufficient for a complete characterization of the distributional properties of the process. If normality is not assumed but if the generating process is taken to be linear, in the sense that X_t is generated by a linear combination of previous X_t's and past and present values of other processes, then once more the major properties of the process are captured in the means and covariances. Throughout most of this work only linear processes will be considered, largely because an adequate and usable theory is available only for such processes. A brief discussion of some nonlinear processes is given in Chapter 10.

It is instructive to ask the question, How would one estimate μ_t? For some processes it is possible to get a number of realizations. An example would be the thickness of steel wire made on a continuous extraction machine. One wire would constitute a single realization, but it is possible for the process to be stopped, the machine to be serviced, and then the process to be started once more. The new wire could be taken to be another realization from the same stochastic process. If the realizations are denoted by x_{jt}, $t = 1, \ldots, n$,

$j = 1, 2, \ldots, k$, then a possible estimate for μ_t would be

$$\hat{\mu}_t = \frac{1}{k} \sum_{j=1}^{k} x_{jt} \qquad (1.2.3)$$

However, for very many situations, it is not possible to obtain more than a single realization. One cannot, for example, stop the economy, go back to some starting point, and let it go once more to see if a different pattern would emerge. With a single realization, it is clearly quite impossible to estimate with any precision μ_t for every t if the μ_t sequence is allowed to take any set of values. It is even more ridiculous to try to estimate $\lambda_{t,t}$, the variance of X_t, at every t if only a single observed series is available.

To overcome such problems, the time series analyst is forced to adopt some restrictive assumptions about the way in which means and covariances can change over time. A restrictive but usable assumption is that of *stationarity* which for our purposes may be defined as follows: a process X_t will be said to be stationary if

$$\text{mean of } X_t = \mu, \qquad \text{variance of } X_t = \sigma_x^2 < \infty \qquad (1.2.4)$$

$$\text{covariance } X_t, X_s = \lambda_{t-s}$$

so that $\sigma_x^2 = \lambda_0$, and the notation usually used will be

$$\text{cov}(X_t, X_{t-\tau}) = \lambda_\tau \qquad (1.2.5)$$

Thus, a stationary process will have mean and variance that do not change through time, and the covariance between values of the process at two time points will depend only on the distance between these time points and not on time itself. Essentially, a stationarity assumption is equivalent to saying that the generating mechanism of the process is itself time-invariant, so that neither the form nor the parameter values of the generation procedure change through time. It certainly cannot be claimed that an assumption of stationarity is generally realistic, but it does enable one to formulate some basic theory and it will be possible to relax the assumption somewhat in later sections.

A stronger form of stationarity than that just introduced is often defined. Denote the distribution function of X_{t+j}, $j = 1, 2, \ldots, N$, by $F(X_{t+1}, X_{t+2}, \ldots, X_{t+N})$. Then the stochastic process is said to be stationary in the stronger sense if, for any finite positive integer N, F does not depend on t. It follows immediately that strong stationarity implies the weaker stationarity defined earlier. Further, if the process is Gaussian, the two definitions are equivalent. In practical applications strong stationarity is virtually impossible to test for, and it is usual to work with the weaker form.

A further requirement is that the process be *ergodic*. Since this is a yet more difficult concept, which cannot be adequately explained without the introduction of considerable mathematical apparatus not required elsewhere, we shall provide only a heuristic explanation (for a rigorous account, see Hannan [1970, p. 201]). What is required is that values of the process sufficiently far apart in time are almost uncorrelated, so that by averaging a series through time one is continually adding new and useful information to the average. Thus, the time average

$$\bar{x}_n = \frac{1}{n} \sum_{t=1}^{n} x_t \qquad (1.2.6)$$

is an unbiased and consistent estimate of the population mean μ, so that $\mathrm{var}(\bar{x}_n) \downarrow 0$ as $n \to \infty$ and $E[\bar{x}_n] = \mu$, all n. Similarly, estimates of λ_τ, to be introduced later, will also be consistent. Thus, given stationarity and ergodicity, one can form good estimates of the quantities of immediate interest by averaging through time rather than being forced to depend on the ensemble averages across realizations considered earlier. Unfortunately, it is not possible to test for ergodicity using a single realization, but one would not expect the data to include strictly cyclical components. A necessary condition for ergodicity, but by no means a sufficient one, is that $\lambda_\tau \to 0$ at a sufficiently fast rate as τ increases. Ergodicity will be assumed to hold in all situations considered in later sections.

The covariances λ_τ will be called *autocovariances* and the quantities

$$\rho_\tau = \lambda_\tau / \lambda_0 \qquad (1.2.7)$$

will be called the *autocorrelations* of a process. The sequence ρ_τ, $\tau = 0, 1, \ldots$, indicates the extent to which one value of the process is correlated with previous values and so can, to some extent, be used to measure the length and strength of the "memory" of the process, that is, the extent to which the value taken at time t depends on that at time $t - \tau$. From the definition (1.2.7), one has

$$\rho_0 = 1, \qquad \rho_{-\tau} = \rho_\tau \qquad (1.2.8)$$

The plot of ρ_τ against τ for $\tau = 0, 1, 2, \ldots$ is called the theoretical correlogram and the values comprising this diagram will be the major quantities that will be used to characterize the (linear) properties of the generating mechanism of the process. However, it is by no means easy to look at a theoretical correlogram and immediately decide on these properties. What is needed are some plausible models that provide correlograms of recognizable shapes. The simplest possible model is that of a sequence of independent (actually, uncorrelated since only linear features are being considered) and identically distributed random variables. The notation to be used in this book whenever possible for such a sequence is ϵ_t. For a sequence of this kind, which henceforth will be called *white noise*,[1] the autocorrelation

---

[1] This is a useful and easily remembered phrase, whose origin cannot be explained until Chapter 2.

sequence is

$$\rho_0 = 1, \qquad \rho_\tau = 0, \quad \tau \neq 0 \tag{1.2.9}$$

so the correlogram takes a very specific and easily recognized shape. One would not expect such a simple model to represent many actual series well, although it will be seen later that one of the objectives of model building will be to transform a given process to a white noise process.

1.3 Some Mathematical Tools

Before more sophisticated models are considered, three mathematical concepts need to be introduced: the backward operator, generating functions, and difference equations.

The *backward operator* B, which is frequently employed for notational convenience, is an operator on a time sequence with the property[1] $BX_t = X_{t-1}$. Thus, on reapplication

$$B^k X_t = X_{t-k} \tag{1.3.1}$$

This operator will often be used in polynomial form, so that

$$d_0 X_t + d_1 X_{t-1} + d_2 X_{t-2} + \cdots + d_p X_{t-p}$$

can be summarized as $d(B)X_t$ where

$$d(B) = d_0 + d_1 B + d_2 B^2 + \cdots + d_p B^p \tag{1.3.2}$$

A *generating function* is a compact and convenient way of recording the information held in some sequence. Consider the sequence $a_0, a_1, a_2, \ldots, a_j, \ldots$, which may be of infinite length; the generating function of this sequence is

$$a(z) = \sum_j a_j z^j \tag{1.3.3}$$

For example, if $a_j = (\lambda^j/j!)e^{-\lambda}$, then $a(z) = \exp(\lambda(z - 1))$. The function $a(z)$ often can be manipulated in simpler ways than can the whole sequence a_j. The quantity z does not necessarily have any interpretation and should be considered as simply the carrier of the information in the sequence, although on occasions it can be given a specific and useful interpretation. Frequently z will be taken to be $z = e^{i\theta}$ since then one can appeal directly to Fourier theory for the existence of the generating function in many circumstances. In what follows, problems of existence will not be explicitly considered. Generating functions occur frequently in probability theory and in mathematical statistics. For example, suppose X is a discrete random variable taking only nonnegative integer values, with $\text{Prob}(X = j) = p_j$; then $p(z) = \sum p_j z^j$ is

---

[1] Strictly the operator lags the whole sequence, so that $B(\ldots, X_{t-1}, X_t, X_{t+1}, \ldots) = (\ldots, X_{t-2}, X_{t-1}, X_t, \ldots)$.

called the probability generating function, with the obvious property that $p(1) = 1$. However $p(e^{it})$ is also the characteristic function of X and so expanding it as a power series in t will give the noncentral moments; i.e.,

$$p(e^{it}) = \sum_j \mu_j \frac{(it)^j}{j!} \quad \text{where} \quad \mu_j = E[X^j]$$

Similarly $p(e^t)$ is the moment generating function, so that

$$p(e^t) = \sum_j \mu_j \frac{(t)^j}{j!}$$

Generating functions have the following additive property: if a_j, b_j, $j = 0, 1, \ldots,$ are two sequences, and if $c_j = a_j + b_j$, then, with obvious notation

$$c(z) = a(z) + b(z) \tag{1.3.4}$$

A more useful property is that of *convolution*. Given two sequences a_j, b_j, $j = 0, 1, \ldots,$ define another sequence c_j, known as their convolution, by

$$c_j = a_0 b_j + a_1 b_{j-1} + a_2 b_{j-2} + \cdots + a_j b_0 = \sum_{k=0}^{j} a_k b_{j-k} \tag{1.3.5}$$

then, the generating functions of the three sequences are related by the equation

$$c(z) = a(z)b(z) \tag{1.3.6}$$

This can be seen by just multiplying out the right-hand side of (1.3.6).

Three particular generating functions will be used frequently:

(i)   given a process X_t, its generating function is

$$X(z) = \sum_{\text{all } t} X_t z^t$$

and may alternatively be called the z-transform of the process;

(ii)   given an observed series x_t, $t = 1, \ldots, n$, its generating function is

$$x(z) = \sum_{t=1}^{n} x_t z^t$$

(iii)   given a sequence of autocovariances λ_τ, the autocovariance generating function will be

$$\lambda(z) = \sum_{\text{all } \tau} \lambda_\tau z^\tau \tag{1.3.7}$$

with corresponding autocorrelation generating function

$$\rho(z) = \sum_{\text{all } \tau} \rho_\tau z^\tau = \frac{\lambda(z)}{\lambda_0} \tag{1.3.8}$$

Here "all τ" means that τ runs through all integers from $-\infty$ to ∞.

Consider a stationary process X_t, with $E(X_t) = 0$, and write

$$X_n(z) = \sum_{t=1}^{n} X_t z^t \qquad (1.3.9)$$

Then $X_n(z)X_n(z^{-1}) = \sum_{t,s} X_t X_s z^{t-s}$ so that

$$E[X_n(z)X_n(z^{-1})] = \sum_{\tau=-n}^{n} (n - |\tau|)\lambda_\tau z^\tau$$

It follows that in (1.3.7)

$$\lambda(z) = \lim_{n \to \infty} \frac{1}{n} E[X_n(z)X_n(z^{-1})] \qquad (1.3.10)$$

In Section 2.1 the function $f(\omega) = (2\pi)^{-1}\lambda(e^{-i\omega})$, called the power spectral function, will be discussed and given a specific and useful interpretation.

A *linear difference equation* of order p is an iterative equation of the form

$$X_t = \sum_{j=1}^{p} a_j X_{t-j} + Y_t \qquad (1.3.11)$$

which determines the sequence X_t from the values of the given time sequence Y_t together with some starting up values. Using the backward operator B, the equation may be written in the form

$$a(B)X_t = Y_t \quad \text{where} \quad a(B) = 1 - \sum_{j=1}^{p} a_j B^j \qquad (1.3.12)$$

Suppose the process starts at time $t = -N$, so that $Y_t = 0$, $t < -N$, and that starting values $X_t = \bar{X}_t$, $t = -N - j$, $j = 1, \ldots, p$, are provided.

The *general solution* of the difference equation (1.3.11) takes the form

$$X_t = X_{1t} + X_{2t}$$

where X_{1t} is the solution of the homogeneous equation $a(B)X_t = 0$ and X_{2t} is given by

$$X_{2t} = b(B)Y_t,$$

where $b(z) = 1/a(z)$, and is called a *particular solution*.

Consider the homogeneous, first-order equation

$$X_t = aX_{t-1} \qquad (1.3.13)$$

Then by continual substitution

$$X_t = a^2 X_{t-2} = a^3 X_{t-3} = \cdots = a^{t+N} X_{-N} \qquad (1.3.14)$$

so that

$$X_t = Aa^t \qquad (1.3.15)$$

where A is a suitable constant, dependent on N.

Now consider the homogeneous second-order equation

$$X_t = a_1 X_{t-1} + a_2 X_{t-2} \qquad (1.3.16)$$

The previous result suggests that a possible solution is of the form

$$X_t = A_1 \theta_1^t + A_2 \theta_2^t \qquad (1.3.17)$$

Substituting this into Eq. (1.3.16) and rearranging gives

$$A_1 \theta_1^t [1 - a_1 \theta_1^{-1} - a_2 \theta_1^{-2}] + A_2 \theta_2^t [1 - a_1 \theta_2^{-1} - a_2 \theta_2^{-2}] = 0$$

and so the solution is correct if θ_1^{-1} and θ_2^{-1} are chosen to be the roots of the equation $a(z) = 1 - a_1 z - a_2 z^2 = 0$, with the constants A_1 and A_2 chosen so that the initial starting values are accounted for.

The more general pth order homogeneous difference equation

$$X_t = \sum_{j=1}^{p} a_j X_{t-j} \qquad (1.3.18)$$

will have the solution

$$X_t = \sum_{k=1}^{p} A_k \theta_k^t \qquad (1.3.19)$$

where θ_k^{-1}, $k = 1, \ldots, p$, are the roots of the equation $a(z) = 0$, assuming no multiple roots, and where again the constants A_k are determined by the initial values.

Provided the a_j are real, Eq. (1.3.19) must produce real values for the sequence X_t, so any complex value of θ_k^{-1} must be matched by its complex conjugate. The corresponding terms will pair to become a term of the form $B|\theta_k|^t \cos(kt + \phi_k)$. The solution to Eq. (1.3.18) will thus either be a mixture of exponentials through time or a mixture of exponentials plus amplitude changing oscillatory terms. For large t the form of the solution will be dominated by $A_0 |\theta_0|^t$, where $|\theta_0| = \max(|\theta_k|, \ k = 1, \ldots, p)$. If $|\theta_0| < 1$, the solution will be said to be stationary; and if $|\theta_0| > 1$, the solution is said to be explosive. From the definition of θ_k, it is seen that a necessary and sufficient condition for the solution to be stationary is that all the roots of the equation $a(z) = 0$ lie outside the unit circle $|z| = 1$. This will be called the *stationarity condition*.

The particular solution to Eq. (1.3.11), X_{2t}, may be written in the form

$$X_{2t} = \sum_{j=0}^{t+N} b_j Y_{t-j} \qquad (1.3.20)$$

It is easily seen that the coefficients b_j will increase in magnitude as j increases unless the stationarity condition holds. A simple example is provided by the first-order equation

$$X_t = a X_{t-1} + Y_t \qquad (1.3.21)$$

which may be written $(1 - aB)X_t = Y_t$ so that

$$X_{2t} = \frac{1}{1 - aB} Y_t = \sum_{j=0}^{t+N} a^j Y_{t-j} \qquad (1.3.22)$$

The stationarity condition for this equation is just $|a| < 1$ since $a(z) = 1 - az$.

In the general case, provided the stationarity condition holds and if one supposes that the process began in the indefinite past, then since[1] $X_{1t} = O(|\theta_0|^{t+N}) \to 0$ as N becomes large, the complete solution is just

$$X_t = b(B)Y_t \qquad \text{for all } t \qquad (1.3.23)$$

It is worth noting that multiplying X_t by z^t and summing over t gives $X(z) = b(z)Y(z)$ since the right-hand sides of Eqs. (1.3.20) and (1.3.23) are convolutions.

1.4 The Linear Cyclic Model

If one plots a white noise series through time, a rather jagged and uneven graph results. (Figure 1.1b, p. 15, is a plot of such a series.) Many actual series have quite a different appearance, being much "smoother" than a white noise series. This smoothness can be explained by ρ_1, the autocorrelation between adjacent values of the series, being positive. The nearer ρ_1 is to unity, the smoother the appearance of the series. There are a number of models that can be introduced to explain this smoothness. Historically, the first to be considered was a process that contained cycles or strictly periodic components. A possible reason for this is that many of the time series first analyzed did appear to contain regular cyclical components when plotted. These series included brightness of rotating twin stars, solar surface activity (sunspot series), and agricultural prices containing a clear seasonal component. A simple model to explain such fluctuation is of the form

$$X_t = d \cos(\omega t + \theta) + \epsilon_t \qquad (1.4.1)$$

so that the process is the sum of a cosine wave with amplitude d, frequency ω (and hence period of $2\pi/\omega$), and phase θ plus a white noise component. However, there is no reason to expect a cyclical component, such as an annual cycle, to be representable by a single cosine term. A periodic function $P(t)$ of period p, defined to have the property

$$P(t + kp) = P(t) \qquad \text{any integer } k$$

may always be represented by the sum of cosines,

$$P(t) = \sum_{j=1}^{p} d_j \cos(j\omega t + \theta_j) \qquad (1.4.2)$$

---

[1] A function of N, $g(N)$, is said to be $O(N)$ if $g(N)/N$ tends to a nonzero constant c as N tends to infinity, and to be $o(N)$ if $g(N)/N \to 0$ as $N \to \infty$.

where $\omega = 2\pi/p$, provided p is an integer multiple of the sampling period. This is the Fourier series representation, ω being known as the *fundamental frequency*, and the frequencies $j\omega$ are the *harmonics* of ω. The somewhat more general model now becomes

$$X_t = P(t) + \epsilon_t = \sum_{j=1}^{p} d_j \cos(j\omega t + \theta_j) + \epsilon_t \qquad (1.4.3)$$

If the period p is known, the parameters d_j, θ_j can be estimated by various techniques including regression.

Suppose now that such a periodic component is fitted to the data and the residuals $X_t - \hat{P}(t)$ are plotted. If again they are too smooth to be represented by a white noise series, it is not unnatural to suppose that this residual smoothness is caused by the presence of further, undetected cycles. The model that would result from such reasoning is of the form

$$X_t = \sum_{k=1}^{m} P_k(t) + \epsilon_t \qquad (1.4.4)$$

where $P_k(t)$ is a periodic function with period p_k and ϵ_t is white noise. Using the Fourier expansion for each periodic function, the model becomes a complicated sum of cosines plus the white noise residual; that is,

$$X_t = \sum_{j,k} d_{jk} \cos(j\omega_k t + \theta_{jk}) + \epsilon_t \qquad (1.4.5)$$

where $\omega_k = 2\pi/p_k$. This will be called the *linear cyclical model*. If the periods p_k, $k = 1, \ldots, m$, are known, the parameters d_{jk}, θ_{jk} can be found by regression methods. If the periods of the components are not known, the classical method of finding them is to use a procedure known as *periodogram analysis*. There are a number of periodogram techniques, but the best known and most used is that due to Schuster [1898]. Given an observed series x_t, $t = 1, \ldots, n$, form the quantity

$$I_n(\lambda) = \frac{1}{n^2}\left[\left(\sum_t x_t \cos t\lambda\right)^2 + \left(\sum_t x_t \sin t\lambda\right)^2\right] \qquad (1.4.6)$$

which may be called the intensity[1] at frequency λ. The plot of $I_n(\lambda)$ against $2\pi/\lambda$ is called the Schuster periodogram, but it is often more convenient to plot $I_n(\lambda)$ against λ, and this plot has been called the *spectrogram*. Both of these diagrams should have clear peaks at points corresponding to the "hidden periods" p_k of the linear cyclic model. This may be seen by considering the very simple case where

$$x_t = a \cos \omega t \qquad (1.4.7)$$

---

[1] It is worth noting that the intensity can be written in the form $I_n(\lambda) = |n^{-1}x(z)|^2$, with $z = e^{-i\lambda}$.

Then

$$\frac{1}{n} \sum_{t=1}^{n} x_t \cos \lambda t = \frac{a}{2n} \sum_{t=1}^{n} (\cos(\omega - \lambda)t + \cos(\omega + \lambda)t) \qquad (1.4.8)$$

Since

$$\sum_{t=1}^{n} \cos tx = \frac{\cos nx \sin((n+1)/2)x}{\sin(x/2)} - 1 \qquad (1.4.9)$$

it follows that

$$\frac{1}{n} \sum_{t=1}^{n} x_t \cos \lambda t = O(n^{-1}), \qquad \lambda \neq \omega$$

but, since $\lim_{x \to 0}(\sin Nx/\sin x) = N$, one has

$$\frac{1}{n} \sum_t x_t \cos \omega t = \frac{a}{2} + O(n^{-1}) \qquad (1.4.10)$$

Similarly

$$\frac{1}{n} \sum_{t=1}^{n} x_t \sin \lambda t = O(n^{-1}) \qquad (1.4.11)$$

so, for this simple model,

$$\begin{aligned} I(\lambda) &= O(n^{-2}), \qquad \lambda \neq \omega \\ &= (a/2)^2, \qquad \lambda = \omega \end{aligned} \qquad (1.4.12)$$

and, if n is sufficient large, the peak at $\lambda = \omega$ should be apparent. The theoretical shape for the linear cyclical model can be derived in a similar fashion, provided that σ_ϵ^2, the variance of the white noise, is small compared to the portion of the variance of x_t attributable to the cyclical components. There are many problems involved with using the periodogram in practice, but these are of no immediate concern.

Since the linear cyclical process contains deterministic time functions, it is difficult at first sight to see how such a process can be stationary. It is, however, possible to make the underlying stochastic process stationary even though any particular realization will not seem to be so. Consider the simple process

$$X_t = a \cos(\omega t + \theta) \qquad (1.4.13)$$

where θ is a random variable rectangularly distributed on the interval $[-\pi, \pi]$. A realization is formed by choosing a value of θ from this population at a time before the starting value of the realization. The process will have a zero mean, by noting that

$$E[X_t] = a \cos \omega t E[\cos \theta] - a \sin \omega t E[\sin \theta] = 0$$

since $E[\cos\theta] = E[\sin\theta] = 0$ if θ is rectangularly distributed on $[-\pi, \pi]$. Since $E[X_t] = 0$, the autocovariances for this simple cyclical process are

$$\lambda_\tau = E[X_t X_{t-\tau}] = a^2 E[\cos(\omega t + \theta)\cos(\omega(t - \tau) + \theta)] \quad (1.4.14)$$

From the formula

$$\cos A \cos B = \tfrac{1}{2}[\cos(A + B) + \cos(A - B)] \quad (1.4.15)$$

it is seen that

$$\lambda_\tau = (a^2/2)E[\cos(\omega(2t - \tau) + 2\theta) + \cos\tau\omega] = (a^2/2)\cos\tau\omega \quad (1.4.16)$$

since the first term vanishes. So λ_τ is seen to be independent of time.

These arguments can be extended to cover the general linear cyclic model (1.4.5) provided the phases θ_{jk} are all independent rectangular random variables. It is found that

$$\mu = E[X_t] = E[\epsilon_t] \quad (1.4.17)$$

and

$$\lambda_\tau = \operatorname{cov}(X_t, X_{t-\tau}) = \tfrac{1}{2}\sum_{j,k} d_{jk}^2 \cos(\omega_{jk}\tau) + \delta(\tau)\sigma_\epsilon^2 \quad (1.4.18)$$

where

$$\delta(\tau) = 1 \quad \text{if} \quad \tau = 0$$
$$= 0 \quad \text{if} \quad \tau \neq 0$$

Although stationarity has been achieved by the use of what may seem to be an artificial device, it is quite justified to consider realizations from the linear cyclic process as though they are stationary, even if they are essentially only marginally stationary.

1.5 The Autoregressive Model

A process generated by the equation

$$X_t = aX_{t-1} + \epsilon_t \quad (1.5.1)$$

where ϵ_t is a zero-mean white noise is called a first-order autoregressive process and is a special case of a much analyzed class of stochastic processes known as Markov processes. Taking expectations of (1.5.1) and denoting $\mu_t = E[X_t]$, one finds that μ_t obeys the simple difference equation

$$\mu_t = a\mu_{t-1} \quad (1.5.2)$$

The solution of this equation, according to Eq. (1.3.14), is

$$\mu_t = a^{t+N}\mu_{-N}$$

if the process starts at time $-N$. Assuming that the process began in the infinite past and that $|a| < 1$, it follows that $\mu_t = 0$ for all t. The model (1.5.1) can easily be generalized to represent stationary processes with nonzero mean μ for, writing $X_t - \mu = a(X_{t-1} - \mu) + \epsilon_t$, it follows from an argument exactly analogous to that just given that X_t has mean μ for all t. Thus, in considering covariance properties, it can be assumed that the process is zero-mean, a state of affairs that can, if necessary, be achieved by subtracting a fixed mean at each time point.

Squaring both sides of (1.5.1) and taking expectations yields the difference equation

$$\text{var}(X_t) = a^2 \text{var}(X_{t-1}) + \sigma_\epsilon^2 \qquad \text{where} \quad \sigma_\epsilon^2 \equiv \text{var}(\epsilon_t)$$

This follows since ϵ_t and X_{t-1} are uncorrelated, for the white noise ϵ_t is by definition uncorrelated with values occurring before time t. (This is readily verified by noting that X_{t-1} can be expressed from (1.5.1) as a linear function of ϵ_{t-j}, $j = 1, 2, \ldots$, plus a distant "starting up" value.) If $|a| < 1$ and the process started in the infinite past, then the solution to the above difference equation is simply the particular solution

$$\lambda_0 = \text{var}(X_t) = \sigma_\epsilon^2/(1 - a^2) \tag{1.5.3}$$

so that variance is constant over time.

The first autocovariance of the process (1.5.1) is given by

$$\lambda_1 = E[X_t X_{t-1}] = aE[X_{t-1}^2] + E[\epsilon_t X_{t-1}]$$

and, since the second term in this expression vanishes, one can write from (1.5.3)

$$\lambda_1 = a\lambda_0 \tag{1.5.4}$$

Thus the autocovariance λ_1, and hence the first autocorrelation, take the same sign as a, the consequence being that for positive a the series X_t will be smoother than a white noise process (smoothness increasing with the magnitude of a), but if a is negative, the process will be less smooth. This is illustrated in Fig. 1.1 which shows plots of generated series from first-order autoregressive processes with $a = -0.5$, 0 (white noise), 0.3, 0.8.

Multiplying both sides of (1.5.1) by $X_{t-\tau}$, $\tau > 0$, and taking expectations gives $\lambda_\tau = a\lambda_{\tau-1}$, so

$$\lambda_\tau = a^\tau \lambda_0, \qquad \tau \geq 0 \tag{1.5.5}$$

Hence the autocorrelation function is simply $\rho_\tau = a^\tau$, $\tau \geq 0$. Autocorrelation functions for the processes generating the data of Fig. 1.1 are shown in Fig. 1.2, the typical exponential decay of such functions as τ increases being clear from these plots. It is seen that X_t is stationary provided $|a| < 1$ since the first and second moments of the process are all time invariant.

Autoregressive processes were first introduced by Yule [1927] and it is not difficult to persuade oneself that they could well arise in practice. For example, the total number of unemployed in one month might be thought to consist of a fixed proportion a of those unemployed in the previous month,

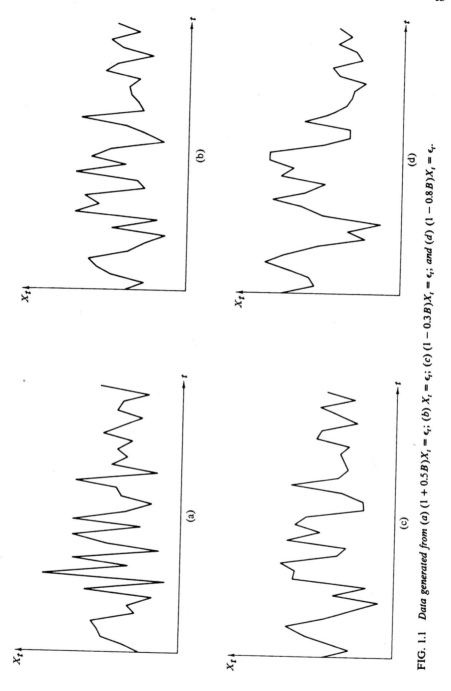

FIG. 1.1 *Data generated from (a)* $(1 + 0.5B)X_t = \varepsilon_t$; *(b)* $X_t = \varepsilon_t$; *(c)* $(1 - 0.3B)X_t = \varepsilon_t$; *and (d)* $(1 - 0.8B)X_t = \varepsilon_t$.

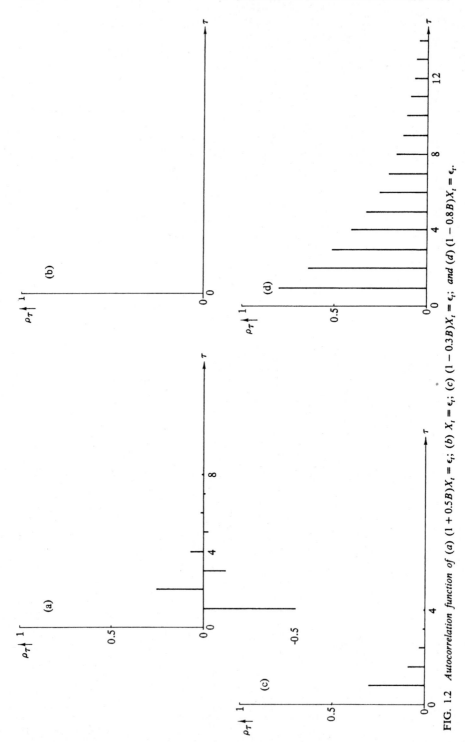

FIG. 1.2 *Autocorrelation function of (a)* $(1 + 0.5B)X_t = \epsilon_t$; *(b)* $X_t = \epsilon_t$; *(c)* $(1 - 0.3B)X_t = \epsilon_t$; *and (d)* $(1 - 0.8B)X_t = \epsilon_t$.

the others having obtained jobs, plus a new group of workers seeking jobs. If the new additions are considered to form a white noise series with positive mean $\mu(1 - a)$, then the unemployment series is first-order autoregressive for if X_t denotes numbers unemployed at time t

$$X_t = aX_{t-1} + (1 - a)\mu + \epsilon_t$$

where ϵ_t is zero-mean white noise. Hence

$$X_t - \mu = a(X_{t-1} - \mu) + \epsilon_t$$

A second example can be constructed as follows. A tank of some chemical holds 10 liters, of which 1 liter is used each working week. The liter removed is replaced at the end of each week from a bottle of the chemical purchased from a manufacturer. The chemical is a mixture of two components; let X_t be the proportion of the first component in the tank in week t. If the bottles of chemical have concentrations of the first component varying randomly over time, with the bottle used at the start of week t having concentration ϵ_t, it follows that

$$X_t = \tfrac{9}{10}X_{t-1} + \tfrac{1}{10}\epsilon_t$$

so a first-order autoregressive series again arises.

Some economic series may be thought to be generated by a mechanism

value at time $t + 1$ = expectation made at time t of value at time

$t + 1$, plus error term

If the error term is white noise and the expectation is just a proportion of current value, a first-order autoregressive process results. However, if expectations are formed from a weighted sum of past and present values of the series, a higher order autoregressive process is obtained.

The general zero-mean autoregressive process is one generated by

$$X_t = \sum_{j=1}^{p} a_j X_{t-j} + \epsilon_t \tag{1.5.6}$$

For processes with nonzero mean μ, the extension is

$$X_t - \mu = \sum_{j=1}^{p} a_j(X_{t-j} - \mu) + \epsilon_t$$

It will again be assumed, without loss of generality, that the process of interest has zero mean. If a process X_t is generated by an equation of the form (1.5.6), it will be called a pth-order autoregressive process and denoted $X_t \sim \text{AR}(p)$. For the process to be stationary, the difference equation will need to obey the stationarity condition introduced in Section 1.3. Thus, the roots of $a(z) = 0$ must all lie outside the unit circle $|z| = 1$, where

$$a(z) = 1 - \sum a_j z^j \tag{1.5.7}$$

In terms of the backward operator, (1.5.6) may be written

$$a(B)X_t = \epsilon_t \tag{1.5.8}$$

and the general solution to this difference equation is just the particular solution

$$X_t = \frac{1}{a(B)}\epsilon_t \tag{1.5.9}$$

provided the stationarity condition holds. Thus, when this condition holds, X_t may be written in the form

$$X_t = \sum_{j=0}^{\infty} b_j\epsilon_{t-j}, \qquad b_0 = 1 \tag{1.5.10}$$

where $b(B) = \sum b_j B^j = 1/a(B)$. In particular, if $X_t \sim \text{AR}(1)$, as in (1.5.1), then $a(z) = 1 - az$ and so

$$X_t = \sum_{j=0}^{\infty} a^j\epsilon_{t-j} \tag{1.5.11}$$

Taking expectations, it is immediately seen that $\mu = E[X_t] = 0$, provided $E[\epsilon_t] = 0$. Squaring both sides of (1.5.11), taking expectations, and noting that $E[\epsilon_t\epsilon_s] = 0$, $s \neq t$, it is immediately seen that

$$\text{var } X_t = \sigma_\epsilon^2 \sum_{j=0}^{\infty} a^{2j} = \frac{\sigma_\epsilon^2}{1 - a^2}$$

thus confirming (1.5.3). This proof very clearly illustrates the explosive nature of the solution for X_t if $|a| \geq 1$.

Multiplying both sides of (1.5.10) by ϵ_s, $s \geq t$ and taking expectations gives

$$\begin{aligned} E[\epsilon_s X_t] &= 0, & s > t \\ &= \sigma_\epsilon^2, & s = t \end{aligned} \tag{1.5.12}$$

This result is needed to find the autocovariance sequence for the $\text{AR}(p)$ process. If both sides of (1.5.6) are multiplied by $X_{t-\tau}$, $\tau \geq 0$, taking expectations gives

$$\lambda_\tau = \sum_{j=1}^{p} a_j\lambda_{\tau-j}, \qquad \tau > 0 \tag{1.5.13}$$

and

$$\lambda_0 = \sum_{j=1}^{p} a_j\lambda_j + \sigma_\epsilon^2 \tag{1.5.14}$$

If $a(z) = \prod_{j=1}^{p}(1 - \theta_j z)$ and $\theta_j \neq \theta_k$, $j \neq k$, with $|\theta_j| < 1$ all j, then the results of Section 1.3 show that the solutions to the difference equations

(1.5.13), (1.5.14) are of the form

$$\lambda_\tau = \sum_{k=1}^{p} A_k \theta_k^\tau + \delta(\tau)\sigma_\epsilon^2 \tag{1.5.15}$$

where

$$\delta(\tau) = 0, \qquad \tau \neq 0$$
$$= 1, \qquad \tau = 0$$

If

$$\frac{1}{a(z)} = \sum_{j=1}^{p} \frac{\phi_j}{1 - \theta_j z} \tag{1.5.16}$$

then it may be shown that

$$A_k = \sigma_\epsilon^2 \frac{\phi_k}{a(\theta_k)} \tag{1.5.17}$$

If any θ_j is complex, then some other θ will be its complex conjugate.

Denoting $\max(|\theta_k|,\ k = 1, \ldots, p)$ by $|\theta_m|$, it follows from (1.5.15) that for τ large $|\lambda_\tau| \approx A_m|\theta_m|^\tau$, so $|\lambda_\tau|$ will decline exponentially to zero as τ becomes large.

It will be shown in Section 1.6 that the autocovariance generating function for an AR(p) process is given by $\lambda(z) = \sigma_\epsilon^2/a(z)a(z^{-1})$.

Dividing (1.5.13) by the variance λ_0 yields a system of equations relating autocorrelations of a pth-order autoregressive process

$$\rho_\tau = \sum_{j=1}^{p} a_j \rho_{\tau-j}, \qquad \tau > 0 \tag{1.5.18}$$

These are known as the Yule–Walker equations, from Yule [1927] and Walker [1931]. Note that the set of equations (1.5.18) with $\tau = 1, 2, \ldots, p$ can be solved for the coefficients a_j in terms of the first p autocorrelations.

The behavior of the autocorrelation function of an autoregressive process is that of a mixture of damped exponentials and/or sine waves. To illustrate, consider in more detail the second-order process

$$X_t - a_1 X_{t-1} - a_2 X_{t-2} = \epsilon_t$$

From the first two equations of (1.5.18), since $\rho_{-\tau} = \rho_\tau$ and $\rho_0 = 1$,

$$\rho_1 = a_1 + a_2\rho_1, \qquad \rho_2 = a_1\rho_1 + a_2$$

Hence

$$\rho_1 = \frac{a_1}{(1 - a_2)}, \qquad \rho_2 = \frac{a_1^2}{(1 - a_2)} + a_2$$

and $\rho_\tau,\ \tau = 3, 4, \ldots$, can be obtained directly from (1.5.18). The stationarity requirement is that the roots of

$$1 - a_1 z - a_2 z^2 = 0 \tag{1.5.19}$$

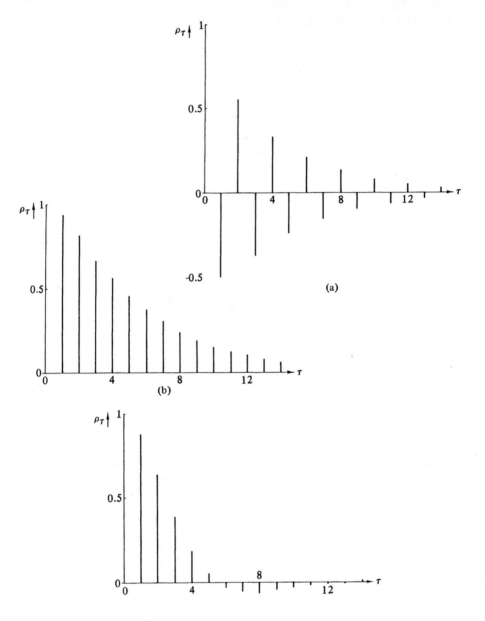

FIG. 1.3 *Autocorrelation function of (a)* $(1 + 0.3B - 0.4B^2)X_t = \epsilon_t$; *(b)* $(1 - 1.3B + 0.4B^2)X_t = \epsilon_t$; *and (c)* $(1 - 1.3B + 0.5B^2)X_t = \epsilon_t$.

lie outside the unit circle $|z| = 1$. If the roots of this equation are real, the autocorrelations die out exponentially, as shown in Figs. 1.3a and 1.3b for the processes

$$(1 - 0.5B)(1 + 0.8B)X_t = (1 + 0.3B - 0.4B^2)X_t = \epsilon_t$$

and

$$(1 - 0.5B)(1 - 0.8B)X_t = (1 - 1.3B + 0.4B^2)X_t = \epsilon_t$$

If the roots of (1.5.19) are complex, then the autocorrelation function exhibits sinusoidal decay. This is illustrated in Fig. 1.3c for the process

$$(1 - 1.3B + 0.5B^2)X_t = \epsilon_t$$

1.6 The Moving Average Model
Suppose that ϵ_t is a zero-mean white noise, then the series

$$X_t = \epsilon_t + \epsilon_{t-1} \qquad (1.6.1)$$

will be smoother than the original white noise series, as will be clear either by simple experimentation or by noting that the first autocorrelation is 0.5. This is a very simple example of a moving average, the more general form for the process being

$$X_t = \sum_{j=0}^{q} b_j \epsilon_{t-j}, \qquad b_0 = 1 \qquad (1.6.2)$$

If a process is generated by such an equation, it is said to be a moving average of order q and denoted $X_t \sim \text{MA}(q)$. If $q = 0$, X_t will be just white noise. The first-order moving average process is, then, $X_t = \epsilon_t + b\epsilon_{t-1}$. For positive b the process will be smoother than white noise, smoothness increasing with the magnitude of b. Figure 1.4 shows generated data from first-order moving average processes with $b = 0.4$ and 0.8.

The mean of the process (1.6.2) is clearly zero. Obviously the model can be extended to deal with the nonzero mean case by writing

$$X_t - \mu = \sum_{j=0}^{q} b_j \epsilon_{t-j}, \qquad b_0 = 1$$

However, it will again be assumed that, if necessary, the mean has been removed by transformation and subsequent analysis will consider (1.6.2). The form of the autocovariances can be seen by writing

$$X_t = \epsilon_t + b_1\epsilon_{t-1} + \cdots + b_{\tau-1}\epsilon_{t-\tau+1} + b_\tau\epsilon_{t-\tau} + b_{\tau+1}\epsilon_{t-\tau-1} + \cdots + b_q\epsilon_{t-q}$$

$$X_{t-\tau} = \qquad\qquad\qquad\qquad \epsilon_{t-\tau} + b_1\epsilon_{t-\tau-1} + \cdots + b_{q-\tau}\epsilon_{t-q}$$

$$+ \cdots + b_q\epsilon_{t-q-\tau}$$

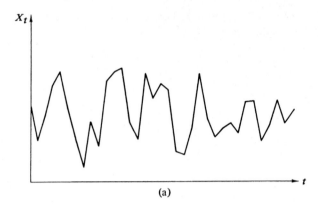

(a)

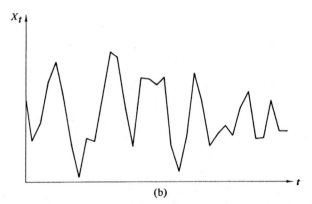

(b)

FIG. 1.4   *Data generated from* (*a*) $X_t = (1 + 0.4B)\epsilon_t$; *and* (*b*) $X_t = (1 + 0.8B)\epsilon_t$.

Remembering that $E[\epsilon_t \epsilon_s] = 0$, $t \neq s$, it follows immediately that

$$\lambda_\tau \equiv E[X_t X_{t-\tau}] = \sigma_\epsilon^2 [b_\tau + b_1 b_{\tau+1} + b_2 b_{\tau+2} + \cdots + b_{q-\tau} b_q],$$

$$\text{for} \quad |\tau| \leqslant q \tag{1.6.3}$$

and

$$\lambda_\tau = 0 \quad \text{for} \quad |\tau| > q \tag{1.6.4}$$

Thus, λ_τ vanishes for sufficiently large τ.

Taking $\tau = 0$ gives

$$\text{var } X_t \equiv \lambda_0 = \sigma_\epsilon^2 \sum_{j=0}^{q} b_j^2 \tag{1.6.5}$$

It is immediately seen that an MA(q) process, with $q < \infty$, is always stationary. It follows from (1.6.4) that, for a moving average process of order

q, the autocorrelations ρ_τ are all zero for $\tau > q$. Thus, the autocorrelation function takes a simple and easily recognized form.

Denoting

$$b(z) = \sum_{j=0}^{q} b_j z^j \tag{1.6.6}$$

then, in terms of the backward operator, the MA(q) model (1.6.2) may be written

$$X_t = b(B)\epsilon_t \tag{1.6.7}$$

and, since the right-hand side of (1.6.2) is a convolution, in terms of generating functions, the model may be written

$$X(z) = b(z)\epsilon(z) \tag{1.6.8}$$

Noting that

$$b(z)b(z^{-1}) = \sum_{j,k=0}^{q} b_j b_k z^{j-k} = \sum_{s=-q}^{q} z^s \sum_{j=0}^{q} b_j b_{j+s} \tag{1.6.9}$$

by putting $j - k = s$ and taking $b_j = 0$, $j > q$, it follows immediately from (1.6.3) and (1.6.4) that the autocovariance generating function is

$$\lambda(z) = \sigma_\epsilon^2 b(z)b(z^{-1}) \tag{1.6.10}$$

It is of some interest to ask if a set of numbers c_j, $j = 0, 1, \ldots$, with $c_j = 0$, $j > q$, can be the autocovariances of an MA(q) scheme. To show that just any set of numbers cannot be used, consider the MA(1) process $X_t = \epsilon_t + b\epsilon_{t-1}$ which has first autocorrelation

$$\rho_1 = b/(1 + b^2) \tag{1.6.11}$$

and clearly $|\rho_1| \leqslant 0.5$. It can easily be proved that the largest possible first autocorrelation ρ_1 achievable from an MA(q) process is

$$\rho_1(\max) = \cos[\pi/(q + 2)] \tag{1.6.12}$$

It follows, for example, that if $\rho_1 = 0.8$, $\rho_j = 0$ for $j > 1$, then there is no corresponding MA(1) process with such autocorrelations. A necessary and sufficient condition that there exists an MA(q) process corresponding to a set of "covariances" c_j, $j = 0, 1, \ldots, q$, has been given by Wold [1954, p. 154] and it is easily shown that the condition is equivalent to $f(\omega) \geqslant 0$, $-\pi \leqslant \omega \leqslant \pi$ where

$$f(\omega) = \lambda(z) = \sum_{j=-q}^{q} c_j z^j \tag{1.6.13}$$

and $z = e^{-i\omega}$. In terms of the power spectral function, to be more fully introduced in Section 2.1, the condition merely states that the spectrum must be nonnegative. The result (1.6.12) has been extended by Davies *et al.* [1974], who show that for a moving average process of order q, the highest value that can be taken by the τth autocorrelation is

$$\rho_\tau(\text{max}) = \cos[\pi/(N+1)] \quad \text{if} \quad \tau \text{ divides } q+1$$
$$= \cos[\pi/(N+2)] \quad \text{if} \quad \tau \text{ does not divide } q+1$$

where N is the largest integer not exceeding $(q+1)/\tau$.

Moving averages were introduced by Yule [1926] and studied in more detail in 1938 by Wold (see Wold [1954]). If some economic variable is in equilibrium but is moved from the equilibrium position by a series of buffeting effects from unpredictable events either from within the economy, such as strikes, or from outside, such as periods of exceptional weather, and if the system is such that the effects of such events are not immediately assimilated, then a moving average model will arise. An example might be a small commodity market that receives a series of news items about the state of crops in producing countries. A particular news item will have both an immediate effect on prices and also a weighted, or discounted, effect over the next few days as the market assimilates the importance and relevance of the news. Let X_t denote price change at time t. The discounting of shocks entering the system may be such that a particular item exerts an influence on price change up to q days after its occurrence. In this case, an appropriate model would be the moving average process

$$X_t = \epsilon_t + b_1\epsilon_{t-1} + \cdots + b_q\epsilon_{t-q}$$

where ϵ_{t-j} is the initial value of the shock that occurs at time $t-j$. If this discounting takes an exponential form, with weight $b_j = a^j$, $0 < a < 1$, so that a news item j days earlier has effect proportional to a^j, then the moving average that results takes the form

$$X_t = \sum_{j=0}^{\infty} a^j\epsilon_{t-j}$$

However, Eq. (1.5.11) indicates that X_t may be represented by

$$X_t = aX_{t-1} + \epsilon_t$$

so in this case an MA(∞) process is found to be equivalent to an AR(1) process.

It was shown in Section 1.5 that a stationary AR(p) process could always be written in an MA(∞) form. It is natural to ask if an MA(q) process is equivalent to an AR(∞) process. Considering (1.6.2) as a difference equation for the ϵ_t given the sequence X_t, the answer is seen immediately to be yes, provided the condition previously called the stationarity condition is obeyed, that is, the roots of $b(z) = 0$ all lie outside the unit circle $|z| = 1$. In this context, this condition will be called the *invertibility condition*. An example where the invertibility condition does not hold is the MA(1) process $X_t = \epsilon_t + b\epsilon_{t-1}$ where $|b| > 1$. Invertibility will be discussed further in Sections 3.4 and 4.8.

If $X_t \sim \text{AR}(p)$, then the corresponding equations using backward operators will be

$$a(B)X_t = \epsilon_t \quad \Rightarrow \quad X_t = b(B)\epsilon_t$$

and in generating function form

$$a(z)X(z) = \epsilon(z) \quad \Rightarrow \quad X(z) = b(z)\epsilon(z) \quad \text{where} \quad a(z)b(z) = 1$$

It follows from this and (1.6.10) that the autocovariance generating function for an AR(p) process is

$$\lambda(z) = \sigma_\epsilon^2/a(z)a(z^{-1})$$

1.7 The Mixed Autoregressive–Moving Average Model

An obvious generalization of the MA and AR models that includes them as special cases is the mixed model in which X_t is generated by

$$X_t = \sum_{j=1}^{p} a_j X_{t-j} + \sum_{j=0}^{q} b_j \epsilon_{t-j} \tag{1.7.1}$$

or if X_t has mean μ

$$X_t - \mu = \sum_{j=1}^{p} a_j(X_{t-j} - \mu) + \sum_{j=0}^{q} b_j \epsilon_{t-j}$$

where ϵ_t is a zero-mean, white noise and $b_0 = 1$. If X_t is generated in this fashion, it is called a mixed ARMA process and denoted $X_t \sim \text{ARMA}(p, q)$. Using the operator B, the model is

$$a(B)X_t = b(B)\epsilon_t \tag{1.7.2}$$

so that the corresponding generating function form is

$$a(z)X(z) = b(z)\epsilon(z) \tag{1.7.3}$$

where

$$a(z) = 1 - \sum_{j=1}^{p} a_j z^j \tag{1.7.4}$$

and

$$b(z) = \sum_{j=0}^{q} b_j z^j \tag{1.7.5}$$

Mixed processes were first studied by Wold in 1938 (see Wold [1954]) and Bartlett [1946].

From the considerations of the previous two sections it is clear that:

(i) the process is stationary if the roots of $a(z) = 0$ all lie outside the unit circle $|z| = 1$;

(ii) if the process is stationary, then there is an equivalent MA(∞) process

$$X_t = \sum_{j=0}^{\infty} c_j \epsilon_{t-j}, \qquad c_0 = 1 \tag{1.7.6}$$

where

$$c(z) = \sum c_j z^j = \frac{b(z)}{a(z)} \tag{1.7.7}$$

(iii) there is an equivalent AR(∞) process

$$X_t = \sum_{j=1}^{\infty} d_j X_{t-j} + \epsilon_t \tag{1.7.8}$$

where

$$d(z) = 1 - \sum_{j=1}^{\infty} d_j z^j = \frac{a(z)}{b(z)} \tag{1.7.9}$$

provided the roots of $b(z) = 0$ all lie outside the unit circle $|z| = 1$, that is, provided the invertibility condition holds.

It thus follows that a stationary ARMA process can always be well approximated by a high-order MA process and that if the process obeys the invertibility condition, it can also be well approximated by a high-order AR process.

A specific form for the autocovariance sequence λ_τ is rather more difficult to find than it was for the AR and MA models. If the model is put into the form

$$\sum_{j=0}^{p} \alpha_j X_{t-j} = \sum_{j=0}^{q} b_j \epsilon_{t-j} \tag{1.7.10}$$

where $\alpha_0 = 1$, $\alpha_j = -a_j$, $j = 1, \ldots, p$, then multiplying both sides of (1.7.10) by $X_{t-\tau}$ and taking expectations gives

$$\sum_{j=0}^{p} \alpha_j \lambda_{\tau-j} = g_\tau \tag{1.7.11}$$

where

$$g_\tau = \sum_{j=0}^{q} b_j \theta_{j-\tau} \tag{1.7.12}$$

and

$$\theta_{j-k} = E[X_{t-k} \epsilon_{t-j}] \tag{1.7.13}$$

From (1.7.6) it is seen that

$$\theta_{j-k} = 0 \qquad \text{for} \quad j < k \tag{1.7.14}$$

Multiplying both sides of (1.7.10) by ϵ_{t-k} and taking expectations gives

$$\sum_{j=0}^{p} \alpha_j \theta_{k-j} = \sigma_\epsilon^2 b_k \tag{1.7.15}$$

In principle an expression for λ_τ can be found by solving the difference equation (1.7.15) for the θ's, substituting into (1.7.12) to find the g's and then solving the difference equation (1.7.11) for the λ's. Since, in general, the results will be rather complicated, the eventual solution is not presented. However, for $\tau > q$, g_τ will be zero by (1.7.14) and so the λ's obey the homogeneous difference equation $\sum_{j=0}^{p} \alpha_j \lambda_{\tau-j} = 0$ so that for $\tau > q$, the λ's will be similar in form to those of the AR(p) process $a(B)X_t = \epsilon_t$, as given in Eq. (1.5.15). It follows that for large enough τ, $|\lambda_\tau|$ will take the exponential form found for AR(p) processes. Dividing by the variance λ_0, it follows that for an ARMA(p, q) process the autocorrelations obey

$$\rho_\tau = \sum_{j=1}^{p} a_j \rho_{\tau-j}, \qquad \tau > q$$

Thus the autocorrelation function for the mixed process eventually, after the setting of q starting values determined by the moving average operator, takes the same shape as that of the autoregressive process $a(B)X_t = \epsilon_t$. McLeod [1975, 1977] gives an algorithm for the computation of the autocovariances in terms of the parameters of an ARMA(p, q) model.

Since the right-hand side of (1.7.12) is a convolution between the b sequence and the reversed θ sequence, it follows that the generating function form of (1.7.11) is

$$a(z)\lambda(z) = b(z)\theta(z^{-1}) \tag{1.7.16}$$

and the generating function form of (1.7.15) is

$$a(z)\theta(z) = \sigma_\epsilon^2 b(z) \tag{1.7.17}$$

Combining these equations gives

$$\lambda(z) = \sigma_\epsilon^2 \frac{b(z)b(z^{-1})}{a(z)a(z^{-1})} \tag{1.7.18}$$

In theory at least, the value of λ_τ can be found as the coefficient of z^τ in the power series expansion of the autocovariance generating function $\lambda(z)$.

For the ARMA(1, 1) process $X_t - aX_{t-1} = \epsilon_t + b\epsilon_{t-1}$ it may be verified from the above equations that

$$\lambda_0 = \frac{(1 + 2ab + b^2)}{1 - a^2}\sigma_\epsilon^2, \qquad \lambda_1 = \frac{(1 + ab)(a + b)}{1 - a^2}\sigma_\epsilon^2,$$

$$\lambda_\tau = a\lambda_{\tau-1}, \qquad \tau \geqslant 2$$

Similarly, the autocorrelations obey $\rho_\tau = a\rho_{\tau-1}$, $\tau \geqslant 2$. However, the distinc-

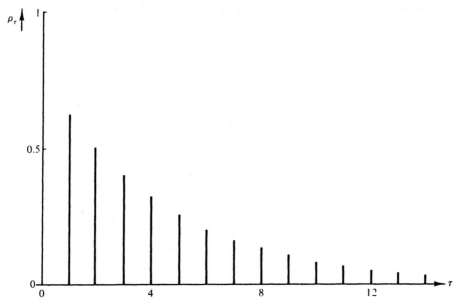

FIG. 1.5   *Autocorrelation function of* $(1 - 0.8B)X_t = (1 - 0.3B)\epsilon_t$.

tion between this process and the first-order autoregressive process is that the relation $\rho_1 = a\rho_0 = a$ now no longer holds unless $b = 0$. Figure 1.5 shows the autocorrelation function of the ARMA$(1, 1)$ process $X_t - 0.8X_{t-1} = \epsilon_t - 0.3\epsilon_{t-1}$.

1.8 Interpreting the Mixed Model

In Sections 1.5 and 1.6 fairly realistic ways in which autoregressive processes and moving average processes could be caused have been suggested, in terms of expectations and by unexpected shocks on the economic system. It would be possible to combine these causes and thereby suggest that a mixed model should arise, but it is difficult to make such explanations completely convincing. There are, however, a number of convincing reasons the mixed model is likely to arise in practice. To illustrate two of these reasons, it is necessary to prove a theorem concerning the form of a process that is the sum of two independent processes.

Suppose X_t and Y_t are two independent, stationary processes with zero means and let

$$Z_t = X_t + Y_t \tag{1.8.1}$$

$$\text{cov}(X_t, X_{t-\tau}) = \lambda_{X,\tau} \tag{1.8.2}$$

and similarly for Y_t, Z_t. Then it follows immediately that

$$\lambda_{Z,\tau} = \lambda_{X,\tau} + \lambda_{Y,\tau} \tag{1.8.3}$$

It then follows, from the condition stated just before Eq. (1.6.13), that if $X_t \sim \text{MA}(m)$, $Y_t \sim \text{MA}(n)$ then

$$Z_t \sim \text{MA}(r) \qquad \text{where} \quad r \leqslant \max(m, n)$$

for both $\lambda_{X, \tau}$ and $\lambda_{Y, \tau}$ are zero for all $\tau > \max(m, n)$

THEOREM   If $X_t \sim \text{ARMA}(p, m)$, $Y_t \sim \text{ARMA}(q, n)$, X_t and Y_t are independent, $Z_t = X_t + Y_t$; then $Z_t \sim \text{ARMA}(x, y)$ where

$$x \leqslant p + q, \qquad y \leqslant \max(p + n, q + m) \tag{1.8.4}$$

Proof.   Let

$$a_1(B) X_t = b_1(B) \epsilon_t \qquad \text{and} \qquad a_2(B) Y_t = b_2(B) \eta_t$$

where a_1, a_2, b_1, b_2 are polynomials in B of order p, q, m, n respectively and ϵ_t, η_t are independent, zero-mean white noise process.

Since $Z_t = X_t + Y_t$ it follows that

$$\begin{aligned} a_1(B) a_2(B) Z_t &= a_2(B) a_1(B) X_t + a_1(B) a_2(B) Y_t \\ &= a_2(B) b_1(B) \epsilon_t + a_1(B) b_2(B) \eta_t \end{aligned}$$

The first term on the right-hand side is $\text{MA}(q + m)$, and the second term is $\text{MA}(p + n)$ so the whole of the expression on the right-hand side is $\text{MA}(y)$ where $y \leqslant \max(p + n, q + m)$. The order of the polynomial $a_1(B) a_2(B)$ is not more than $p + q$, and so the theorem is established.

The theorem also holds if X and Y have nonzero means μ_X and μ_Y. It has just been shown that

$$a(B)(X_t + Y_t - \mu_X - \mu_Y) = b(B) e_t$$

where

$$a(B) = 1 - a_1 B - \cdots - a_{p+q} B^{p+q} = a_1(B) a_2(B)$$

$$b(B) e_t = 1 + b_1 e_{t-1} + \cdots + b_y e_{t-y} = a_2(B) b_1(B) \epsilon_t + a_1(B) b_2(B) \eta_t$$

and e_t is white noise. Hence, it follows that, if $Z_t = X_t + Y_t$,

$$a(B)(Z_t - \mu_Z) = b(B) e_t \qquad \text{where} \quad \mu_Z = \mu_X + \mu_Y.$$

The need for the inequalities in the expressions for any x and y in the above theorem partly arises from the fact that the polynomials $a_1(B)$ and $a_2(B)$ may contain common roots and so part of the operator need not be applied twice. For example, if

$$(1 - \alpha B) X_t = \epsilon_t \qquad \text{i.e.,} \quad X_t \sim \text{AR}(1)$$

$$(1 - \alpha B)(1 - \beta B) Y_t = \eta_t \qquad \text{i.e.,} \quad Y_t \sim \text{AR}(2)$$

then with $Z_t = X_t + Y_t$ one has

$$(1 - \alpha B)(1 - \beta B) Z_t = (1 - \beta B) \epsilon_t + \eta_t$$

that is,

$$Z_t \sim \text{ARMA}(2,1)$$

In general, if the polynomials $a_1(B)$, $a_2(B)$ have just k roots in common, the inequalities (1.8.4) become

$$x \leqslant p + q - k, \qquad y \leqslant \max(p + n - k, q + m - k) \qquad (1.8.5)$$

The inequalities in this expression are still necessary since the possibility remains of cancellation on both sides of the equation. For example, in the simple case just considered write

$$(1 - \beta B)\epsilon_t + \eta_t = (1 + bB)e_t$$

Equating variances and first autocovariances on both sides of this expression produces

$$(1 + \beta^2)\sigma_\epsilon^2 + \sigma_\eta^2 = (1 + b^2)\sigma_e^2, \qquad -\beta\sigma_\epsilon^2 = b\sigma_e^2$$

Hence

$$\frac{b}{1 + b^2} = \frac{-\beta}{(1 + \beta^2) + \sigma_\eta^2/\sigma_\epsilon^2}$$

and if either $\beta < \alpha < 0$ or $\beta > \alpha > 0$ it is possible to find a $\sigma_\eta^2/\sigma_\epsilon^2$ such that $b = -\alpha$, in which case Z_t follows the AR(1) process $(1 - \beta B)Z_t = e_t$.

That the inequality for y in (1.8.5) is still required is further demonstrated by the following example. Suppose

$$(1 - \alpha B)X_t = \epsilon_t \qquad \text{i.e.,} \qquad X_t \sim \text{AR}(1)$$

$$(1 + \alpha B)Y_t = \eta_t \qquad \text{i.e.,} \qquad Y_t \sim \text{AR}(1)$$

and also the variance of $\epsilon = $ variance of $\eta = \sigma^2$.

If $Z_t = X_t + Y_t$, then $(1 - \alpha B)(1 + \alpha B)Z_t = (1 + \alpha B)\epsilon_t + (1 - \alpha B)\eta_t$. Denote the right-hand side by $Q_t = \epsilon_t + \alpha\epsilon_{t-1} + \eta_t - \alpha\eta_{t-1}$. Then

$$\text{var } Q_t = 2(1 + \alpha^2)\sigma^2 \qquad \text{and} \qquad E\{Q_t Q_{t-k}\} = 0, \qquad \text{all } k > 0$$

so Q_t is a white noise process and $Z_t \sim \text{AR}(2)$ rather than ARMA(2,1), which would generally occur when two independent AR(1) processes are added together. Those situations in which a simpler model arises than might generally be expected will be called "coincidental situations."

Two situations where series are added are of particular interpretational importance. The first is where series are aggregated to form some total, and the second is where the observed series is the sum of the true process plus observational error, corresponding to the classical "signal plus noise" situation. Most macroeconomic series, such as GNP, employment, or exports, are aggregates and there is no particular reason to suppose that all of the component series will obey exactly the same model. Virtually any macroeconomic series, other than certain prices or interest rates, contains important observation errors. It would be highly coincidental if the "true" series and the observational error series obeyed models having common roots, apart possibly from the root unity, or that the parameters of these models should be such that the cancelling of terms produces a value of y in (1.8.4) less than the maximum possible.

It follows from the theorem that if the series being analyzed is the sum of two independent components each of which is AR(1), then the series will be ARMA(2, 1), for example. If the observed series is the sum of a "true" series that is AR(p) plus a white noise observation error, then an ARMA(p, p) series results. It may be thought to be unrealistic to suppose that the components of an aggregate series are independent. However, if the components can be written in the form

$$X_t = c_1 F_t + W_{1t}, \qquad Y_t = c_2 F_t + W_{2t},$$

where F_t is some common factor explaining the relatedness of X_t and Y_t, W_{1t} and W_{2t} are independent AR processes and F_t is itself an AR process, then

$$Z_t = (c_1 + c_2) F_2 + W_{1t} + W_{2t}$$

and applying the basic theorem twice, the sum of the three components will in general be an ARMA process.

The situations considered in this section have been analyzed in more detail by Granger and Morris [1976], where it is also pointed out that the mixed model may also arise in various other ways, for example, from an AR process with lags that are not integer multiples of the sampling period or from a feedback mechanism between two or more series. Thus, on purely theoretical grounds, it is seen that the mixed model is very likely to arise in practice, and that arguments as to the difficulty of its interpretation (for example, Chatfield and Prothero [1973]) can be overcome in a number of ways.

There is also a sound statistical reason for considering ARMA models. It is often the case that one has the choice of either fitting an ARMA(p, q) model or an AR(p') model to some data. Experience suggests that the mixed model may achieve as good a fit as the AR model but using fewer parameters, i.e., $p + q < p'$. Since the actual amount of data available is usually very limited, the statistician prefers to fit a model involving as few parameters as possible. Box and Jenkins [1970] have called this the *principle of parsimony* and the application of this principle will often lead one to a mixed model.

The results of this section can be generalized, as discussed by Engel [1984], where conditions are provided to assure that the sum of two dependent Gaussian ARMA processes is ARMA. Engel further shows that if X_t is Gaussian ARMA with zero mean, then any polynomial of finite order in X_t will also be ARMA; however, $\exp(X_t)$ will not, in general, be ARMA, though it can typically be well approximated by an ARMA process of finite order.

Engel also discusses the products of ARMA processes. Let X_{it} be m independent, zero mean ARMA(p_i, q_i) processes. Then their product is ARMA(p, q), where

$$p \leqslant \prod_{i=1}^{m} p_i; \qquad q \leqslant p + \max_{i}(q_i - p_i)$$

For example, if X_{1t} and X_{2t} are independent AR(p) processes, their product is ARMA($p^2, p^2 - p$).

1.9 Filters

If a series Y_t is formed by a linear combination of terms of a series X_t, so that

$$Y_t = \sum_{j=-s}^{m} c_j X_{t-j} \tag{1.9.1}$$

then Y_t is called a *filtered* version of X_t. If only past and present terms of X_t are involved, so that

$$Y_t = \sum_{j=0}^{m} c_j X_{t-j} \tag{1.9.2}$$

then Y_t might be called a one-sided or backward-looking filter. In terms of the backward operator B, this type of filter may be written as

$$Y_t = c(B) X_t \tag{1.9.3}$$

where

$$c(z) = \sum_{j=0}^{m} c_j z^j \tag{1.9.4}$$

Provided $\Sigma c_j^2 < \infty$, m need not be finite.

It is seen immediately that if Y_t is an MA process, then it is a backward-looking filter applied to a white noise process. If X_t is an AR(p) process, it may be described in the following way: an appropriate finite backward-looking filter applied to X_t will produce a white noise series. Similarly, the ARMA process can be said to be one for which a finite, backward-looking filter applied to the process produces a backward filter applied to a white noise process.

In terms of generating functions, (1.9.1) may be written $Y(z) = c(z)X(z)$. It then follows from (1.3.10) that the autocovariance functions of X_t and Y_t, denoted $\lambda_x(z)$ and $\lambda_y(z)$, are related by the equation

$$\lambda_y(z) = c(z)c(z^{-1})\lambda_x(z) \tag{1.9.5}$$

Filters are frequently used to remove, or reduce in importance, components of series that are troublesome. However, it is inconvenient to try to determine the effects of filters using the tools introduced in this chapter. These effects can be very simply described by using the spectral theory to be introduced in Chapter 2.

Filters are also associated with the idea of a "black box" relationship between two series. Suppose a "box" is observed to have an input series X_t and output series Y_t, with the box having a memory property, so that Y_t can be a function of current and past X_t. Diagramatically, this can be shown as

$$X_t \rightarrow \boxed{\begin{array}{c} \text{BLACK} \\ \text{BOX} \end{array}} \rightarrow Y_t$$

The analyses associated with this type of construct involve either deriving the properties of the output series given those of the input series and the box, or characterization of the properties of the box given the input and output series. The first problem is simply that of filtering discussed above, while the second involves estimation of the "transfer function" $c(z)$, defined in (1.9.4), of the box. A method for doing this is briefly mentioned in Section 2.5, and black box constructs are discussed further in Chapter 7.

If Y_t is a backward-looking filter, with finite m, applied to an ARMA(p, q) process, then $Y_t \sim$ ARMA($p, q + m$). This is seen by taking $a(B)X_t = b(B)\epsilon_t$ where a, b are polynomials of order p, q. Write $Y_t = c(B)X_t$ and hence $a(B)Y_t = c(B)a(B)X_t = c(B)b(B)\epsilon_t$, and $c(B)b(B)$ will be a polynomial in B of order $q + m$.

1.10 Deterministic Components

A time sequence M_t will be called *deterministic* if there exists a function of past and present values $g_t = g(M_{t-j}, j = 0, 1, \ldots)$ such that

$$E\left[(M_{t+1} - g_t)^2\right] = 0 \qquad (1.10.1)$$

If the function g_t is a linear function of M_{t-j}, $j \geqslant 0$, then M_t will be called *linear deterministic*. Consider the sequence $M_t = ae^{bt}$ so that $M_{t+1} = e^b M_t$. If b is known, then the sequence is linear deterministic. If b is not known, it can be perfectly estimated from the past of the series, but the estimate will be a nonlinear function of the sequence; for instance

$$b = \tfrac{1}{2}[\log M_t^2 - \log M_{t-1}^2]$$

allowing for the fact that a may be negative.

Other functions that are linearly deterministic are:

(i) the periodic sequence

$$M_t = a \cos(\omega t + \theta) \qquad (1.10.2)$$

provided ω is known and there exists an integer k such that $2\pi k/\omega$ is an integer. For example, if $M_t = a \cos(2\pi t/12 + \theta)$, then

$$M_{t+1} = M_{t-11} \tag{1.10.3}$$

so that M_t is clearly linear deterministic. If ω has to be estimated from past data, the sequence becomes nonlinear deterministic.

(ii) $$M_t = \sum_{j=0}^{m} d_j t^j \tag{1.10.4}$$

so that the sequence is a polynomial in t. To show that such polynomials are linear deterministic, consider the simple sequence $M_t = a + bt$. Then $M_t - M_{t-1} = b$ so, if b is known, it follows that

$$M_{t+1} = b + M_t \tag{1.10.5}$$

The difference operator is defined by

$$\Delta M_t = M_t - M_{t-1} \tag{1.10.6}$$

It can be shown that if M_t is a polynomial or order m, then $\Delta^m M_t = m! d_m$ and

$$\Delta^{m+1} M_t = 0 \tag{1.10.7}$$

It is thus seen that the M_t sequence obeys a homogeneous linear difference equation, and so is linear deterministic. However, one needs to know the value of m, or at least a value m' such that $m' > m$, to use this procedure.

These types of functions are of considerable importance in practice since the plots of many time series, particularly economic series, appear to contain trends and seasonal components. A classical model involving these components is to assume an economic variable to be represented by

$$X_t = T(t) + S(t) + Y_t \tag{1.10.8}$$

where $T(t)$ is a deterministic component representing the trend, the seasonal $S(t)$ is also deterministic and is a periodic component with period 12 months and Y_t is a stationary process with no deterministic components.

If the variable measured some macroeconomic quantity, it was once usual to add further periodic components, with periods greater than 12 months, to represent business cycles. It is now generally accepted that this is not a useful way to represent the business cycle component, since these "cycles" are by no means strictly periodic. In fact, there is virtually no evidence that modern macroeconomic series contain periodic components other than seasonal ones.

Given a length of series representable as (1.10.8), the estimated variance can be approximately decomposed:

$$\widehat{\mathrm{var}}(X_t) = \widehat{\mathrm{var}}(T(t)) + \widehat{\mathrm{var}}(S(t)) + \widehat{\mathrm{var}}(Y_t) \tag{1.10.9}$$

In practice, the first two components dominate in the sense that they contribute a great deal more to the overall variance of the series than does Y_t. However, for testing hypotheses or investigating relationships between variables, it is the term Y_t that is often of greatest interest. For this reason, as well as others to be explained later, it is usually thought desirable to implement techniques that either remove the trend and seasonal components or, at least, greatly reduce their importance.

The trend term is very difficult to define, given only a finite series to analyze. It is usually taken to be some monotonically increasing or monotonically decreasing function of time. For an observed series it is often possible to approximate the trend by a polynomial in t or an exponential function of time. To extrapolate this trend outside of the observed period can lead to disastrous results. Suppose, for example, one measured outdoor temperatures at some location every minute from 4 A.M. to 11:30 A.M. The data would almost certainly appear to contain a clear-cut upward trend, but when this segment of data is considered in the context of temperature readings taken over several days, the apparent trend is seen to be just a segment of a daily cycle in temperature.

There are two basic methods of estimating a trend term. One is to assume that $T(t)$ can be well approximated by some time function, such as a polynomial in t, an exponential in t, or some combination of these, and then to estimate the parameters of the function by a regression procedure. The alternative is to view trend as the current mean of the series, i.e., $T(t) = E[X_t]$, where clearly X_t is now nonstationary. One might estimate this current mean by either

$$\hat{T}(t) = \frac{1}{2m+1} \sum_{j=-m}^{m} x_{t-j} \qquad (1.10.10)$$

or

$$\hat{T}(t) = \alpha \hat{T}(t-1) + (1-\alpha)x_t \qquad (1.10.11)$$

where α is near one. This second estimate may be written as

$$\hat{T}(t) = (1-\alpha) \sum_{j=0}^{\infty} \alpha^j x_{t-j} \qquad (1.10.12)$$

so that the most recent value of the series is given greatest weight, but if $E[X_t] = \mu$, a constant, then $E[\hat{T}(t-1)] = \mu$. Estimates of the form (1.10.11) form the basis of a forecasting technique known as "exponential smoothing" which will be discussed in more detail in Chapter 5. Both of these estimates involve filters that greatly smooth the input series x, and this underlying smooth component is then equated with the trend. Once trend has been "estimated," trend removal (strictly trend reduction) consists of forming a new series

$$x'_t = x_t - \hat{T}(t) \qquad (1.10.13)$$

A different approach to trend removal is considered in the following section.

If X_t is a trend-free zero-mean process but with a seasonal component, so that

$$X_t = S(t) + Y_t$$

then there is a wide variety of techniques for estimating $S(t)$. If a monthly sampling period is being used, $S(t)$ may be taken to have period 12 months and so, from (1.4.2), may be represented by

$$S(t) = \sum_{j=1}^{6} d_j \cos\left(\frac{2\pi jt}{12} + \theta_j\right) = \sum_{j=1}^{6} \left\{ d_j' \cos\left(\frac{2\pi jt}{12}\right) + d_j'' \sin\left(\frac{2\pi jt}{12}\right)\right\}$$

$$(1.10.14)$$

The quantities d_j' and d_j'' may be estimated by least-squares regression. An equivalent procedure is to use dummy variables D_{jt}, $j = 0, \ldots, 11$, such that $D_{jt} = 1$ if $(t - j - 1)/12$ is an integer and zero otherwise, so that $D_{0t} = 1$ every January and is zero in every other month, and so forth (assuming x_1 is a January figure). $S(t)$ may then be represented by

$$S(t) = \sum_{j=0}^{11} d_j D_{jt} \qquad (1.10.15)$$

with the side condition that $\sum_{j=0}^{11} d_j = 0$, and the d_j found once more by regression.

An alternative, but easier, procedure is to form

$$\bar{S}_0 = \text{average of all January } x\text{'s}$$

$$\bar{S}_1 = \text{average of all February } x\text{'s, etc.}$$

and then to take

$$\hat{S}(t) = \sum_{j=0}^{11} \bar{S}_j D_{jt} \qquad (1.10.16)$$

again assuming the series starts in January. However, one may suspect that the seasonal component is slowly changing either in amplitude or shape through time. In this case $\bar{S}_0$ may be taken to be the average of all recent January figures, or a time-changing $S_0(k)$ figure for January in year k derived from

$$\hat{S}_0(k) = \alpha \hat{S}_0(k - 1) + (1 - \alpha)[\text{most recent January figure}] \quad (1.10.17)$$

and similarly for the other months. This class of methods of estimating the seasonal components may be thought of as linear filters, and their properties can be determined from the theory to be introduced in Section 2.2. On occasions, one may fear that not only is the seasonal component changing through time, so that averages over just the recent past should be used, but that some years are very untypical, due to freak weather conditions say, and that the figures for these years should not be included in the averages. Thus, $\bar{S}_0$ may be estimated as the average over the last m January x's, excluding the largest and smallest x in this period. This is a nonlinear procedure, and its effects can be determined only by simulation. The results of such a simulation will be described in Section 2.8.

Once the seasonal component has been estimated, the *seasonally adjusted* series is $x_t' = x_t - \hat{S}(t)$. An alternative method of removing the seasonal component is considered in Section 1.14. It should be emphasized that the foregoing discussion of seasonal analysis is only a brief survey of a difficult and complicated problem. Further papers can be found in Zellner [1978].

Many early textbooks dealing with time series analysis (see, for example, Croxton and Cowden [1955]) concentrated almost exclusively on procedures for the removal of the deterministic components in (1.10.8), paying relatively little attention to the properties of Y_t. The more modern view is that, as far as possible, the trend, seasonal, and "irregular" components should be handled simultaneously in a single model aimed at depicting as faithfully as possible the behavior of a given time series. Trend is generally treated by differencing, leading to the consideration of "integrated processes" in Section 1.13. (An alternative is to transform the series, by taking logarithms for example, before differencing.) Seasonality can be treated, as will be seen in Section 1.14, through a generalization of the ARMA models discussed earlier.

1.11 Wold's Decomposition

The models that have been introduced so far may appear to the reader to have been selected rather arbitrarily. One might well expect that there are many other models that could have been considered. In fact, a famous theorem due to Wold [1954] suggests otherwise. He proved that any stationary process X_t can be uniquely represented as the sum of two mutually uncorrelated processes $X_t = D_t + Y_t$ where D_t is linearly deterministic and Y_t is an MA(∞) process. The Y_t component is said to be *purely nondeterministic*.

Even though the process may be generated nonlinearly, the decomposition is a linear one and is determined entirely by the second moments of the process.

The theorem is probably more satisfying to theoreticians than to practical time series analysts. It does, however, mean that it is reasonable to hope that the true generating mechanism of a process can be adequately approximated by a mechanism that generates some simple type of linearly deterministic process plus some stationary ARMA process. It does not necessarily follow that a nonlinear model may not provide a better explanation. Wold's decomposition does suggest a wide class of stationary processes that should be considered and, given stationarity, will usually be difficult to better.

1.12 Nonstationary Processes

In series arising in many disciplines it is generally agreed that an assumption of stationarity is too restrictive and that series actually met are in some way nonstationary. The immediate problem when considering nonstationarity is that there are unlimited ways in which a process could be nonstationary. There is naturally a strong temptation not to venture too boldly into such uncharted territory, but rather to consider models that are in some way close to those met under a stationarity assumption. One such model, in which a stationary process had added to it a trend in mean, was briefly discussed in Section 1.10. With economic data it is frequently observed that the extent of the fluctuations of a series are roughly proportional to the current level. This suggests that the model

$$X_t = T(t) \cdot Y_t \tag{1.12.1}$$

where Y_t may be a stationary series, might be appropriate. If X_t is necessarily nonnegative, for example, a price or level of production, then a logarithmic transformation of the data will produce the previous model in which trend is only found in the mean. Alternatively, a transformation such as

$$X_t' = X_t \bigg/ \frac{1}{m} \sum_{j=0}^{m-1} X_{t-j} \tag{1.12.2}$$

could produce a series that is apparently stationary (see, for instance, Granger and Hughes [1971]). No completely satisfactory techniques are available for testing whether or not a series contains a trend in mean and/or variance. A number of sensible procedures can be suggested, but a decision based on the plot of the data is likely to be a reasonable one, provided the analyst is sufficiently experienced.

Even when a series appears to contain no clear-cut trend in mean or variance, there are various more subtle ways in which it can be nonstationary. An obvious class of models are ARMA processes with time-changing parameters. An example would be a process generated by

$$X_t = a(t) X_{t-1} + b(t) \epsilon_t \tag{1.12.3}$$

where ϵ_t is stationary white noise. Provided that $\prod_{j=0}^{n} a(t-j) \to 0$ as $n \to \infty$ for every t, this particular difference equation has the solution

$$X_t = \sum_{j=0}^{\infty} c_j(t) \epsilon_{t-j} \tag{1.12.4}$$

where

$$c_j(t) = \left\{ \prod_{k=0}^{j-1} a(t-k) \right\} b(t-j), \qquad j > 0 \tag{1.12.5}$$

and $c_0(t) = b(t)$. It can be shown that any ARMA process with time-changing parameters will have a solution of the form (1.12.4) with an appropriate sequence of functions $c_j(t)$ provided some kind of stability condition holds. This class of nonstationary models may be considered of real importance due to a generalization of Wold's decomposition theorem provided by Cramér [1961], which states that for *any* process X_t, there is a uniquely determined decomposition $X_t = D_t + Y_t$ where D_t and Y_t are uncorrelated, D_t is deterministic, Y_t is purely nondeterministic representable as

$$Y_t = \sum_{j=0}^{\infty} c_j(t)\epsilon_{t-j}$$

where

$$\sum_{j=0}^{\infty} [c_j(t)]^2 < \infty, \quad \text{all } t \qquad (1.12.6)$$

If the parameters of the ARMA process, or equivalently the $c_j(t)$, change too quickly with time, they clearly cannot be estimated at all satisfactorily given a single realization of the process for analysis, for the same reasons as discussed in Section 1.2. It is therefore natural to consider processes for which the parameters are only slowly changing with time. A systematic account of such processes which may be called *evolutionary processes* has been given by Priestley [1965].

It was seen in Section 1.3 that generating mechanisms with time invariant parameters could produce nonstationary outcomes. For example, if

$$X_t = aX_{t-1} + \epsilon_t \qquad (1.12.7)$$

where $a > 1$ and ϵ_t is a zero-mean white noise process, with the process starting at time $t = -N$, then the difference equation has the solution

$$X_t = Aa^{t+N} + \sum_{j=0}^{t+N} a^j\epsilon_{t-j} \qquad (1.12.8)$$

Even if initial conditions make $A = 0$, it is seen that the variance of X_t is given by

$$\text{var } X_t = \frac{a^{2(t+N+1)} - 1}{a^2 - 1}\text{var}(\epsilon) \qquad (1.12.9)$$

which depends on time, is increasing with t, and becomes infinite as $N \to \infty$. In general, then, X_t will have a trend both in mean and variance and these effects should be noticeable from a plot of a realization of the process. Such processes may be called *explosive*. Figure 1.6 shows a plot of generated data from the process (1.12.7), with $a = 1.05$ and ϵ_t a zero-mean Gaussian white noise process with variance 16. The calculations were started by setting $X_0 = 100$.

The solution of (1.12.7) is thus explosive if $a > 1$ but is stationary if $|a| < 1$. The case $a = 1$ provides a process that is neatly balanced between an

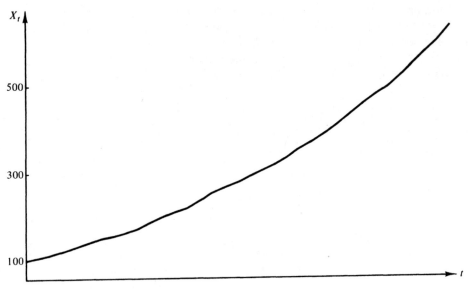

FIG. 1.6   *Data generated from* $X_t = 1.05 X_{t-1} + \epsilon_t$.

overtly nonstationary one and the stationary situation. If X_t is generated by the model

$$X_t = X_{t-1} + \epsilon_t + m \qquad (1.12.10)$$

then it is known as a *random walk*, provided ϵ_t is a zero-mean white noise process. If $m \neq 0$, X_t will be a *random walk with drift*. If the process starts at time $t = -N$ with $X_{-N} = A$, then

$$X_t = A + (t + N)m + \sum_{j=0}^{t+N-1} \epsilon_{t-j}$$

so that

$$\mu_t = E[X_t] = A + (t + N)m$$

$$\lambda_{0,t} = \text{var}[X_t] = (t + N)\sigma_\epsilon^2 \quad \text{and} \quad \lambda_{\tau,t} = \text{cov}[X_t, X_{t-\tau}], \qquad \tau \geq 0$$

$$= (t + N - \tau)\sigma_\epsilon^2$$

where σ_ϵ^2 is the variance of ϵ_t and is assumed to be finite. Thus,

$$\rho_{\tau,t} = \text{corr}(X_t, X_{t-\tau}) = \frac{(t + N - \tau)}{\sqrt{(t + N)(t + N - \tau)}} = \sqrt{\frac{t + N - \tau}{t + N}}$$

Provided $t + N$ is large compared to τ, it is seen that all $\rho_{\tau,t}$ approximate unity. It follows that the sequence X_t is exceptionally smooth, but is also nonstationary since its variance is either increasing with t or, if $N = \infty$, then this variance is infinite. Figure 1.7 shows plots of the random walk (1.12.10)

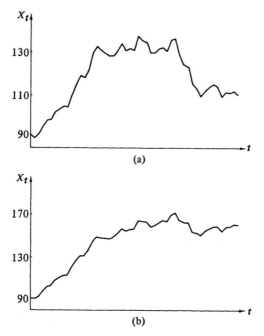

FIG. 1.7   *Data generated from (a) random walk; and (b) random walk with drift.*

with $m = 0$, and the random walk with drift, obtained by setting $m = 1$ in (1.12.10). In both cases the series are generated from a zero-mean Gaussian white noise process ϵ_t with variance 16, and by setting $X_0 = 100$.

A random walk is an example of a class of nonstationary processes known as *integrated processes* that can be made stationary by the application of a time-invariant filter. If X_t is a random walk, then $\Delta X_t = X_t - X_{t-1} = m + \epsilon_t$ is a white noise process. Integrated processes are considered in more detail in the next section. Although they clearly do not represent a very wide class of nonstationary processes, they may introduce sufficient nonstationarity into the models as to produce adequate approximations to actually observed processes in many cases.

1.13 Integrated Processes

A process X_t is said to be an integrated process if it is generated by an equation of the form

$$a(B)(1 - B)^d X_t = b(B)\epsilon_t \qquad (1.13.1)$$

where ϵ_t is zero-mean white noise, $a(B), b(B)$ are polynomials in B of orders p, q respectively ($a(B)$ being a stationary operator), and d is an integer. Such a process will be denoted $X_t \sim \text{ARIMA}(p, d, q)$ (autoregressive integrated moving average of order p, d, q) and it will generally be assumed that the roots of $a(z) = 0$ all lie outside the unit circle. Thus the process obtained by differencing d times, $Y_t = (1 - B)^d X_t$, will be a stationary ARMA(p, q) process. Experience suggests that $d = 0$ or 1 will be appropriate for most observed processes, although occasionally $d = 2$ is required.

In the case $d = 1$, (1.13.1) has solution

$$X_t = \sum_{j=0}^{t+N-1} Y_{t-j}$$

if the process starts at time $t = -N$ and $X_{-N} = 0$. It follows that var(X_t) $= O(N + t)$ and, noting that

$$\text{cov}(X_t, X_{t-\tau}) = \text{var}(X_{t-\tau}) + \text{cov}\left(\sum_{j=0}^{\tau-1} Y_{t-j}, \sum_{j=0}^{N+t-\tau-1} Y_{t-j-\tau}\right)$$

as the second term in this expression is $O(\tau)$, it follows that

$$\text{corr}(X_t, X_{t-\tau}) = \frac{O(N + t - \tau)}{\sqrt{O(N + t)O(N + t - \tau)}} = \sqrt{\frac{O(N + t - \tau)}{O(N + t)}}$$

so, if τ is small compared to $t + N$, corr($X_t, X_{t-\tau}$) ≈ 1. Thus, for an integrated process, the theoretical correlogram will take values near one for all nonlarge τ. For example, consider the process

$$X_t - aX_{t-1} = \epsilon_t + b\epsilon_{t-1} \tag{1.13.2}$$

The autocovariances for this process were derived in Section 1.7, from which it follows that the autocorrelations are

$$\rho_1 = \frac{(1 + ab)(a + b)}{1 + 2ab + b^2}, \qquad \rho_\tau = a\rho_{\tau-1}, \tau \geqslant 2 \tag{1.13.3}$$

Now, as $a \to 1$ in (1.13.2), the resulting process is ARIMA(0, 1, 1):

$$X_t - X_{t-1} = \epsilon_t + b\epsilon_{t-1}$$

and it is seen that the autocorrelations (1.13.3) all tend to one. If d is greater than one, the same result holds. It follows that a plausible technique for determining the value of d is to form correlograms for the process differenced once, twice, etc. until a correlogram is obtained that does not display the shape found for integrated processes. This procedure is discussed further in Chapter 3.

It will be seen in subsequent chapters that integrated processes play a central role in the analysis of economic time series. This observed fact becomes crucially important when considering methods appropriate for analyzing the relationships among such series.

1.14 Models for Seasonal Time Series

In Section 1.10 the problem of dealing with time series possessing a deterministic seasonal component was discussed. There are two difficulties with such an approach. First, one would rarely, if ever, be in the happy position of *knowing* the exact functional form of the deterministic component. Further, it is extremely difficult to identify this form from actual time series of length typically available in practical applications. An analogous problem is that of fitting deterministic trend curves to a given (nonseasonal) time series. It is well known that one can very often find two or three fairly simple curves that fit the data almost equally well. However, when these curves are projected forward, the resulting forecasts can be markedly different (see Newbold [1973a]). Secondly, the seasonal component may well not be deterministic, but rather stochastic in nature.

Accordingly, it is worth investigating whether or not some extension of the nonseasonal autoregressive integrated moving average model of the previous section might provide a useful form for the representation of seasonal time series. Such a model is developed by Box *et al.* [1967] and further examined by Box and Jenkins [1970]. Suppose that X_t is a seasonal time series, with period s, so that $s = 4$ for quarterly and 12 for monthly data. One would like, in some way, to remove the effects of seasonality from this series to produce a nonseasonal series to which an ARIMA model could be built. Now, denote the resulting nonseasonal series by u_t; then it is reasonable to think in terms of the seasonal ARIMA filter

$$a_s(B^s)(1 - B^s)^D X_t = b_s(B^s)u_t \qquad (1.14.1)$$

where

$$a_s(B^s) = 1 - a_{1,s}B^s - \cdots - a_{P,s}B^{Ps}$$
$$b_s(B^s) = 1 + b_{1,s}B^s + \cdots + b_{Q,s}B^{Qs}$$

The rationale behind this is that if one were dealing with, say, monthly time series it would be expected that one January would be pretty much like the previous January, and indeed be similar to the last few previous Januarys and similarly for other months of the year. Further, if the same relationship between years held for every month of the year, (1.14.1) would be an appropriate representation, with the operator B^s indicating a relationship between points s time periods apart. It is important to note that nothing has been said about the autocorrelation properties of the series u_t. In particular, it is *not* assumed that the transformation (1.14.1) is such that

$$\text{corr}(u_t u_{t-ks}) = 0 \qquad \text{for all} \quad k > 0 \qquad (1.14.2)$$

It will not in general be possible (or, indeed, desirable) to find such a transformation. The only requirement is the weaker one that the filtered series u_t be free from seasonality. (Note that the series $u_t - a_1 u_{t-1} = \epsilon_t$, where ϵ_t is white noise, is nonseasonal without (1.14.2) holding.) Since u_t is a nonseasonal series, the possibility can be considered of approximating its behavior with the ARIMA model

$$a(B)(1 - B)^d u_t = b(B)\epsilon_t \qquad (1.14.3)$$

where

$$a(B) = 1 - a_1 B - \cdots - a_p B^p \qquad \text{and} \qquad b(B) = 1 + b_1 B + \cdots + b_q B^q$$

Combining (1.14.1) and (1.14.3) yields the multiplicative model

$$a(B)a_s(B^s)(1 - B)^d (1 - B^s)^D X_t = b(B)b_s(B^s)\epsilon_t \qquad (1.14.4)$$

The problem of fitting the model (1.14.4) to actual series will be examined in Chapter 3.

All is flux, nothing is stationary.

HERACLEITUS 513 B.C.

2.1 Introduction

The previous chapter was largely concerned with the description of time series in terms of models—known as the time-domain approach. There is, however, an alternative approach, known as spectral or frequency-domain analysis, that often provides useful insights into the properties of a series. Since spectral results will only occasionally be used in later chapters, it will be sufficient to give just a brief survey of the basic concepts and interpretations of this theory.

Let X_t be a zero-mean stationary process with autocovariances $\lambda_\tau = \text{cov}(X_t, X_{t-\tau})$ and corresponding autocorrelations $\rho_\tau = \lambda_\tau/\lambda_0$. The autocovariance generating function $\lambda(z)$ was introduced in Section 1.3 and was defined by

$$\lambda(z) = \sum_{\text{all } \tau} \lambda_\tau z^\tau \qquad (2.1.1)$$

and it will be assumed that this function exists, at least for $|z| = 1$. The function of particular interest in this chapter is defined by

$$s(\omega) = \frac{1}{2\pi}\lambda(z), \qquad z = e^{-i\omega} \qquad (2.1.2)$$

so that

$$s(\omega) = \frac{1}{2\pi} \sum_{\text{all } \tau} \lambda_\tau e^{-i\tau\omega} \qquad (2.1.3)$$

or

$$s(\omega) = \frac{\lambda_0}{2\pi} + \frac{1}{\pi} \sum_{\tau \geqslant 1} \lambda_\tau \cos \tau\omega \qquad (2.1.4)$$

as $\lambda_\tau = \lambda_{-\tau}$. The function $s(\omega)$ is called the power spectrum (strictly the power spectral density function) and from (1.3.10) is

45

seen to be both real and positive. From the definition it is also seen that

$$s(\omega + 2\pi k) = s(\omega) \qquad \text{for integer } k \qquad (2.1.5)$$

so that the function $s(\omega)$ is periodic outside the interval $(-\pi, \pi)$ and thus one needs to consider the function only over this interval. From (2.1.4) it also follows that

$$s(-\omega) = s(\omega) \qquad (2.1.6)$$

and so it is usual to plot $s(\omega)$ against ω only for $0 \leqslant \omega \leqslant \pi$. One further important property follows from the fact that

$$\int_{-\pi}^{\pi} e^{i(k-\tau)\omega}\, d\omega = 0 \qquad \text{if} \quad k \neq \tau$$

$$= 2\pi \qquad \text{if} \quad k = \tau \qquad (2.1.7)$$

and so by direct evaluation one finds from (2.1.3) that

$$\lambda_\tau = \int_{-\pi}^{\pi} e^{i\tau\omega} s(\omega)\, d\omega \qquad (2.1.8)$$

Thus, the sequence λ_τ and the function $s(\omega)$ comprise a Fourier transform pair, with one being uniquely determined from the other, so that the time-domain approach, which concentrates on the λ_τ sequence and the models derived from it, and the frequency-domain approach, which is based on interpretation of $s(\omega)$, are theoretically equivalent to one other. A result achieved in one domain may always be found in the other. The reason for considering the frequency domain is that on occasions results are easier to prove and interpretations are easier to make using the spectral approach.

The function $s(\omega)/\lambda_0$ has the properties of a probability density function over the range $-\pi \leqslant \omega \leqslant \pi$ since $s(\omega) \geqslant 0$ and, from (2.1.8) with $\tau = 0$,

$$\int_{-\pi}^{\pi} \frac{s(\omega)}{\lambda_0}\, d\omega = 1 \qquad (2.1.9)$$

In describing how spectral techniques are interpreted, it is convenient to define the rather more general spectral distribution function, given by

$$S(\omega) = \int_{-\pi}^{\omega} \frac{s(\omega)}{\lambda_0}\, d\omega \qquad (2.1.10)$$

so that $S(\omega)$ is monotonically nondecreasing as ω goes from $-\pi$ to π, with further properties $S(-\pi) = 0$, $S(\pi) = 1$, and $1 - S(-\omega) = S(\omega)$, from which it follows that $S(0) = \frac{1}{2}$.

Equation (2.1.8) may now be written in the alternative form

$$\rho_\tau = \frac{\lambda_\tau}{\lambda_0} = \int_{-\pi}^{\pi} e^{i\tau\omega}\, dS(\omega) \qquad (2.1.11)$$

Equation (2.1.11) is called the spectral representation of the autocorrelation sequence ρ_τ. This representation is one of the two fundamental relationships that need to be understood and interpreted for a proper appreciation of the spectral approach. The other fundamental relation, called the spectral representation of the stationary series X_t, is

$$X_t = \int_{-\pi}^{\pi} e^{it\omega} \, dz(\omega) \qquad (2.1.12)$$

where

$$E\{ dz(\omega) \overline{dz(\lambda)} \} = 0, \qquad \omega \neq \lambda$$
$$= \lambda_0 \, dS(\omega), \qquad \omega = \lambda \qquad (2.1.13)$$

To explain the importance and interpretation of these two representations, it is necessary to consider a sequence of models of increasing generality. First consider the simple linear cyclical process

$$X_t = a \cos(\omega_1 t + \theta) \qquad (2.1.14)$$

discussed in Section 1.4, where θ is a random variable rectangularly distributed on $(-\pi, \pi)$ and whose value is taken to have been determined at time $t = -\infty$ for the process to be considered stationary. It was shown in Section 1.4 that the autocovariance sequence for this process is given by $\lambda_\tau = (a^2/2) \cos \tau \omega_1$, and so (2.1.11) holds with

$$S(\omega) = \tfrac{1}{2}, \qquad 0 \leqslant \omega < \omega_1$$
$$= 1, \qquad \omega_1 \leqslant \omega \leqslant \pi$$

as may be seen by direct substitution. Thus $S(\omega)$ is the simple step function shown in Fig. 2.1.

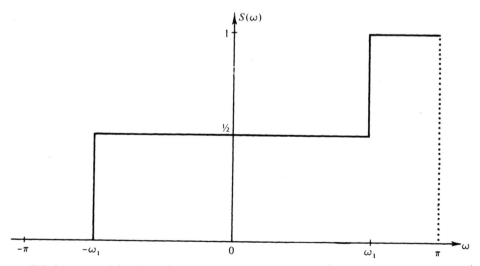

FIG. 2.1 *Spectral distribution function for model* (2.1.14).

Now consider the rather more general linear cyclical process

$$X_t = \sum_{j=1}^{m} a_j \cos(\omega_j t + \theta_j), \qquad 0 \leqslant \omega_j < \omega_{j+1} \leqslant \pi, \quad \text{all } j \quad (2.1.15)$$

where θ_j, $j = 1,\ldots, m$, is a set of independent random variables, each rectangularly distributed on $(-\pi, \pi)$. By the arguments used in Section 1.4, it follows that

$$\lambda_\tau = \tfrac{1}{2} \sum a_j^2 \cos \tau \omega_j \qquad (2.1.16)$$

and the power spectral distribution function corresponding to this covariance sequence is

$$S(\omega) = \tfrac{1}{2}, \qquad 0 \leqslant \omega < \omega_1$$

$$= \tfrac{1}{2}\left(\lambda_0 + \tfrac{1}{2} \sum_{j=1}^{k} a_j^2\right)\Big/\lambda_0, \qquad \omega_k \leqslant \omega < \omega_{k+1}, \quad k = 1,\ldots, m - 1$$

$$= 1, \qquad \omega_m \leqslant \omega \leqslant \pi \qquad (2.1.17)$$

where, of course, $\lambda_0 = \tfrac{1}{2}\sum_{j=1}^{m} a_j^2$ is the variance of X_t. There are a number of features of this example that are particularly noteworthy:

(i)　X_t is the sum of m components, the jth component being $X_{j,t} = a_j \cos(\omega_j t + \theta_j)$, and is thus completely associated with the frequency ω_j.

(ii)　The components are uncorrelated with one another, which can be verified by noting that

$$X_{j,t} = a_j \cos \theta_j \cos \omega_j t - a_j \sin \theta_j \sin \omega_j t \quad \text{and} \quad E[\cos \theta_j] = E[\sin \theta_j] = 0$$

and then by remembering that θ_j, θ_k are independent and thus any function of θ_j will be independent of any function of θ_k.

(iii)　The variance of $X_{j,t}$ is $\tfrac{1}{2}a_j^2$ so that one can say that the contribution to the total variance of X_t is $\tfrac{1}{2}a_j^2$.

(iv)　$S(\omega)$ is a monotonically nondecreasing step function, with steps at $\omega = \pm\omega_j$, $j = 1,\ldots, m$, and with a step of size $a_j^2/4\lambda_0$ at frequency $\omega = \omega_j$.

(v)　The probability function corresponding to this distribution function takes the form shown in Fig. 2.2, having peaks of height $a_j^2/4$ at frequencies $\omega = \pm\omega_j$.

A natural generalization of model (2.1.15) follows by allowing the number of components to tend to infinity, i.e., letting $m \to \infty$, giving

$$X_t = \sum_{j=1}^{\infty} a_j \cos(\omega_j t + \theta_j) \qquad (2.1.18)$$

i.e.,

$$X_t = \sum_{j=1}^{\infty} (a_j \cos \theta_j \cos \omega_j t - a_j \sin \theta_j \sin \omega_j t) \qquad (2.1.19)$$

Probability

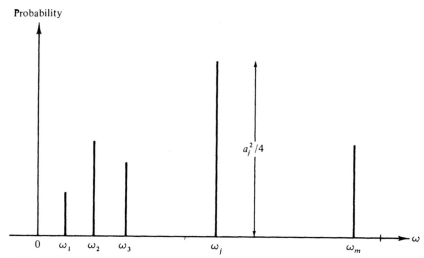

FIG. 2.2   *Probability function corresponding to spectral distribution function* (2.1.17).

with $0 \leqslant \omega_j < \omega_{j+1} \leqslant \pi$ for all j and the θ_j still being independent random variables rectangularly distributed on $(-\pi, \pi)$. Thus X_t now consists of a countably infinite number of components, but since X_t is required to have finite variance, the condition

$$\lim_{m \to \infty} \tfrac{1}{2} \sum_{j=1}^{m} a_j^2 = \text{var}(X_t) < \infty$$

needs to be imposed.

The model in (2.1.18) is a fairly general one, but it is possible to go further. One could ask, Why should there be only a countably infinite number of components rather than an uncountably infinite number?[1] If one takes this further step, (2.1.19) becomes

$$X_t = \int_0^{\pi} \cos \omega t \, du(\omega) - \int_0^{\pi} \sin \omega t \, dv(\omega) \qquad (2.1.20)$$

where $du(\omega)$ and $dv(\omega)$ are random variables such that

$$\begin{aligned}
E[du(\omega) \, du(\lambda)] &= 0, & \omega \neq \lambda \\
E[du(\omega) \, dv(\lambda)] &= 0, & \text{all } \omega, \lambda \\
E[dv(\omega) \, dv(\lambda)] &= 0, & \omega \neq \lambda
\end{aligned} \qquad (2.1.21)$$

Viewing the integral sign as an elongated S, denoting a sum, then (2.1.20) has X_t as a "sum" of an uncountable number of uncorrelated components of the

---

[1] If the objects in a set can each be associated with an integer, they are said to be countable, for example, the positive even integers, but if the objects in a set are too numerous for this, such as the number of points on the line $(0, 1)$, they are said to be uncountably infinite.

form

$$X_t(\omega) = \cos t\omega \, du(\omega) - \sin t\omega \, dv(\omega) \qquad (2.1.22)$$

so that each component is associated with a specific frequency ω. If, further, $\text{var}(du(\omega)) = \text{var}(dv(\omega)) = 2\lambda_0 \, dS(\omega)$, then

$$\text{var}(X_t(\omega)) = (\cos t\omega)^2 \text{var}(du(\omega)) + (\sin t\omega)^2 \text{var}(dv(\omega)) = 2\lambda_0 \, dS(\omega)$$

and so

$$\lambda_0 = \text{var } X_t = \int_0^\pi \text{var}(X_t(\omega)) \, d\omega = 2\int_0^\pi \lambda_0 \, dS(\omega)$$

$$= 2\lambda_0(S(\pi) - S(0)) = \lambda_0$$

as required since $S(\pi) = 1$ and $S(0) = \frac{1}{2}$.

A more convenient form of (2.1.20) is achieved by defining the complex random variable

$$dz(\omega) = \frac{1}{2}\{du(\omega) + i \, dv(\omega)\} \qquad (2.1.23)$$

since then (2.1.20) becomes

$$X_t = \int_{-\pi}^\pi e^{it\omega} \, dz(\omega) \qquad (2.1.24)$$

with

$$E\left[dz(\omega)\,\overline{dz(\lambda)}\right] = 0, \qquad \omega \neq \lambda$$
$$= \lambda_0 \, dS(\omega), \qquad \omega = \lambda \qquad (2.1.25)$$

where $\overline{X}$ denotes the complex conjugate of X. The more general model, so derived, has not been considered simply out of curiosity but because it can be shown that *any* stationary series may be represented in the form (2.1.20) or equivalently by (2.1.24) together with the condition (2.1.25). An elementary proof may be found in Chapter 17 of Wilks [1962].

There is one important way in which X_t generated by (2.1.24) is more general than X_t generated by the linear cyclical models (2.1.15) or (2.1.18). In theory at least, a series generated by such a linear cyclical model is deterministic, that is, it can be predicted without error given the infinite past of the series, but X_t generated by (2.1.24) need not have this property. (Deterministic and nondeterministic series are discussed further in Section 4.1.) This aspect of the general model appears mathematically in the following way: there is a classical result in mathematics that states that any monotonically nondecreasing function can always be decomposed into three monotonic components, one of which is continuous and differentiable, the second is a step function, and the third has more unusual mathematical properties which cannot be interpreted in the present context and can safely be ignored. Thus the spectral distribution function $S(\omega)$ may be written

$$S(\omega) \approx S_1(\omega) + S_2(\omega) \qquad (2.1.26)$$

where $S_1(\omega)$ is the continuous component and $S_2(\omega)$ the step function. This decomposition matches exactly Wold's decomposition of a stationary series, discussed in Section 1.11, with $S_1(\omega)$ being the spectral distribution function of the purely nondeterministic (MA(∞)) component and $S_2(\omega)$ corresponding to the deterministic component, as in (2.1.17) for example.

Suppose now that X_t is purely nondeterministic, so that $S(\omega) = S_1(\omega)$, and let $\lambda_0 \, dS(\omega)/d\omega = s(\omega)$. Then one has

$$X_t = \int_{-\pi}^{\pi} e^{it\omega} \, dz(\omega) \tag{2.1.27}$$

with[1]

$$E\left[dz(\omega)\,\overline{dz(\lambda)}\right] = 0, \qquad \omega \neq \lambda$$
$$= s(\omega)\,d\omega, \qquad \omega = \lambda \tag{2.1.28}$$

As stated earlier, this formula together with (2.1.8) make up the two most important relationships in spectral analysis. Unfortunately it is likely to appear rather complicated and of an unfamiliar form to many readers, and so some further explanation is in order. The need to use complex conjugates in the expectation term arises as follows. Let A and B be two complex random variables with zero means; then the covariance between them is defined as $\mathrm{cov}(A, B) = E\{A\,\overline{B}\}$. This form is necessary so that the variance of A is real, remembering that variance is a measure of dispersion and thus needs to be real, i.e.,

$$\mathrm{var}(A) \equiv \mathrm{cov}(A, A) = E\{|A|^2\} \tag{2.1.29}$$

If $E\{dz(\omega)\} = 0$, which will be assumed to be so, then

$$\lambda_\tau \equiv \mathrm{cov}(X_t, X_{t-\tau}) = E[X_t \overline{X}_{t-\tau}] = \int_{-\pi}^{\pi} \int_{-\pi}^{\pi} e^{it\omega} e^{-i(t-\tau)\lambda} E\left[dz(\omega)\,\overline{dz(\lambda)}\right] \tag{2.1.30}$$

The need for condition (2.1.28) is now seen as a requirement for X_t to be stationary, for otherwise λ_τ will be a function of time t, which is not possible under stationarity. Using (2.1.28), the double integral in (2.1.30) becomes just the integral along the line $\omega = \lambda$ and so this integral becomes

$$\lambda_\tau = \int_{-\pi}^{\pi} e^{i\tau\omega} s(\omega) \, d\omega \tag{2.1.31}$$

Thus, the spectral representation of the series X_t, alternatively called the Cramér representation, and the spectral representation of the covariance sequence λ_τ, given by (2.1.31), have been derived. The method used above to reach these relationships leads immediately to the interpretation of the

---

[1] The reason it is necessary to use the more awkward-looking terms $du(\omega)$ and $dz(\omega)$ rather than, say, $a(\omega)\,d\omega$, is clear from (2.1.28) where it is seen that $dz(\omega)$ is $O(\sqrt{d\omega})$ rather than $O(d\omega)$.

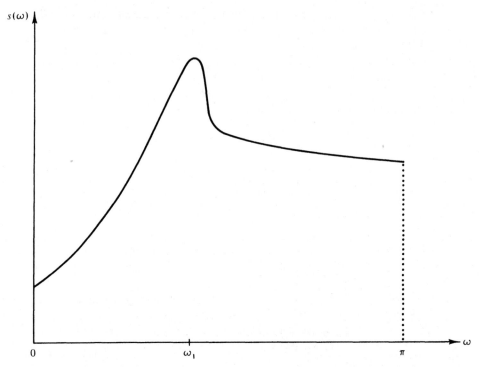

FIG. 2.3   *Example of a spectrum, with frequency components around ω_1 of most importance.*

spectrum $s(\omega)$ since $s(\omega)\, d\omega$ is the contribution to the variance of X_t attributable to the component $X_t(\omega)$ of X_t with frequencies in the range $(\omega, \omega + d\omega)$. Thus, if $s(\omega)$ had the shape shown in Fig. 2.3, one could say that the low-frequency (long-period) components were of little importance since they contribute little to $\mathrm{var}(X_t)$, the components near frequency ω_1 were of greatest importance, and the high-frequency components (short periods, ω near π) are of intermediate importance. Note that, from its definition, the area under the curve $s(\omega)$ over the range $0 \leqslant \omega \leqslant \pi$ is $\frac{1}{2}\,\mathrm{var}\,X_t$.

To summarize this section, it has been proposed that any stationary time series can be thought of as the sum of (possibly) a noncountably infinite number of uncorrelated components, each associated with a particular frequency, and the importance of any group of components with frequencies falling into some narrow band is measured by their composite variance. This variance when plotted against frequency is the power spectral function.

As an illustration of these ideas, consider the simplest type of series, a zero-mean white noise, so that $X_t = \epsilon_t$. Then $\lambda_\tau = 0$, $\tau \neq 0$, and the corresponding spectrum is seen from (2.1.4) to be $s_\epsilon(\omega) = \sigma_\epsilon^2/2\pi$, i.e., a constant over the whole frequency range. Thus white noise is made up of components of all frequencies and all components are equally important, when measured in terms of their contribution to the variance of the series. This explains how the expression "white noise" arose to describe a purely random sequence, as if one considers visual light, a light for which one component is more important than others will appear as a color, but light in which all color components are present in equal amounts will appear white.

2.2 Filters

If X_t is a zero-mean stationary series with Cramér representation $X_t = \int_{-\pi}^{\pi} e^{it\omega} \, dz_x(\omega)$, then clearly $B^k X_t = X_{t-k} = \int_{-\pi}^{\pi} e^{i(t-k)\omega} \, dz_x(\omega)$. It then follows that if Y_t is a filtered version of X_t, given by

$$Y_t = \sum_{j=0}^{m} c_j X_{t-j} \tag{2.2.1}$$

i.e.,

$$Y_t = c(B) X_t \quad \text{where} \quad c(B) = \sum_{j=0}^{m} c_j B^j \tag{2.2.2}$$

then the Cramér representation of Y_t is just $Y_t = \int_{-\pi}^{\pi} e^{it\omega} c(e^{-i\omega}) \, dz_x(\omega)$. The spectrum of Y_t is then found by considering $\lambda_\tau^{(y)} \equiv \text{cov}(Y_t, Y_{t-\tau})$, i.e.,

$$E[Y_t \overline{Y}_{t-\tau}] = \int_{-\pi}^{\pi} \int_{-\pi}^{\pi} e^{it\omega} e^{-i(t-\tau)\lambda} c(e^{-i\omega}) c(e^{i\lambda}) E\left[dz_x(\omega) \overline{dz_x(\lambda)} \right]$$

which, from the orthogonality condition for $dz_x(\omega)$, becomes, as with (2.1.30),

$$\lambda_\tau^{(y)} = \int_{-\pi}^{\pi} e^{i\tau\omega} c(e^{-i\omega}) c(e^{i\omega}) s_x(\omega) \, d\omega$$

so that, comparing with (2.1.31), one obtains

$$s_y(\omega) = |c(e^{i\omega})|^2 s_x(\omega) \tag{2.2.3}$$

where $|c(e^{i\omega})|^2$ may be called the *filter function*. It is possible to interpret the effect on a series of applying a filter from this formula. Suppose, for example, that the coefficients c_j were such that the shape of $|c(e^{i\omega})|^2$ when plotted against ω is as shown in Fig. 2.4.

The spectrum of Y_t will then be the spectrum of X_t multiplied by this shape. If X_t were white noise, then the spectrum of Y_t would be shaped exactly as in Fig. 2.4. Since this shape has a peak at $\pi/2$, it follows that the component of Y_t with this frequency will be important compared to other frequencies, and thus Y_t will tend to appear to contain a cycle with frequency approximately equal to $\pi/2$. Thus, in this case one outcome of filtering a white noise series has been to produce a series that appears to have a cyclical component, at least over some sample lengths. A possible set of coefficients producing such an effect is $c_0 = 1$, $c_2 = -2$, $c_4 = 1$, and all the other $c_j = 0$;

$|c(e^{i\omega})|^2$

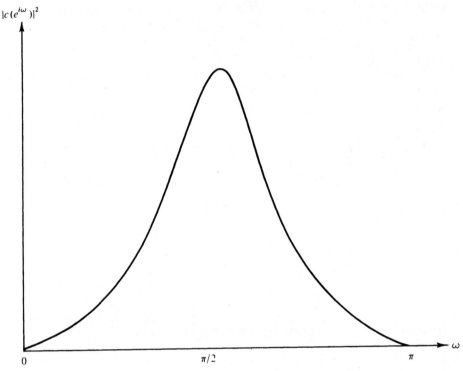

0	$\pi/2$ π ω

FIG. 2.4   *Example of a filter function.*

then $|c(e^{i\omega})|^2 = 4(1 - \cos 2\omega)^2$ which has the shape shown in the figure. Early time series analysts were very concerned about the possibility of a filter inserting a spurious cycle into their data—the so-called Slutzky-effect. When using only time-domain analysis, it is difficult to investigate this possibility; but using spectral methods it is seen that interpretation becomes much easier.

As a second example of a filter, consider $Y_t = \sum_{j=0}^{m} X_{t-j}$, i.e., a moving average with constant weights. Then

$$|c(e^{i\omega})|^2 = [1 - \cos(m + 1)\omega]/(1 - \cos \omega)$$

which has the form shown in Fig. 2.5. If m is quite large, the first peak, around zero frequency, becomes of dominating importance, and so it follows that Y_t will consist almost exclusively of the low-frequency component of the original series X_t. Such a filter is called a *low-band pass* filter. It was suggested in Section 1.10 that such a moving average can be used to estimate the trend component of a series. The reason for this can now be seen since a trend component will correspond to the very low (near zero) frequency component, since a trend is essentially monotonic and so does not repeat itself, meaning that trend has infinite period and hence zero frequency.

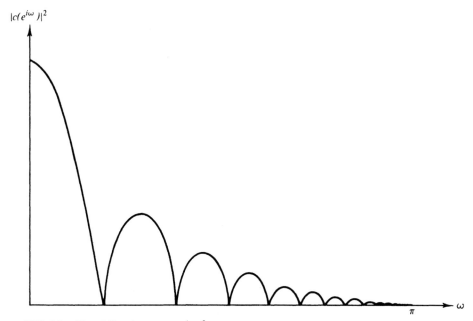

$|c(e^{i\omega})|^2$

FIG. 2.5 *Plot of filter function* $|c(e^{i\omega})|^2 = [1 - \cos(m + 1)\omega]/(1 - \cos \omega)$.

2.3 The Spectrum of Some Common Models

In the previous sections the shape of the spectrum of certain models was determined, in particular:

(i)   A white noise series has a flat spectrum over the whole range $0 \leqslant \omega \leqslant \pi$.

(ii)   A series with a cyclical component of frequency ω_0 has a spectrum with a tall, narrow peak at that frequency (theoretically, an infinitely tall, infinitely narrow, peak having finite area). In particular, a series with a seasonal component will have a spectrum with peaks at $j\omega_s$, $j = 1, 2, \ldots$, where ω_s is the principal seasonal frequency, so that $\omega_s = 2\pi/12$ for monthly data, and $\omega_s = 2\pi/4$ for quarterly data, and so forth. The secondary seasonal frequencies $j\omega_s$, $j > 1$ and $j\omega_s \leqslant \pi$, correspond to the harmonics of the seasonal component.

(iii)   A series with an important trend component will have a strong peak at the very low frequencies.

Now consider a stationary series generated by an ARMA(p, q) model, so that

$$a(B)X_t = b(B)\epsilon_t \tag{2.3.1}$$

which has a corresponding MA(∞) representation $X_t = c(B)\epsilon_t$, where

$$c(z) = b(z)/a(z) \tag{2.3.2}$$

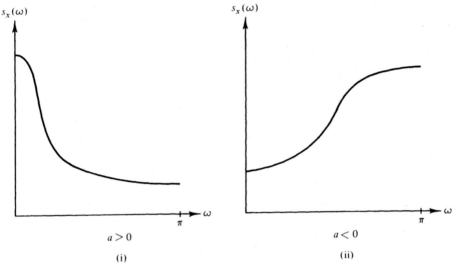

FIG. 2.6   *Spectrum of first-order autoregressive process.*

The MA(∞) form indicates that X_t is merely a filtered version of the white noise series ϵ_t, and thus from (2.2.3) it follows that

$$s_x(\omega) = |c(z)|^2(\sigma_\epsilon^2/2\pi), \qquad z = e^{-i\omega} \tag{2.3.3}$$

i.e.,

$$s_x(\omega) = |b(e^{i\omega})/a(e^{i\omega})|^2(\sigma_\epsilon^2/2\pi) \tag{2.3.4}$$

This result can also be obtained from the definition of $s_x(\omega)$ in terms of the autocovariance generating function, obtained in Chapter 1, using Eqs. (2.1.2) and (1.7.18).

As a particular example, consider the AR(1) process $X_t = aX_{t-1} + \epsilon_t$. Then, from (2.3.4), this process has spectrum

$$s_x(\omega) = |1 - ae^{i\omega}|^{-2}(\sigma_\epsilon^2/2\pi) = \sigma_\epsilon^2/2\pi(1 + a^2 - 2a\cos\omega) \tag{2.3.5}$$

which has the shape shown in Fig. 2.6. When the parameter a is positive, the low frequency (long-period) components are seen to be the more important, and it therefore follows that the series will be smoother than white noise. If a is negative, the high-frequency (short-period) components will dominate and the series will be less smooth, or more ragged, even than a white noise series. These interpretations agree exactly, of course, with those achieved from the time-domain considerations of Section 1.5.

As a nears one, the low frequency peak will increase in height until, in the limit as $a \to 1$, the peak becomes infinite in height, as can be seen from the fact that

$$s_x(0) = \sigma_\epsilon^2/2\pi(1 - a)^2$$

Thus, in this limiting sense, the spectrum of the random walk series $X_t = X_{t-1} + \epsilon_t$ is of the form

$$s_x(\omega) = \sigma_\epsilon^2/4\pi(1 - \cos \omega) \qquad (2.3.6)$$

Strictly speaking a random walk does not possess a spectrum since it does not have a finite variance, but apart from a possible problem at the zero frequency the function given in (2.3.6) can be taken to be the spectrum of a random walk. Similarly, the spectrum of an ARIMA($p, 1, q$) process can be taken to be of the form

$$s_x(\omega) = (\sigma_\epsilon^2/4\pi)|b(e^{i\omega})/a(e^{i\omega})|^2(1 - \cos \omega)^{-1} \qquad (2.3.7)$$

This spectrum will have basically the same shape as that of a random walk since its shape is largely determined by the term $(1 - \cos \omega)^{-1}$ in (2.3.7). This fact alone strongly illustrates the necessity of first differencing such series before further detailed analysis is possible.

If a series W_t is the sum of the two zero-mean independent series X_t and Y_t, i.e., $W_t = X_t + Y_t$, then

$$s_w(\omega) = s_x(\omega) + s_y(\omega) \qquad (2.3.8)$$

as can be seen from (2.1.2) and the fact that $\lambda_\tau^{(w)} = \lambda_\tau^{(x)} + \lambda_\tau^{(y)}$. Thus, if W_t is the sum of a stationary ARMA series and a seasonal component, its spectrum will have the peaks arising from the seasonal superimposed on the spectrum of the ARMA series.

It is generally not possible to decide on the exact generating model of a series by looking at its spectrum, but for the reasons just outlined the spectrum can be useful in helping to decide whether or not to first difference a series and whether to allow for a seasonal component when modeling. Further, if a series has a rather flat spectrum, this is an excellent indication that the series is a white noise, or at least very nearly so. Thus, if one believes that X_t is generated by $a(B)X_t = b(B)\epsilon_t$, then the spectrum of the filtered series $\epsilon_t = b^{-1}(B)a(B)X_t$ will be flat if one's belief is correct.

2.4 Aliasing

Economists find that the sampling interval of their data is rarely at their disposal, so that data are provided with a daily or a monthly or a quarterly sampling interval. For many series, the sampling interval could have been shorter and in some cases the series could have been recorded continuously, for example, an interest rate series or a temperature. The fact that one is sampling such a series at equally spaced intervals of time does imply certain important considerations in the interpretation of a spectrum. Suppose that the continuous series $X(t)$ contains a cyclical component of frequency $2\pi/\Delta$, where Δ is the sampling interval. Then the sampled series $\{X_t\}$ will contain no information about this component, which will seem to be a constant. As

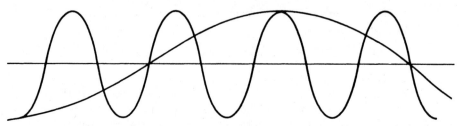

FIG. 2.7   *Illustration of aliasing.*

an example, if one recorded the temperature daily at noon one would have no information about daily cycle of temperature variation. However, if recordings were taken at noon and at midnight, the importance of the daily fluctuation in temperature could be estimated. In general, the highest frequency about which we have direct information is π/Δ and this is known as the "Nyquist frequency."

If this Nyquist frequency is denoted by ω_0, then its power will appear at $\omega = \pi$ in the power spectrum when defined as in the previous sections since $\lambda_\tau = E\{ X_t X_{t-\tau} \}$ is strictly $\lambda_{\tau\Delta} = E\{ X(t)X(t - \tau\Delta) \}$ in terms of the continuous series. If $X(t)$ contains a cycle with frequency greater than ω_0, then this component will be confused—or "aliased"—with a component having frequency less than ω_0. This follows because a high-frequency cosine wave systematically sampled at regular intervals appears the same as a low-frequency wave, as illustrated in Fig. 2.7. With Nyquist frequency ω_0, then if $\omega < \omega_0$, the frequencies $\omega, 2\omega_0 - \omega, 2\omega_0 + \omega, 4\omega_0 - \omega, 4\omega_0 + \omega, \ldots$ are all confounded and are aliases of one another, and the sum of all of their powers will appear at frequency ω in $s(\omega)$. As an example, suppose one's data are measured monthly, but the underlying continuous series contains a weekly cycle. Of course, there are not exactly four weeks to a month, so the weekly cycle will be seen as a peak in the spectrum—but at what frequency? Taking into account leap years, the average number of days in a month is 30.437 and so there are 4.348 weeks in the average month. Thus, the weekly cycle will induce a spike into the spectrum at frequency 0.348π since here π corresponds to the Nyquist frequency.

2.5 The Cross Spectrum

Cross-spectral analysis has nothing to do with angry ghosts, but is the generalization of the power spectrum to the two-series case and provides a sophisticated method of interpreting the relationship between a pair of series. Suppose that X_t and Y_t are both zero-mean, stationary series that are also jointly stationary so that

$$\lambda_\tau^{(x)} = E[X_t X_{t-\tau}], \quad \lambda_\tau^{(y)} = E[Y_t Y_{t-\tau}], \quad \lambda_\tau^{(xy)} = E[X_t Y_{t-\tau}] = \lambda_{-\tau}^{(yx)} \quad (2.5.1)$$

are all independent of t. This essentially means that the relationship between the two series is time invariate. Denote the cross-covariance generating function by $\lambda^{(xy)}(z)$, so that

$$\lambda^{(xy)}(z) = \sum_{\text{all } \tau} \lambda^{(xy)}_{\tau} z^{\tau} \qquad (2.5.2)$$

Then the cross spectrum (strictly, cross-spectral density function) between the series X_t, Y_t is defined to be

$$s_{xy}(\omega) = \frac{\lambda^{(xy)}(z)}{2\pi}, \qquad z = e^{-i\omega} \qquad (2.5.3)$$

The corresponding inverse relation is

$$\lambda^{(xy)}_{\tau} = \int_{-\pi}^{\pi} e^{i\omega\tau} s_{xy}(\omega)\, d\omega \qquad (2.5.4)$$

as is seen by multiplying both sides of (2.5.3) by $e^{i\tau\omega}$ and then integrating over $(-\pi, \pi)$. Since $\lambda^{(xy)}_{\tau} \neq \lambda^{(xy)}_{-\tau}$, in general, it follows that $s_{xy}(\omega)$ will usually be a complex function of ω, and so one could write

$$s_{xy}(\omega) = \mathrm{co}(\omega) + iq(\omega)$$

where $\mathrm{co}(\omega)$ and $q(\omega)$ are real functions, known as the cospectrum and the quadrature spectrum, respectively. These functions are all quite difficult to interpret as they stand, and so it is usual to define three further functions, that are much easier to interpret, from them. These are:

(i) $$C(\omega) = \frac{|s_{xy}(\omega)|^2}{s_{xx}(\omega) s_{yy}(\omega)} = \frac{\mathrm{co}^2(\omega) + q^2(\omega)}{s_{xx}(\omega) s_{yy}(\omega)} \qquad (2.5.5)$$

where $s_{xx}(\omega)$, $s_{yy}(\omega)$ are respectively the spectral density functions of X_t, Y_t. $C(\omega)$ will here be called the coherence function.[1]

(ii) $$\phi(\omega) = \tan^{-1}[q(\omega)/\mathrm{co}(\omega)] \qquad (2.5.6)$$

which is called the phase.

(iii) $$R_{xy}(\omega) = |s_{xy}(\omega)|/s_{yy}(\omega) \qquad (2.5.7)$$

known as the gain function.

All three of these functions are real and so can be conveniently plotted against ω, and due to symmetry it is only necessary to plot them over the range $0 \leqslant \omega \leqslant \pi$.

To learn how to interpret these plots, it is convenient to use the Cramér representations of the series:

$$X_t = \int_{-\pi}^{\pi} e^{it\omega}\, dz_x(\omega), \qquad Y_t = \int_{-\pi}^{\pi} e^{it\omega}\, dz_y(\omega) \qquad (2.5.8)$$

---

[1] Some other writers call $C(\omega)$ the coherency function, whereas others use this name for $\{C(\omega)\}^{1/2}$.

It was seen earlier that to ensure that X_t is stationary it is necessary that $E\{dz_x(\omega)\overline{dz_x(\lambda)}\} = 0$, $\omega \neq \lambda$. For X_t and Y_t to be jointly stationary requires

$$E\left\{dz_x(\omega)\overline{dz_y(\lambda)}\right\} = 0, \qquad \omega \neq \lambda \tag{2.5.9}$$

Consider now $\lambda_\tau^{(xy)} = E\{X_tY_{t-\tau}\}$, which from (2.5.8) may be written

$$\lambda_\tau^{(xy)} = \int_{-\pi}^{\pi}\int_{-\pi}^{\pi} e^{it\omega}e^{-i(t-\tau)\lambda}E\left\{dz_x(\omega)\overline{dz_y(\lambda)}\right\} \tag{2.5.10}$$

Hence, from (2.5.9), one gets

$$\lambda_\tau^{(xy)} = \int_{-\pi}^{\pi} e^{i\tau\omega}E\left\{dz_x(\omega)\overline{dz_y(\omega)}\right\}$$

so that

$$s_{xy}(\omega)\,d\omega = E\left\{dz_x(\omega)\overline{dz_y(\omega)}\right\} \tag{2.5.11}$$

It is possible to give immediately an interpretation to the coherence $C(\omega)$ by noting that it can be written

$$C(\omega) = \frac{\left(E\left\{dz_x(\omega)\overline{dz_y(\omega)}\right\}\right)}{E\left\{dz_x(\omega)\overline{dz_x(\omega)}\right\}E\left\{dz_y(\omega)\overline{dz_y(\omega)}\right\}} \tag{2.5.12}$$

Thus $C(\omega)$ is the square of the coefficient of correlation of $dz_x(\omega)$ and $dz_y(\omega)$. It follows that $0 \leqslant C(\omega) \leqslant 1$ and $C(\omega)$ should be interpreted in exactly the same way as the square of a correlation coefficient. Thus if $C(\omega)$ is near one, it means that the ω-frequency components of the two series are highly (linearly) related, but a value near zero means that these corresponding frequency components are only slightly related. The stationarity condition (2.5.9) implies that if X_t and Y_t are related, then they are related only through their corresponding frequency components. Similarly, by its construction, the gain function $R_{xy}(\omega)$ is the regression coefficient of the ω-frequency component of X_t on the corresponding ω-frequency component of Y_t, and can be interpreted accordingly.

To understand the use of the phase function $\phi(\omega)$, it is useful to consider a model of the form

$$X_t = aY_{t-k} + V_t \tag{2.5.13}$$

where Y_t and V_t are independent stationary series. Putting the terms of the model into the Cramér representation form gives

$$\int_{-\pi}^{\pi} e^{it\omega}\,dz_x(\omega) = \int_{-\pi}^{\pi} e^{it\omega}ae^{-ik\omega}\,dz_y(\omega) + \int_{-\pi}^{\pi} e^{it\omega}\,dz_v(\omega)$$

so that

$$dz_x(\omega) = ae^{-ik\omega}\,dz_y(\omega) + dz_v(\omega) \tag{2.5.14}$$

Then multiplying by $\overline{dz_y}(\omega)$ and taking expectations, from (2.5.11), yields

$$s_{xy}(\omega)\,d\omega = ae^{-ik\omega}E\{dz_y(\omega)\overline{dz_y}(\omega)\} = ae^{-ik\omega}s_{yy}(\omega)\,d\omega \quad (2.5.15)$$

since $E\{dz_v(\omega)\overline{dz_y}(\omega)\} = 0$, since Y_t, V_t were taken to be independent. It follows immediately from (2.5.15) and the definition of $\phi(\omega)$ that

$$\phi(\omega) = \tan^{-1}\left|\frac{-a\sin k\omega s_{yy}(\omega)}{a\cos k\omega s_{yy}(\omega)}\right| = -k\omega$$

Thus, the phase diagram, being the plot of $\phi(\omega)$ against ω, will be useful in finding any lag relationship between the series one is investigating. If $\phi(\omega)$ is a straight line over some frequency band, then the direction of slope tells one which series is leading and the amount of the slope gives the extent of the lag. It is important to note that the lag k need not be an integer multiple of the sampling period, so that it is possible to detect a lag of say 1.5 months when using monthly data. When investigating lags using a time-domain approach, it is much more difficult to pick up such noninteger lags.

In interpreting a phase diagram it is important to realize that one has to have a causal model of the form (2.5.13) in mind since if there is a feedback relationship between the two series, then the above interpretation is no longer appropriate. If the two series X_t and Y_t are related in a more complicated manner, such as a filter form $X_t = \sum_{j=0}^{m}a_jY_{t-j}$, then the phase diagram is no longer easy to interpret. This is seen by noting that

$$dz_x(\omega) = a(\omega)\,dz_y(\omega) \quad \text{where} \quad a(\omega) = \sum_{j=0}^{m}a_je^{-ij\omega}$$

so that $C(\omega) = 1$ for all ω. However,

$$\phi(\omega) = \tan^{-1}\left[\frac{-\sum a_j\sin j\omega}{\sum a_j\cos j\omega}\right]$$

which will typically be of a nonsimple form.

It should also be noted that there is a degree of ambiguity in the definition of $\phi(\omega)$ since it is a periodic function, with $\phi(\omega + 2j\pi) = \phi(\omega)$ if j is an integer. It is usual to restrict $\phi(\omega)$ to the region $-\pi < \phi(\omega) \leqslant \pi$, but the periodic nature of the function is important to remember when interpreting the diagram. An example is when $X_t = -aY_t$ since then $dz_x(\omega) = -a\,dz_y(\omega)$, which may be written $dz_x(\omega) = ae^{i\pi}\,dz_y(\omega)$ and so $\phi(\omega) = \pi$. However, the estimate of $\phi(\omega)$ will be inclined to lie about the value π; and, from the periodic nature of the definition, this means that some values will lie just under π and others just above $-\pi$, having "flipped over" by the amount 2π.

Some examples of the use of spectral and cross-spectral analysis are given in Section 2.7, after the estimation problem has been discussed in the following section.

2.6 Estimation of Spectral Functions

The estimation of a spectrum has proved to be, for the statistician, one of the more interesting and difficult estimation problems so far encountered. One aspect of this difficulty arises because one is attempting to estimate all the uncountably infinite number of points of a continuous curve $s(\omega)$, $0 \leqslant \omega \leqslant \pi$, from just a finite amount of data x_t, $t = 1, \ldots, n$. An obvious starting point in such an attempt is the definition (2.1.4)

$$s(\omega) = \frac{\lambda_0}{2\pi} + \frac{1}{\pi} \sum_{\tau=1}^{\infty} \lambda_\tau \cos \tau\omega \tag{2.6.1}$$

Some of the λ_τ may be estimated from the data by

$$\hat{\lambda}_\tau = \frac{1}{n(\tau)} \sum_{t=1}^{n-\tau} (x_t - \bar{x})(x_{t+\tau} - \bar{x}), \qquad \tau = 0, 1, \ldots, n-1 \tag{2.6.2}$$

where $n(\tau)$ could be n or $n - |\tau|$ or some other appropriate quantity. In fact, it turns out that the choice of $n(\tau) = n$ has certain advantages, even though it means that a biased estimate of λ_τ is being used. The proposed estimate is thus

$$\hat{s}(\omega) = \frac{\hat{\lambda}_0}{2\pi} + \frac{1}{\pi} \sum_{\tau=1}^{n-1} \hat{\lambda}_\tau \cos \tau\omega = \frac{1}{2\pi} \sum_{\tau=-n+1}^{n-1} \hat{\lambda}_\tau \cos \tau\omega \tag{2.6.3}$$

If, in (2.6.2), $n(\tau) = n$, then (2.6.3) is seen, after some algebra, to be just

$$\hat{s}(\omega) = \frac{1}{2\pi n} \left| \sum_{t=1}^{n} (x_t - \bar{x}) e^{i\omega t} \right|^2 \tag{2.6.4}$$

so that this estimate of the spectrum is seen to be proportional to the periodogram discussed in Section 1.4. Thus, in a sense, Schuster, when introducing the periodogram at the very beginning of this century, was anticipating the development of spectral analysis. However, it has been found that in many ways the estimate (2.6.4) is an unsatisfactory estimate, and in particular it is not consistent since the variance of $\hat{s}(\omega)$ does not tend to zero as n, the sample size, tends to infinity. Further, the covariance between $\hat{s}(\omega_1)$ and $\hat{s}(\omega_2)$, that is, the covariance between estimates at two different frequencies, does tend to zero as $n \to \infty$, so that for large n, $\hat{s}(\omega)$ has a tendency to become very jagged and the possibility of finding spurious "cycles" in one's data is enhanced. This is the reason the periodogram proved to be an unsatisfactory tool of analysis and has been largely superseded by the spectrum.

To produce estimates having better properties, the following class has been considered by many writers:

$$\hat{s}_k(\omega) = \frac{1}{2\pi} \sum_{\tau=-n+1}^{n-1} k_n(\tau) \hat{\lambda}_\tau \cos \tau\omega \tag{2.6.5}$$

where the constants $k_n(\tau)$ are derived from a function $k(\ )$ by

$$k_n(\tau) = k(\tau/M_n) \tag{2.6.6}$$

for some number M_n depending on n. The function $k(\ )$ is known as the "lag window generator" and M_n is called the "truncation point." There has been considerable debate about how these quantities should be selected, largely because there is no single criterion that is generally accepted to be the best for use in selecting among possible estimates. A widely used function, suggested by Parzen [1961], is

$$
\begin{aligned}
k(u) &= 1 - 6u^2 + 6|u|^3, & |u| &\leqslant 0.5 \\
&= 2(1 - |u|)^3, & 0.5 &< |u| < 1.0 \\
&= 0, & |u| &\geqslant 1
\end{aligned}
\tag{2.6.7}
$$

This produces consistent estimates, provided $M_n \to \infty$ and $M_n/n \to 0$ as $n \to \infty$, and also ensures that the spectral estimate cannot take negative values. However, one pays for consistency by having a biased estimate, the bias being approximately proportional at frequency ω to the value of the actual spectrum $s(\omega)$.

If the sequence $k_n(\tau)$, for fixed n, has Fourier transform window $k_n(\omega)$, so that

$$k_n(\tau) = \int_{-\pi}^{\pi} \cos \tau \omega k_n(\omega)\, d\omega \tag{2.6.8}$$

then it may be shown that

$$\hat{s}_k(\omega) = \int_{-\pi}^{\pi} k_n(\lambda)\hat{s}(\omega - \lambda)\, d\lambda$$

where $\hat{s}(\omega)$ is given by (2.6.4) and is proportional to the periodogram. Thus, since $k_n(\lambda)$ takes its main maximum at $\lambda = 0$, $\hat{s}_k(\omega)$ for given ω is seen to be a weighted average of periodogram-type estimates at frequencies centered on ω. This may be thought of as viewing a periodogram through a Gothic window and averaging what one sees. As one moves to an adjacent frequency value ω', $\hat{s}_k(\omega')$ will still contain part of the periodogram used in forming $\hat{s}_k(\omega)$, and this will ensure a positive covariance between $\hat{s}_k(\omega)$ and $\hat{s}_k(\omega')$, provided ω and ω' are sufficiently near, and so an estimated curve that is smoother than a periodogram will result. The value of M_n chosen will determine the "width" of the window and hence the size of this covariance. The value of M_n chosen is for the analyst to decide. As a rule of thumb, for typical sample sizes found in economics, M_n is usually not more than $n/3$, and experienced analysts find it helpful in interpreting possible cyclical peaks in the spectrum to superimpose three estimates of the spectrum using three different values of M_n, such as $n/5$, $n/4$, and $n/3$.

The cross spectrum may be estimated using (2.6.5) but with $\hat{\lambda}_\tau$ being replaced by an estimate of the corresponding cross variance, i.e.,

$$\hat{\lambda}_\tau^{xy} = \frac{1}{n} \sum_{t=\tau+1}^{n} (x_t - \bar{x})(y_{t-\tau} - \bar{y})$$

Estimates of coherence and phase may be derived directly from the estimate of the cross spectrum.

It will be seen from (2.6.4) that, since the mean is subtracted from the data, it necessarily follows that $\hat{s}(0) = 0$ and, since $\hat{s}_k(\omega)$ is a smoothed periodogram, it then follows that spectral estimates at zero frequency are not very reliable, and similarly for the cross spectrum.

Asymptotic values for the mean, variance, and covariance of spectral estimates are available, and Neave [1970] has provided exact formulas for these quantities, although these depend on the actual autocovariance sequence of the process. Asymptotically $\hat{s}_k(\omega)$ is normally distributed, but a chi-squared approximation seems more appropriate for series of fewer than 200 terms. Some suggestions have also been made in the literature on the distribution of the coherence and phase functions, and many of these possibilities have been investigated, using simulation techniques, by Granger and Hughes [1968], although the conclusions there reached for the spectral estimate $\hat{s}_k(\omega)$ have to be somewhat modified in the light of comments made by Neave [1972]. In general terms, the simulation studies indicate that the main shape of a spectrum should be observed even when estimated from quite short series and, similarly, simple lags between series should be detected, but the estimated coherence derived from short series is less satisfactory since the estimates appear to be biased toward the value 0.5.

One important feature of the phase diagram does result from the theory and is supported by the simulations: the estimate of phase is rectangularly distributed over $(-\pi, \pi)$ if the true coherence is zero. This is intuitively sensible since one cannot hope to estimate a measure of lag between two unrelated components. It follows that if the phase diagram is extremely unstable, then this is good evidence that the two series are uncorrelated over the appropriate set of frequencies.

Considerably more detail relating to the problems of estimation, the properties of the estimates, and various alternative procedures can be found in the books by Parzen [1967], Hannan [1970], Koopmans [1974], and Priestley [1981] and also in the Special Issue on Spectral Estimation, *Proc. IEEE* **70**, (9) (September, 1982).

The following two sections of this chapter discuss some applications of spectral techniques.

2.7 The Typical Spectral Shape and Its Interpretation

The interpretation of the power spectrum of a single series depends upon the existence of any underlying smooth shape in the estimated spectrum plus the position and height of any possibly significant peaks. The peaks can be interpreted as indicating "cyclical" components in the series, having almost constant periods. The underlying smooth shape conceptually can be used to suggest possible models for the noncyclical component. The original uses of spectral analysis in economics concentrated on these aspects. Peaks at the seasonal frequencies were interpreted as a clear indication that the series contained a seasonal component and so looking at the spectrum of a seasonally adjusted series is helpful in evaluating the effectiveness of the adjustment process. The use of spectral techniques in dealing with problems of seasonal adjustment is considered further in the next section. The only other possibly meaningful peaks would be those corresponding to the business cycles in the economy. Although it is now generally accepted that the business cycle cannot be well represented by the sum of a few purely periodic components, the possibility of there being extra power at a low-frequency band, corresponding to the business cycle component, has been considered by a number of writers, for example, Howrey [1968]. Given sufficient data, very subtle cycles can be detected.

If the estimated spectrum appears flat, without peaks and without any clear tendency to follow a smooth curve, then this suggests that the series is white noise. Confidence bands can also be constructed to test the hypothesis that the series is white noise. This procedure has been used to test the hypothesis that prices from speculative markets follow a random walk, by forming the spectrum of price changes, in Granger and Morgenstern [1970] and Labys and Granger [1970]. If the underlying shape is not flat, this observation might be used to suggest a model for the series; but since there are usually many models that could produce almost identical shapes, the estimated spectrum is rarely found to be useful in the model identification problem to be discussed in Chapter 3.

When economic data were first analyzed by spectral methods in the early 1960s, a somewhat unexpected result was the observation that most of the estimated spectra had almost identical shapes, being very high at very low frequencies, falling steeply as frequency increased, becoming flat at high frequencies (ω near π) and with only the occasional peak at a seasonal frequency to break up the inherent smoothness. Such curves were called the "typical spectral shape" [Granger, 1966], and an example is shown in Fig. 2.8, which shows the spectrum of the Federal Reserve Board index of industrial production using 486 monthly observations, and is from Nerlove [1964]. One consequence of this shape is that it is very difficult to observe subtle features of the spectrum at low frequencies, due to an estimation problem called leakage, which means that the estimate of the spectrum near a peak is badly upward biased. The basic reason for the typical spectral shape arising is the very high correlation observed between adjacent values of the levels of most economic series when observed frequently, such as at monthly intervals. It might be said that the economy has considerable momentum and that the size of changes in economic variables is generally small compared to the current level of the variable. Since spectral analysis requires rather large samples for efficient estimation, most of the series originally analyzed were those recorded monthly or at even shorter intervals.

It was originally suggested that an appropriate model for a series having a typical spectral shape, without seasonal peaks, was a process of the form

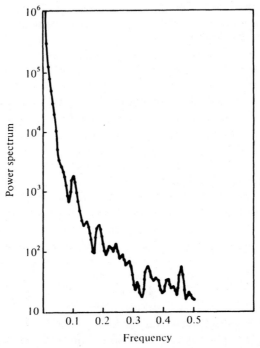

FIG. 2.8   *Spectrum of Federal Reserve Board index of industrial production.*

$X_t = aX_{t-1} + \epsilon_t$ where ϵ_t is white noise and a is very near one, values for a of 0.95 or greater being suggested. While such a model would produce a typical spectral shape, it is now recognized that a wider, and potentially more fruitful, class will also produce this spectral shape, namely the ARIMA class considered in Section 1.13, as can be seen from Eq. (2.3.7). In any case, the most important consequence of the observed typical spectral shape is that it will be very difficult to perform subtle analysis on the levels of most economic variables, a point which will be repeated elsewhere in this book. If the series is first filtered, to remove or at least greatly reduce the considerable peak at zero frequency, it becomes much easier to identify other features of the series. Experience suggests that an appropriate filter is the first difference, so that changes (or possibly proportional changes) should be used rather than levels. The spectra of most change series do not have the typical shape and usually are not flat, suggesting that an ARMA model is appropriate. The properties of the estimates of a spectrum that is near-flat are also much more satisfactory, this also being true for the cross-spectral estimates.

2.8 Seasonal Adjustment: An Application of the Cross Spectrum

A very casual glance at many raw economic series will indicate the presence of an important seasonal component. Obvious examples include personal consumption, production, sales and inventories, food prices, and imports and exports. Since this seasonal component is easily explained, at least superficially, and is occasionally of such overpowering importance, in terms of its contribution to the total variance of the series, that other components are difficult to observe in the plot of the data, analysts frequently want to remove the seasonal component so that they can better observe components of the series that are operationally more important, in particular the long swings. A method of removing the seasonal component from a series is called a seasonal adjustment technique. There are a number of problems that arise from the use of such techniques, and spectral analysis has proved useful in connection with several of these problems.

It is first necessary to define the seasonal component of a series, and this is best done by considering the spectrum of the series. Loosely, a possible definition of the seasonal is that component of the series that causes the spectrum to have peaks at or around seasonal frequencies, that is, frequencies $\omega_{sk} = 2\pi k/p_s$ where $k = 1, 2, 3, \ldots$ and p_s is the period of the seasonal, and thus takes the value 4 for data recorded at quarterly intervals, 12 for monthly data, and so forth. If the seasonal consists of an unchanging, strictly periodic component, then it will contribute power in the theoretical spectrum only at the seasonal frequencies and not elsewhere in the frequency band surrounding these frequencies. However, if the seasonal component is taken to change somewhat from year to year, due possibly to random elements in the causal mechanism, the seasonal component will then contribute power to the whole narrow frequency band surrounding the seasonal frequencies. There is a lot that can be said in favor of this more general definition of a seasonal component. Under either definition, the estimated spectrum will have peaks at and around the seasonal frequencies. It is important to note that the seasonal component causes there to be *extra* power at these frequencies, leading to peaks. The seasonal component cannot be defined simply as giving *some* power at the seasonal frequencies since, for example, white noise does not have zero power at these frequencies. In fact, virtually any ARMA process has a spectrum with some power at the seasonal frequencies. Although the above definition can be made both more rigorous and more satisfactory, as it stands it does provide a useful and usable criterion for whether or not a given series does contain a seasonal component. Consequently, it also provides the first step in evaluating the effectiveness of a method of seasonal adjustment. This follows from the fact that a good seasonal adjustment technique should remove the seasonal component, and no more, and thus the estimated spectrum of the seasonally adjusted series should contain no peaks at seasonal frequencies.

An example of this use of the spectrum is shown in Figs. 2.9 and 2.10 from Nerlove [1964]. The continuous lines show the spectra of total U.S. employed (monthly data, July 1947–December 1961) and a particular subset of the employed, being males aged 14–19. The broken lines show the estimated spectra of these series after being seasonally adjusted by a technique used by

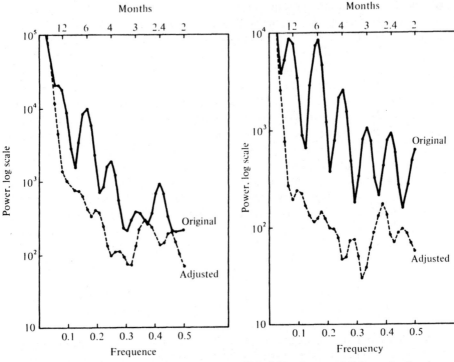

FIG. 2.9 *Spectra of total U.S. employed,*
before and after seasonal adjustment.

FIG. 2.10 *Spectra of U.S. employed males,*
14–19, before and after seasonal adjustment.

the Bureau of Labor Statistics in the early 1960s. The original series show
strong evidence of seasonal components, that for the teenagers being extremely strong since a large cohort enters the job market at the same time
each year. The adjusted series have spectra of the "typical" shape, since
levels of employment were used, and no peaks at seasonal frequencies.
Unfortunately, the peaks have often been replaced by dips, suggesting that
the adjustment procedure has removed rather too much power at seasonal
frequencies. Several seasonal adjustment methods are inclined to have this
undesirable property. In the time domain, the presence of a seasonal component is shown by high positive correlogram values at lags 12, 24, 36, etc., if
using monthly data, whereas the adjusted series may now contain negative
autocorrelations at some of these lags. For integrated processes, this statement applies to the first differences of the series.

Some methods of seasonal adjustment consist of simply applying an
appropriate filter to the series. An example of such a filter is the series Y_t
formed from the original monthly series X_t by

$$Y_t = X_t - \frac{1}{m+s+1} \sum_{k=-s}^{m} X_{t-12k}$$

Thus, the new January figure is the old figure minus the average January value over adjacent years. Two particular cases are important: (i) $s = m$ so that a symmetric filter is used, and (ii) $s = 0$, giving a completely one-sided filter. Symmetric filters are typically used in adjusting historical data, but to adjust a current series up to the most recent value a one-sided filter has to be used. Since the spectrum of Y_t can be determined from that of X_t and the filter function, as explained in Section 2.2, the effect of a seasonal adjustment filter can be evaluated theoretically rather than by using real data as illustrated above. To give a simple example, consider the twelfth-differencing method introduced in Section 1.14, so that $Y_t = X_t - X_{t-12}$, and, in terms of spectra,

$$s_y(\omega) = 2(1 - \cos 12\omega)s_x(\omega)$$

If $s_x(\omega)$ is finite for all ω, it is seen that $s_y(\omega) = 0$ at $\omega = 2\pi k/12$, $k = 0, 1, \ldots$, so Y_t will have no seasonal component but will have induced zero spectral values at the zero and seasonal frequencies. It is to allow for this overadjustment that the more complicated seasonal filter considered in (1.14.1) has been suggested.

Unfortunately, the seasonal adjustment methods used in practice, particularly those of government agencies, do not correspond to simple filters and so cannot be completely evaluated by the method just proposed. The nonlinearities introduced are designed to cope with values taken in exceptional years, due to events such as dock strikes, or very poor harvests, or with fairly rapidly changing seasonal patterns. A further problem is the tendency to use a symmetric filter as the current value is approached until eventually a one-sided filter is used on the most recent term of the series. This corresponds to a nonstationary filter and induces a variable lagging of the low-frequency component. Because the available theory is not always able to cope with the evaluation of actual seasonal adjustment techniques, it becomes necessary to analyze these techniques by simulation.

To illustrate this, consider the series X_t generated by

$$X_t = S(t) + X_t' \tag{2.8.1}$$

where $S(t)$ is a pure seasonal component, having spectrum with power *only* over narrow frequency bands surrounding the seasonal frequency, and X_t' contains no seasonal component. Suppose a seasonal adjustment procedure is applied to X_t, producing the series $A(X_t)$. A strong criterion for a good method of adjustment is that $A(X_t)$ should closely approximate X_t'. A first step in evaluating this approximation consists of comparing the spectra of $A(X_t)$ and X_t' to see if they have similar shapes. This corresponds to the method used by Nerlove mentioned above. The obvious second step is to estimate the cross spectrum between $A(X_t)$ and X_t'. With real data, X_t' is not observable, so that simulated data have to be used. There is little point in forming the cross spectrum between X_t and $A(X_t)$ since the presence of the important seasonal component $S(t)$ will spoil the estimates over various important frequency bands. The simulation technique has been used by Godfrey and Karreman [1967] for various simulated series and a number of adjustment methods. The kind of result they obtained is illustrated in Fig. 2.11, in which a Bureau of the Census method, known as X11, is applied to a series without a seasonal component and generated by an AR(2) model. The spectra of the original and the adjusted series suggest that the method passes the first test quite well since no "seasonal" has been removed and no dips induced in the spectrum. The method is used on historical data, not up to the last few values, and the flat phase estimate, lying around zero in part (ii) of the figure, suggests that no lags are induced in the adjusted series compared to the original nonseasonal data. However, the coherence diagram, in part (iii) of the figure, does give cause for concern about the method of adjust-

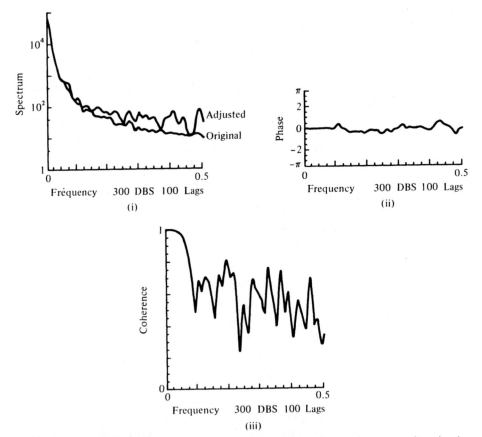

FIG. 2.11   (*i*) *Spectra,* (*ii*) *phase diagram, and* (*iii*) *coherence diagram between unadjusted and seasonally adjusted series.* (*From Godfrey and Karreman* [1967], *reprinted by permission of Princeton University Press.*)

ment. An ideal method should produce a coherence diagram with values near one at all frequencies. In practice, the low-frequency component has remained unchanged, but coherence at higher frequencies is considerably reduced. These results can be interpreted as follows: let

$$X_t = X_t^{(1)} + X_t^{(2)} \quad \text{and} \quad A(X_t) = A_t^{(1)} + A_t^{(2)}$$

where X_t is the original nonseasonal series and $A(X_t)$ is the adjusted series. $X_t^{(1)}$ and $A_t^{(1)}$ are the low frequency components of the series, with frequencies of say less then $2\pi/20$, and $X_t^{(2)}$, $A_t^{(2)}$ are the other frequency components. Ideally $X_t^{(1)} = A_t^{(1)}$ and $X_t^{(2)} = A_t^{(2)}$, but in practice the first equality holds but not the second, even though $X_t^{(2)}$ and $A_t^{(2)}$ have similar spectral shapes. Thus, the adjustment mechanism has removed part of the higher frequency component $X_t^{(2)}$ and replaced it with "noise" having similar spectral shape. It follows that the low-frequency component, which is the one economists are most interested in, is virtually unaffected by the adjustment method, but the higher frequency component is much affected. This certainly has important implications for model building. Godfrey and Karreman find similar results when the input series does contain a seasonal and for various nonlinear adjustment techniques. The results might suggest that since the low frequency component is the one of greatest interest and since the higher frequency component is spoiled by the adjustment method, a simpler procedure would be to just filter out the higher frequency component of the original series, including any seasonal, leaving just that part of the series of greatest interest.

A great deal more could be said on the problem of seasonal adjustment, but to do so would take us too far from the stated objectives of this book. Nevertheless, the results shown here do suggest that time series analysts should usually prefer to work with seasonally unadjusted data and to perform their own methods of reducing the importance of any seasonal component since the consequences of the method used can usually then be determined.

It is not our purpose in this book to consider the problem of how best to seasonally adjust an economic time series, though the past few years have witnessed many interesting developments in this area: a survey is provided by Bell and Hillmer [1984]. Of particular interest are papers by Burman [1980] and Hillmer and Tiao [1982], which discuss the decomposition of a series generated by the seasonal ARIMA models of Section 1.14 into additive trend, seasonal, and irregular components.

2.9 Advanced Spectral Techniques

The interpretation of the spectral representation of a stationary series X_t, given in (2.1.12), as a decomposition of X_t into uncorrelated frequency components is potentially an important one. A number of interesting gener-

alizations of the ideas discussed above have been based on this representation. The fact that some of these frequency components can be associated
with fundamental ideas in economics, such as long-run, short-run, and
seasonal components, increases the importance of these generalizations. As
economists believe that relationships between economic variables can differ
between the long and short run, it is natural to consider regression models
for different frequency components. The idea can be illustrated by the
equation

$$x_t(\omega) = \sum_j \beta_j(\omega) z_{jt}(\omega) + \text{residual} \qquad (2.9.1)$$

where the z_{jt} are explanatory variables, $z_t(\omega)$ represents the ω frequency
component of z_t, and the $\beta_j(\omega)$ will generally be complex regression parameters. No lag terms are required as these are included within the formula that
generates the β's. This procedure has been called "band spectrum regression"
by Engle [1974], who points out that if (2.9.1) is estimated by generalized
least squares, the $\beta_j(\omega)$'s will just be functions of the spectra and cross
spectra between the variables in the regression. Thus, the frequency-depen-
dent regression parameters can be derived directly from estimates of spectra
and cross spectra rather than by trying to estimate frequency components
and performing the regression (2.9.1) directly. As an application, Engle
looked at the consumption function to determine whether the marginal
propensity to consume an additional dollar of income appeared to be
different for high and low frequencies. Interpreting high frequencies as the
transitory component and low frequencies as the permanent component of
income, the permanent income hypothesis would suggest a substantial difference, but none was observed. In Engle [1980] these techniques are generalized
to include lagged dependent variables and simultaneous relationships.

A further justification for running regressions on separate spectral bands is
as a specification test. If a model is well specified, the estimates should not be
significantly different. Engle [1978] performed such a test on a set of price
equations but found some rather significant differences. These techniques can
be considered as multivariate generalizations of the gain function (2.5.7).

A quite different type of multivariate analysis is frequency domain factor
analysis, which first appeared in Geweke [1977] and Sargent and Sims [1977],
although previously the first edition of Brillinger [1981] had discussed the
related frequency-domain principal component analysis. The question being
asked is whether the dynamic relationships between a number of variables
can be simply explained by the presence of a number of unobserved common
factors. Thus, the model considered is simply

$$y_{jt} = \sum_{s=0}^{\infty} A_{js} z_{t-s} + e_{jt} \qquad (2.9.2)$$

for the N series y_{jt}, $j = 1, \ldots, N$, where z_t is a $1 \times k$ vector of independent white noise series and e_{jt} is a series (not necessarily white noise) that is independent of z_{t-s} and all e_{st}, $s \neq j$. Each component of z has zero mean and unit variance. If the vector e_t has spectral density matrix $F_e(\omega)$ it is seen that the spectral density of y_t is given by

$$F_y(\omega) = \bar{A}(\omega)\bar{A}(\omega)^\dagger + F_e(\omega)$$

where $A(\omega)$ is the Fourier transform of the series A_s given by

$$\bar{A}(\omega) = \sum_{s=0}^{\infty} A_s e^{i\omega s}.$$

The estimation problem is to find F_e and $\bar{A}$ at each frequency based on data $F_y(\omega)$ at that frequency. However, this is simply the familiar factor analytic model used in cross-section studies but with complex covariances. Standard estimation techniques adapted for complex arithmetic can therefore be applied for each frequency separately because the frequency bands are independent.

The economic question asked by both Sargent and Sims [1977] and Singleton [1980] is what is the dimension k of z, that is, how many independent noise sources are there acting as common factors in the economy? Singleton, considering the term structure of interest rates, finds just $k = 2$.

The traditional spectral techniques deal just with stationary series, linear relationships, and second moments, but various extensions removing these assumptions have been proposed. For example, Brillinger and Rosenblatt [1967a, b] have provided a theory for Fourier transforms of sets of higher lagged moments, expressed most conveniently in terms of lagged cumulants. As a particular example, suppose that X_t is a stationary series with mean $E[X_t] = \mu$, variance $\sigma^2 = E[(X_t - \mu)^2]$, autocovariance $R(s) = \text{cov}(X_t, X_{t-s})$, and third-order automoments

$$C(p, q) = E[(X_t - \mu)(X_{t-p} - \mu)(X_{t-q} - \mu)]$$

with corresponding spectrum

$$f(\omega) = \frac{1}{2\pi} \sum_{s=-\infty}^{\infty} R_s e^{-is\omega}$$

and bispectrum

$$f(\omega, \lambda) = (2\pi)^{-2} \sum_{p=-\infty}^{\infty} \sum_{q=-\infty}^{\infty} C(p, q) e^{-(ip\omega + iq\lambda)}$$

Define

$$G_{ij} = \frac{|f(\omega_i, \lambda_j)|^2}{f(\omega_i)f(\lambda_j)f(\omega_i + \lambda_j)}$$

Consider now the Wold decomposition

$$X_t = \sum_{j=0}^{\infty} C_j \epsilon_{t-j}$$

where the ϵ_t's are all zero mean and independent, identically distributed. In this case, X_t is a linear process and it follows that $G_{ij} = \mu_3^2/2\pi\sigma_s^2$, that is, it is a constant, for all ω and λ. Here μ_3 is the third moment of ϵ. If the ϵ's are merely uncorrelated, as opposed to independent, G_{ij} will not be a constant as ω and λ vary. Subba Rao and Gabr [1980] based a test for linearity on this observation.

Because it seems likely that the generating mechanism for an economic variable changes through time, due to changes in tastes, technology or laws such as tax laws, a number of writers have considered series whose spectra change through time and are thus nonstationary. In particular, Priestley [1965, 1981, Vol. 2] considers series with spectral representation

$$X_t = \int_{-\pi}^{\pi} A_t(\omega) e^{i\omega t} dz(\omega)$$

with

$$E\left[dz(\omega)\overline{dz(\lambda)}\right] = \begin{cases} 0, & \omega \neq \lambda \\ dF(\omega), & \omega = \lambda \end{cases}$$

as before. Here $A_t(\omega)$ is a deterministic, time-varying function of frequency. If $A_t(\omega)$ consists only of zero or low-frequency components for each ω, X_t is said to be slowly changing, and then a slowly changing spectrum for X_t can be defined. If the future spectral shape is predictable, it is clear that forecasts of X_t superior to those achievable with the stationarity assumption may be possible. Some time-domain models that correspond to the slowly varying frequency-domain models are discussed in Chapter 10.

A wider class of nonstationary processes, with an attractive interpretation, are known as harmonizable processes and have been discussed by Loève [1963], Blanc-Lapierre and Fortet [1965], and Joyeux [1979] among others. Such a process has a spectral representation

$$X_t = \int_{-\pi}^{\pi} e^{it\omega} dz(\omega)$$

where

$$E\left[dz(\omega)\overline{dz(\lambda)}\right] = ddF(\omega, \lambda)$$

If $F(\omega, \lambda)$ is everywhere differentiable, then one can write

$$ddF(\omega, \lambda) = f(\omega, \lambda)\, d\omega\, d\lambda.$$

With these processes, frequency components are no longer independent of each other, so that the amplitude of the seasonal frequency, say, can be a function of the business cycle. Many nonstationary models can be represented in this form and, in particular, Joyeux has shown that Priestley's slowly changing processes are a special case. In her paper, Joyeux discussed the interpretation and estimation of the harmonizable spectrum $F(\omega, \lambda)$ and applied the methods to two individual economic series.

With new housing starts, it was found that the high- and low-frequency components were correlated, suggesting that the series is nonstationary. When the method was applied to a personal income series, the high- and low-frequency components were found to be uncorrelated, which agrees with the economic theory that suggests that the permanent and transitory components of income are independent. These techniques do require a great deal of data, and the results are not always easily interpreted but when generalized to the multivariate case may prove to be quite important.

A discussion of most of the topics in this section, with more detail plus a history of the use of spectral methods in econometrics, can be found in the survey article by Granger and Engle [1984].

CHAPTER THREE

BUILDING LINEAR TIME SERIES MODELS

Today is the tomorrow you were worrying about yesterday.

GRAFFITI

In this chapter, a unified approach to the fitting of linear models to a given time series is presented. Such an approach was devised by Box and Jenkins in a series of articles and a subsequent book [1970], and the material in this chapter draws heavily from Chapters 6–9 of that book. The objective, given a particular time series realization $x_1, x_2, \ldots, x_n$, is to derive a linear stochastic model that could have generated the series. As will be seen in Chapter 5, this model can then be employed to generate forecasts of future values of the series.

3.1 Model Building Philosophy

It is convenient, initially, to describe a model building procedure for nonseasonal time series. In Section 3.7 it is shown how this approach can be generalized to deal with seasonal series.

In Chapter 1, the autoregressive integrated moving average process

$$a(B)(1 - B)^d X_t = b(B)\epsilon_t \qquad (3.1.1)$$

where

$$a(B) = \left(1 - a_1 B - a_2 B^2 - \cdots - a_p B^p\right)$$

$$b(B) = \left(1 + b_1 B + b_2 B^2 + \cdots + b_q B^q\right)$$

was introduced. It is assumed that the time series under consideration can be represented by a model from this class (3.1.1)—possibly after the removal of any deterministic component, including a nonzero mean, and/or the application of some suitable transformation to the data.

A strategy for constructing autoregressive integrated moving average models can be based on a three-step iterative cycle of

    (i)   model identification,
    (ii) model estimation,
    (iii) diagnostic checks on model adequacy.

At the identification stage one chooses a particular model from the class (3.1.1), that is, one selects values for p, d, and q. The procedures employed at this stage are, of necessity, inexact and require a good deal of judgment. However, one is not irrevocably committed to the chosen model if subsequent analysis suggests that some alternative form might provide more adequate representation of the given data. Because of the nature of the estimation techniques employed, it is also necessary at this stage to obtain initial rough estimates of the coefficients $a_1, a_2, \ldots, a_p, b_1, b_2, \ldots, b_q$ of the identified model.

At the estimation stage of the model building cycle, the coefficients of the identified model are estimated using efficient statistical techniques. Approximate standard errors are obtained for the estimated coefficients and, provided one is prepared to make specific distributional assumptions, tests of hypotheses and confidence intervals can be derived.

Finally, diagnostic checks are applied to determine whether or not the chosen model adequately represents the given set of data. Any inadequacies revealed may suggest an alternative model specification. If this is the case, the whole iterative cycle of identification, estimation, and diagnostic checking is repeated until a satisfactory model is obtained.

3.2 Identification

There can be little doubt that the most difficult step in the model building cycle is identification. This is so since, although a number of general principles can be laid down, there exists no surefire deterministic approach to the problem. Rather, it is necessary to exert a degree of judgment, the facility for which is greatly improved by experience. (Indeed it has been said that identification is a technique that should not be attempted for the first time.) It is worth reemphasizing that in selecting a model at this stage one is committed to no more than an assessment of its validity. The initially chosen model can always be discarded at a later stage of the analysis, should this course appear desirable. It is also possible that one may wish to carry forward from the identification stage not one, but two or more possible models.

The Tools of the Trade

The two most useful tools in any attempt at model identification are the sample autocorrelation function and the sample partial autocorrelation function. Given a time series $x_1, x_2, \ldots, x_n$, the sample autocorrelation function, which is a plot of the sample autocorrelations,

$$r_\tau = \frac{\displaystyle\sum_{t=\tau+1}^{n} (x_t - \bar{x})(x_{t-\tau} - \bar{x})}{\displaystyle\sum_{t=1}^{n} (x_t - \bar{x})^2}, \qquad \tau = 0, 1, 2, \ldots$$

against τ provides an obvious estimate of the autocorrelation function ρ_τ, defined in (1.2.7), of the underlying stochastic process.

The usefulness of the partial autocorrelation function can best be illustrated by considering the autoregressive process

$$\left(1 - a_1 B - a_2 B^2 - \cdots - a_p B^p\right) X_t = \epsilon_t$$

From (1.5.13) it is seen that the autocovariances for such a process obey

$$\lambda_\tau = \sum_{j=1}^{p} a_j \lambda_{\tau-j}, \qquad \tau > 0$$

Dividing this expression by the variance λ_0, it follows that the autocorrelations obey

$$\rho_\tau = \sum_{j=1}^{p} a_j \rho_{\tau-j}, \qquad \tau > 0 \qquad (3.2.1)$$

The partial autocorrelation of order K for any stochastic process is defined as a_{KK} given by solving the set of simultaneous linear equations in a_{Kj}

$$\rho_\tau = \sum_{j=1}^{K} a_{Kj} \rho_{\tau-j}, \qquad \tau = 1, 2, \ldots, K \qquad (3.2.2)$$

Thus $a_{Kj}, j = 1, 2, \ldots, K$, is substituted for a_j and K for p in (3.2.1). The first K equations of this system are then solved for a_{Kj}, and the resulting a_{KK} denoted as the partial autocorrelation. It follows from (3.2.1) that for an autoregressive process of order p, $a_{pp} = a_p$. Furthermore, for such a process, the partial autocorrelations of order greater than p will clearly all be zero. To see this, note that from (3.2.1) it follows that for any positive integer m

$$\rho_\tau = \sum_{j=1}^{p} a_j \rho_{\tau-j}, \qquad \tau = 1, 2, \ldots, p + m$$

Alternatively this system of equations can be written

$$\rho_\tau = \sum_{j=1}^{p+m} a_j^* \rho_{\tau-j}, \qquad \tau = 1, 2, \ldots, p + m$$

where

$$a_j^* = a_j, \qquad j = 1, 2, \ldots, p$$
$$= 0, \qquad j = p + 1, \ldots, p + m$$

Hence, solving the equations (3.2.2) for $K = p + m$ yields $a_{p+m,\,p+m} = a_{p+m}^* = 0$. An obvious estimate of the partial autocorrelations is obtained by substituting the sample autocorrelations r_τ or ρ_τ in (3.2.2) and solving the resulting equations. Thus the sample partial autocorrelation of order K is $\hat{a}_{KK}$ given as the solution of the set of equations

$$r_\tau = \sum_{j=1}^{K} \hat{a}_{Kj} r_{\tau-j}, \qquad \tau = 1, 2, \ldots, K$$

A computationally efficient algorithm, which works well if $a(B) = 0$ does not have a root near the unit circle, for obtaining the sample partial autocorrelations is given by Durbin [1960].

Characterization of Stochastic Processes

It is convenient at this stage to examine the characteristic behavior of the autocorrelation and partial autocorrelation functions of the various members of the class of stochastic processes (3.1.1). First consider those processes that require differencing to induce stationarity, i.e., $d \geqslant 1$ in (3.1.1). Let X_t be generated by the process $(1 - B)X_t = Y_t$ where Y_t is stationary. It was shown in Section 1.13 that if this process is viewed as starting in the infinite past, then $\mathrm{corr}(X_t X_{t-\tau}) \approx 1$ for finite τ. However, the sample autocorrelations for series generated by such processes can behave very differently. To see this, write

$$X_t = X_0 + \sum_{j=1}^{t} Y_j$$

The sample autocovariances are

$$c_\tau = \frac{1}{n} \sum_{t=\tau+1}^{n} (x_t - \bar{x})(x_{t-\tau} - \bar{x})$$

based on the sample $x_1, x_2, \ldots, x_n$, and the difference here from the population case considered earlier is that appeal cannot be made to limiting cases as t tends to infinity. To get some insight into the behavior of c_τ, note that for a stationary process Y, the population autocovariances tend to zero at high lags. (This follows, for example, from (1.7.18).) These quantities are estimated by

$$\frac{1}{n} \sum_{t=\tau+1}^{n} y_t y_{t-\tau} = \frac{1}{n} \sum_{t=\tau+1}^{n} (x_t - x_{t-1})(x_{t-\tau} - x_{t-\tau-1})$$
$$= \frac{1}{n} \sum_{t=\tau+1}^{n} [(x_t - \bar{x}) - (x_{t-1} - \bar{x})]$$
$$\times [(x_{t-\tau} - \bar{x}) - (x_{t-\tau-1} - \bar{x})]$$

Thus, apart from end terms which will make very little difference, since the above expression is close to zero, it follows that, subject to the restriction that c_τ is bounded above by c_0,

$$2c_\tau \approx c_{\tau+1} + c_{\tau-1}$$

for sufficiently large τ. Hence the sample autocovariances and therefore the sample autocorrelations will typically behave as a very smooth function, and thus not die out rapidly, at high lags. The failure of the sample autocorrelation function to die out at high lags thus indicates that differencing is required. This is so even though the first few sample autocorrelations need not necessarily be large. The behavior of the sample autocorrelation function for the process $X_t - X_{t-1} = \epsilon_t + b\epsilon_{t-1}$ is studied in some detail by Wichern [1973] who found by simulation that, for samples of size 50, $E(r_1) = 0.62$ for $b = -0.5$ and $E(r_1) = 0.21$ for $b = -0.8$.

If differencing is found to be necessary, the sample autocorrelations and partial autocorrelations of the differenced series are far more likely than those of the original series to yield useful information about the underlying stochastic process. This is because any information contained in the latter is swamped by the behavior induced by nonstationarity, rendering further interpretation virtually impossible.

Assume now that the process X_t has been differenced a sufficient number of times as to produce the stationary process $Y_t = (1 - B)^d X_t$. Then, summarizing results derived in Chapter 1 and earlier in this chapter:

  (i) If Y_t is an autoregressive process of order p, i.e., $q = 0$, its autocorrelations will die out according to the difference equation

$$\rho_\tau = \sum_{j=1}^{p} a_j \rho_{\tau-j} \qquad \text{for all } \tau > 0$$

that is, according to a mixture of damped exponentials and/or sine waves, and its partial autocorrelations will obey

$$a_{KK} = 0 \qquad \text{for all } K > p$$

  (ii) If Y_t is a moving average process of order q, i.e., $p = 0$, its autocorrelations will obey

$$\rho_\tau = 0 \qquad \text{for all } \tau > q$$

and its partial autocorrelations will die out, though not according to any clearly recognizable pattern.

  (iii) If Y_t is a mixed autoregressive moving average process of order (p, q), with $p, q \neq 0$, its autocorrelations will die out according to

$$\rho_\tau = \sum_{j=1}^{p} a_j \rho_{\tau-j} \qquad \text{for all } \tau > q$$

and its partial autocorrelations will also die out, though again not according to any clearly recognizable pattern.

These three characteristics of members of the class of processes (3.1.1) can be employed as the basis of an attempt to identify an appropriate model for the suitably differenced time series. It can often happen, however, that model selection based on these criteria is rather tenuous. We have found it useful also to employ a procedure proposed by Hannan and Rissanen [1982].

Model Identification in Practice

In practice, of course, one never knows the autocorrelations and partial autocorrelations of the underlying stochastic process and must estimate them from the given time series realization. In identifying an appropriate model, then, it is necessary to rely on the sample autocorrelation and partial autocorrelation functions imitating sufficiently closely the behavior of the corresponding parent quantities. Clearly, the larger the number of sample observations the more likely, in general, is this requirement to hold. Therefore, in order to have any reasonable hope of success in model identification, a moderately long series of observations is needed. It is not possible to be completely dogmatic on this point since the degree of difficulty of an identification is a function of the characteristics of the individual process. However, we would not be terribly confident of success with much less than 40–50 observations.

The first step in the identification process is to calculate the sample autocorrelations and partial autocorrelations of the given time series and its first one or two differences. Failure of the sample autocorrelations to die out quickly at high lags and the appearance of smooth behavior in these quantities at high lags is an indication that further differencing is required. After stationarity is achieved by suitable differencing, the sample autocorrelations and partial autocorrelations can be examined to help identify typical autoregressive, moving average, or mixed behavior. As a rough guide for determining whether the parent autocorrelations are in fact zero after the qth, Bartlett [1946] shows that, for a sample of n observations from an $MA(q)$ process, the standard deviation of r_τ is appropriately

$$n^{-1/2}\left(1 + 2\left(\rho_1^2 + \rho_2^2 + \cdots + \rho_q^2\right)\right)^{1/2} \quad \text{for} \quad \tau > q$$

Davies and Newbold [1980a] show that a slightly better approximation is obtained if n is replaced by $n(n + 2)/(n - \tau)$. Quenouille [1949] has shown that, for a pth order autoregressive process, the standard deviations of the sample partial autocorrelations $\hat{a}_{KK}$ are approximately $n^{-1/2}$ for $K > p$. By appealing to a result of Anderson [1942], one can assume normality in moderately large samples, and so the use of limits of plus or minus two standard deviations about zero should provide a reasonable guide in assessing whether the parent autocorrelations and partial autocorrelations are in fact zero. Thus, in the examples that follow, for samples of size n, comparison of the sample quantities with $\pm 2n^{-1/2}$ gives a useful guide to statistical significance.

As a further tool in model selection, we will employ a procedure proposed by Hannan and Rissanen [1982]. We will assume that an appropriate degree of differencing has been achieved and that n observations are available on the stationary process Y_t. For convenience of exposition, it will also be assumed that this process has zero mean. In practice, if this assumption is untenable, the sample mean can be subtracted from the observations before proceeding. The ARMA(p, q) model for this process is then

$$Y_t = a_1 Y_{t-1} + \cdots + a_p Y_{t-p} + \epsilon_t + b_1 \epsilon_{t-1} + \cdots + b_q \epsilon_{t-q}$$

As a first step, an attempt is made to approximate this process by an autoregression of order K, where K remains to be determined;

$$Y_t = a_{K1} Y_{t-1} + a_{K2} Y_{t-2} + \cdots + a_{KK} Y_{t-K} + \epsilon_t$$

Given the sample autocorrelations r_t, the coefficients a_{Kj} can be estimated recursively through the algorithm of Durbin [1960], which yields

$$\hat{a}_{11} = r_1, \qquad \hat{a}_{K,K} = \frac{r_K - \sum_{j=1}^{K-1} \hat{a}_{K-1,j} r_{K-j}}{1 - \sum_{j=1}^{K-1} \hat{a}_{K-1,j} r_j}$$

$$\hat{a}_{K,j} = \hat{a}_{K-1,j} - \hat{a}_{K,K} \hat{a}_{K-1,K-j}, \qquad j = 1, 2, \ldots, K-1$$

The $\hat{a}_{KK}$ are the sample partial autocorrelations. The estimated error variances from the fitted autoregressions can also be found recursively, from

$$\hat{\sigma}_1^2 = (1 - r_1^2) \sum_{t=1}^{n} \frac{y_t^2}{n}, \qquad \hat{\sigma}_K^2 = (1 - \hat{a}_{K,K}^2) \hat{\sigma}_{K-1}^2$$

One possibility for determining an appropriate value for K, the order of the approximating autoregression, is to use an information criterion such as the AIC criterion of Akaike [1969]. This requires that we select that value of K for which

$$\log \hat{\sigma}_K^2 + 2K/n$$

is smallest. The second term in this expression can be thought of as a penalty for heavily parameterized models. In fact, as shown by Shibata [1976], the AIC criterion is not consistent, but rather overestimates, asymptotically, the true order of a model. However, at this point our objective is not to estimate the order of a true model but rather to approximate a mixed model by an autoregression of sufficiently high order. Therefore, a rather liberal criterion might be appropriate for choosing this order.

Now, the purpose of estimating an approximating autoregression is to obtain estimates of the innovations ϵ_t. If the chosen value for K is K^*, we can use for this the residuals

$$\hat{\epsilon}_t = Y_t - \hat{a}_{K^*,1} Y_{t-1} - \hat{a}_{K^*,2} Y_{t-2} - \cdots - \hat{a}_{K^*,K^*} Y_{t-K^*}$$

These residuals can then be used in place of the true lagged innovations ϵ_{t-j} in the ARMA(p, q) formulation, so that approximately we can write

$$Y_t = a_1 Y_{t-1} + \cdots + a_p Y_{t-p} + b_1 \hat{\epsilon}_{t-1} + \cdots + b_q \hat{\epsilon}_{t-q} + \epsilon_t \quad (3.2.3)$$

The attraction of such an approach is that, using (3.2.3), the parameters $a_1, \ldots, a_p, b_1, \ldots, b_q$ can now be relatively cheaply estimated by ordinary least squares regression methods.

In practice, for combinations of values (p, q), (3.2.3) is estimated by least squares. Let $\hat{\sigma}_{p,q}^2$ denote the usual maximum likelihood error variance estimate. Then, Hannan and Rissanen propose that the particular values (p, q) for which

$$\log \hat{\sigma}_{p,q}^2 + (p + q) \log n/n$$

is smallest be chosen. Hannan and Rissanen establish that such a procedure has desirable asymptotic properties.

Newbold and Bos [1982] have investigated the performance of this procedure in moderate sample sizes, both through extensive simulation experiments and the analysis of real data sets. It was found, generally, to perform very satisfactorily. Our view is not that one should invariably proceed with the model picked out by the Hannan–Rissanen criterion, but rather that it should be sensibly used in conjunction with an examination of the sample autocorrelations and partial autocorrelations. It is often useful, rather than restricting attention to the single most preferred model, to look at the two or three that rate highest according to the criterion.

In the examples that follow, the maximum permitted value for the approximating autoregression was fixed at 10, while any values of p or q up to 5 were permitted. In practice, though, attention can be restricted to values of p that do not exceed K^*.

The Hannan–Rissanen procedure just described will often yield consistent estimators of autoregressive–moving average order. However, it may not do so when the moving average operator of the true process has a root close to the boundary of the invertibility region. Hannan and Kavalieris (1984) propose various modifications of the original procedure that give consistent order estimates. One possibility is to add a third stage, based on the residuals $\hat{\hat{\epsilon}}_t$ from the least squares estimation of (3.2.3) using the values of p and q selected by the second stage. The second stage computations are then repeated but with $\hat{\hat{\epsilon}}_{t-j}$ in place of $\hat{\epsilon}_{t-j}$ ($j = 1, 2, \ldots, q$) in (3.2.3). This adds somewhat to the computational burden, which however is still not high, since estimation is through ordinary least squares. In fact, our experience with several real data sets suggests that very often the original Hannan–Rissanen choice of p and q will be retained when this modification is employed.

EXAMPLE 1   Our first example is a series of 140 quarterly observations on the ratio of consumer installment debt to personal income in the U.S. Table 3.1 shows the sample autocorrelations r_K and partial autocorrelations $\hat{a}_{KK}$ for the series and its first two differences. Note that $2n^{-1/2} \simeq 0.17$.

The sample autocorrelations of the original series fail to damp out quickly at high lags, suggesting that differencing is required to induce stationarity. For the first differenced series, however, the sample autocorrelations quickly become rather small. The sample partial autocorrelations of this series are all very small after the first (save, perhaps, for a value of moderate size at lag 4). This suggests the possibility of a first-order autoregressive model for the first differences. This particular time series has exhibited fairly steady growth through time, the first differences appearing to have positive mean. Hence, the model suggested is

$$(1 - a_1 B)(1 - B) X_t = b_0 + \epsilon_t$$

Applying the Hannan–Rissanen criterion to the series of first differences, with mean subtracted, the model selected was also first-order autoregressive. (The order of the approximating autoregression picked out by the AIC criterion was one.)

Table 3.1   *Sample autocorrelations and partial autocorrelations for data on the ratio of installment debt to personal income*

	K	1	2	3	4	5	6	7	8	9	10
	r_K	.97	.94	.91	.88	.85	.82	.79	.76	.73	.71
	$\hat{a}_{KK}$	.97	−.02	−.04	−.01	−.01	−.01	−.02	−.01	.01	.01
X_t											
	K	11	12	13	14	15	16	17	18	19	20
	r_K	.68	.66	.63	.61	.59	.57	.55	.53	.51	.49
	$\hat{a}_{KK}$	.01	.02	−.02	.02	.02	−.02	−.03	−.04	−.03	−.02
	K	1	2	3	4	5	6	7	8	9	10
	r_K	.73	.50	.35	.16	.01	−.10	−.12	−.14	−.11	−.03
	$\hat{a}_{KK}$	.73	−.06	.02	−.18	−.08	−.06	.08	−.05	.06	.06
$(1 - B)X_t$											
	K	11	12	13	14	15	16	17	18	19	20
	r_K	−.03	−.02	−.00	−.03	−.01	.04	.08	.11	.15	.17
	$\hat{a}_{KK}$	−.09	−.00	−.01	−.06	.08	.11	.01	.06	.02	.02
	K	1	2	3	4	5	6	7	8	9	10
	r_K	−.07	−.15	.05	−.07	−.09	−.16	.01	−.09	−.10	.15
	$\hat{a}_{KK}$	−.07	−.16	.03	−.09	−.10	−.21	−.05	−.18	−.17	.02
$(1 - B)^2 X_t$											
	K	11	12	13	14	15	16	17	18	19	20
	r_K	.04	−.07	.09	−.01	−.06	.04	−.02	−.01	−.01	.03
	$\hat{a}_{KK}$	−.04	−.12	−.00	−.11	−.11	−.01	−.10	−.06	−.04	−.05

EXAMPLE 2   Our second example is a series of 122 monthly observations on the U.S.–U.K. exchange rate. Table 3.2 shows the sample autocorrelations r_K and partial autocorrelations $\hat{a}_{KK}$ for the original series and its first two differences. Here $2n^{-1/2} \simeq 0.18$.

The sample autocorrelations of the original series die out only very slowly at high lags, suggesting that differencing is needed. For the series of first differences, the sample autocorrelations quickly become very small, so that no further differencing is indicated. Looking at the sample autocorrelations and partial autocorrelations for the series of first differences, a number of possibilities suggest themselves. The sample autocorrelations are all quite small after the first, so that an MA(1) model could be appropriate. Still, the second sample autocorrelation is of moderate size. Similarly, only the first sample partial autocorrelation is terribly large (if we ignore, as seems sensible, the aberrant values at lags 18 and 19). This could indicate an AR(1) model, but again the second sample partial autocorrelation is moderately large. These values for the second sample autocorrelation and partial autocorrelation raise the possibility of a two-parameter model—either AR(2), MA(2), or ARMA(1, 1). The mixed model could be justified by noting that there is little in the behavior of the sample autocorrelations to contradict the possibility that the population quantities follow a difference equation close to

$$\rho_\tau = (0.10/0.46)\rho_{\tau-1} = 0.22\rho_{\tau-1}, \qquad \tau = 2, 3, 4, \ldots$$

Table 3.2   *Sample autocorrelations and partial autocorrelations for data on U.S.–U.K. exchange rate*

	K	1	2	3	4	5	6	7	8	9	10
	r_K	.97	.92	.88	.83	.77	.72	.67	.63	.59	.55
	$\hat{a}_{KK}$	.97	−.26	−.03	−.02	−.08	−.01	.05	−.02	.05	.02
X_t											
	K	11	12	13	14	15	16	17	18	19	20
	r_K	.52	.48	.45	.41	.37	.33	.29	.25	.21	.17
	$\hat{a}_{KK}$	−.03	−.07	−.04	−.03	−.08	.07	−.07	−.07	−.06	.04
	K	1	2	3	4	5	6	7	8	9	10
	r_K	.46	.10	.01	.01	.03	.04	−.06	−.05	.03	.08
	$\hat{a}_{KK}$	.46	−.13	.02	.01	.03	.01	−.10	.02	.06	.04
$(1 - B)X_t$											
	K	11	12	13	14	15	16	17	18	19	20
	r_K	.12	.09	.02	−.02	−.08	−.03	−.00	.13	−.02	−.10
	$\hat{a}_{KK}$	.08	.01	−.03	−.02	−.09	.06	−.02	.19	−.21	.00
	K	1	2	3	4	5	6	7	8	9	10
	r_K	−.17	−.24	−.08	−.02	.03	.06	−.09	−.07	.03	.01
	$\hat{a}_{KK}$	−.17	−.28	−.20	−.18	−.12	−.03	−.14	−.16	−.12	−.14
$(1 - B)^2X_t$											
	K	11	12	13	14	15	16	17	18	19	20
	r_K	.06	.04	−.02	.01	−.11	.03	−.09	.27	−.07	−.14
	$\hat{a}_{KK}$	−.07	−.04	−.03	.02	−.13	−.04	−.23	.18	−.03	−.06

whereas

$$\rho_1 = 0.22\rho_0 = 0.22$$

is unlikely, given an observed value of 0.46 for the first sample autocorrelation.

Applying the Hannan–Rissanen criterion to the series of first differences, the model chosen was ARMA(1, 1). (The order of the approximating autoregression picked out by the AIC criterion was two.) We therefore choose to proceed with the model

$$(1 - a_1 B)(1 - B) X_t = (1 + b_1 B)\epsilon_t$$

EXAMPLE 3 Our final example of nonseasonal model identification is for a series of 131 monthly observations on the U.S. 30-day commercial paper yield. Table 3.3 presents the sample autocorrelations r_K and sample partial autocorrelations $\hat{a}_{KK}$ for these data and the first two differences of the series. We have $2n^{-1/2} \simeq 0.17$.

The sample autocorrelations for the raw data die out only very slowly at high lags, so that we next consider the series of first differences. Here, although the sample autocorrelations do not suggest the need for further differencing, their pattern is very difficult to interpret. More light is shed by looking at the sample partial autocorrelations of the first differenced series.

Table 3.3 *Sample autocorrelations and partial autocorrelations for data on 30-day commercial paper yield*

	K	1	2	3	4	5	6	7	8	9	10
	r_K	.95	.88	.82	.78	.74	.69	.66	.64	.60	.55
	$\hat{a}_{KK}$	.95	−.21	.12	.05	−.02	−.00	.06	.06	−.16	−.15
X_t	K	11	12	13	14	15	16	17	18	19	20
	r_K	.50	.46	.44	.41	.36	.31	.27	.22	.19	.16
	$\hat{a}_{KK}$	.10	.03	.03	−.12	−.11	.02	−.11	.08	.02	.00
	K	1	2	3	4	5	6	7	8	9	10
	r_K	.34	−.12	−.18	−.15	−.06	−.19	−.17	.15	.22	.03
	$\hat{a}_{KK}$	.34	−.27	−.04	−.11	−.01	−.27	−.06	.19	.00	−.10
$(1 - B) X_t$	K	11	12	13	14	15	16	17	18	19	20
	r_K	−.16	−.20	.04	.14	.11	.12	.03	.00	−.08	−.14
	$\hat{a}_{KK}$	−.13	−.09	.08	.06	.11	.09	−.09	−.01	−.02	.06
	K	1	2	3	4	5	6	7	8	9	10
	r_K	−.14	−.30	−.05	−.06	.17	−.12	−.25	.21	.17	.03
	$\hat{a}_{KK}$	−.14	−.33	−.17	−.24	.04	−.22	−.35	−.08	−.01	.03
$(1 - B)^2 X_t$	K	11	12	13	14	15	16	17	18	19	20
	r_K	−.10	−.20	.09	.06	−.03	.09	−.04	.04	−.01	−.08
	$\hat{a}_{KK}$	−.04	−.17	−.12	−.16	−.07	.07	−.01	−.02	−.09	−.02

The first two of these are quite large, whereas the remainder (except for the sixth, which we choose to ignore) are relatively small. This suggests an AR(2) model might be fitted to the first differences, that is,

$$(1 - a_1B - a_2B^2)(1 - B)X_t = \epsilon_t$$

When the Hannan–Rissanen criterion was applied to the series of first differences, the ARMA(1, 1) model was chosen. (The order of approximating autoregression, obtained through the AIC criterion, was two.) However, it is difficult to find strong support for this model in the sample autocorrelations for the first differences. Accordingly, we are reluctant to abandon the AR(2) specification. According to the Hannan–Rissanen criterion, the ARMA(2, 1) model is also preferred to the AR(2). Since AR(2) and ARMA(1, 1) are both special cases of ARMA(2, 1), it seems reasonable to fit this model also. Accordingly, for this particular series, we will proceed to further analysis, not with a single chosen model, but with three possibilities. It does on occasion happen that the evidence examined at the model selection stage does not point terribly clearly in the direction of a single model. In that case it is sensible to carry forward two or more possible structures for further analysis. We will see in Section 3.5 how to distinguish among these models.

3.3 Initial Estimates for Coefficients

Assume, now, that a model

$$\left(1 - a_1B - a_2B^2 - \cdots - a_pB^p\right)Y_t = \left(1 + b_1B + b_2B^2 + \cdots + b_qB^q\right)\epsilon_t$$
$$(3.3.1)$$

where $Y_t = (1 - B)^d X_t$ has been selected. The estimation procedure to be described in Section 3.5 requires initial estimates of the coefficients $a_1, a_2, \ldots, a_p, b_1, b_2, \ldots, b_q$. These can be obtained directly from the sample autocovariances, employed in the identification process.

Given a series of observations $y_1, y_2, \ldots, y_n$ on the process Y_t of (3.3.1), with sample autocovariances denoted by

$$c_\tau = \frac{1}{n}\sum_{t=\tau+1}^{n}(y_t - \bar{y})(y_{t-\tau} - \bar{y}), \qquad \tau = 0, 1, 2, \ldots$$

and $c_{-\tau} = c_\tau$, it follows from (1.7.11)–(1.7.14) that the autoregressive coefficients $a_1, a_2, \ldots, a_p$ can be estimated by solving the set of equations

$$c_\tau = \sum_{j=1}^{p} \hat{a}_j c_{\tau-j}, \qquad \tau = q + 1, q + 2, \ldots, q + p$$

Assuming, now, that one can write

$$\left(1 - \hat{a}_1B - \hat{a}_2B^2 - \cdots - \hat{a}_pB^p\right)Y_t = \tilde{Y}_t$$
$$\approx \left(1 + b_1B + b_2B^2 + \cdots + b_qB^q\right)\epsilon_t$$

the coefficients $b_1, b_2, \ldots, b_q$ can be estimated using the autocovariance properties of the moving average process $\tilde{Y}_t$. Denote the sample autocovariances of this process as $\tilde{c}_\tau$. It can then be shown that

$$\tilde{c}_\tau = \sum_{j=0}^{p} a_j^2 c_\tau + \sum_{j=1}^{p} (a_0 a_j + a_1 a_{j+1} + \cdots + a_{p-j} a_p)(c_{\tau+j} + c_{\tau-j}),$$

$$\tau = 0, 1, 2, \ldots, q$$

where $a_0 = -1$. A Newton–Raphson algorithm, due to Wilson [1969], can then be employed to generate estimates of the moving average coefficients by an iterative procedure. Define a vector

$$\boldsymbol{\beta}' = (\beta_0, \beta_1, \beta_2, \ldots, \beta_q)$$

where

$$\beta_0^2 = \sigma_\epsilon^2, \qquad \beta_j = \beta_0 b_j, \qquad j = 1, 2, \ldots, q \tag{3.3.2}$$

Let $\boldsymbol{\beta}^{(i)}$ denote the value of $\boldsymbol{\beta}$ obtained at the ith iteration. This estimate is then updated according to

$$\boldsymbol{\beta}^{(i+1)} = \boldsymbol{\beta}^{(i)} - (\mathbf{A}^{(i)})^{-1} \mathbf{g}^{(i)}$$

where

$$\mathbf{g}' = (g_0, g_1, \ldots, g_q), \qquad g_j = \sum_{i=0}^{q-j} \beta_i \beta_{i+j} - \tilde{c}_j$$

and

$$\mathbf{A} = \begin{bmatrix} \beta_0 & \beta_1 & \cdots & \beta_{q-2} & \beta_{q-1} & \beta_q \\ \beta_1 & \beta_2 & \cdots & \beta_{q-1} & \beta_q & 0 \\ \beta_2 & \beta_3 & \cdots & \beta_q & 0 & 0 \\ & & \vdots & & & \\ \beta_q & 0 & \cdots & 0 & 0 & 0 \end{bmatrix} + \begin{bmatrix} \beta_0 & \beta_1 & \cdots & \beta_{q-2} & \beta_{q-1} & \beta_q \\ 0 & \beta_0 & \cdots & \beta_{q-3} & \beta_{q-2} & \beta_{q-1} \\ 0 & 0 & \cdots & \beta_{q-4} & \beta_{q-3} & \beta_{q-2} \\ & & \vdots & & & \\ 0 & 0 & \cdots & 0 & 0 & \beta_0 \end{bmatrix}$$

The iterative procedure is continued until satisfactory convergence is obtained, when estimates of the b_j can then be obtained from (3.3.2). The iteration process can be started off by setting $\sigma_\epsilon^2 = \tilde{c}_0$ and $b_1, b_2, \ldots, b_q = 0$.

3.4 The Autocorrelation Function as a Characteristic of Process Behavior

Up to this point it has been implicitly assumed that the behavior of the autocorrelations ρ_τ characterized the behavior of linear stationary stochastic processes of the form (3.3.1). It will now be proved that, given the requirement of invertibility introduced in Chapter 1, this is indeed so. Indeed, were it possible for two or more processes to possess the same autocorrelation structure, the identification process in Section 3.2 would be of very little value.

It is convenient initially to consider the pth-order autoregressive process

$$a(B)X_t = \epsilon_t \qquad (3.4.1)$$

whose autocorrelations are ρ_τ, and to prove that no other finite order autoregressive process can have these autocorrelations. Let

$$a^*(B)X_t = \epsilon_t^* \qquad (3.4.2)$$

denote such a process, of order p^*. It has been shown that for processes of the form (3.4.1), the autocorrelations obey

$$\rho_\tau = \sum_{j=1}^{p} a_j \rho_{\tau-j}, \qquad \tau > 0 \qquad (3.4.3)$$

Consider, then, the set of equations

$$\rho_\tau = \sum_{j=1}^{\max(p,\,p^*)} e_j \rho_{\tau-j}, \qquad \tau = 1, 2, \ldots, \max(p, p^*)$$

It follows from (3.4.3) that these equations must have the unique solution

$$e_j = a_j, \qquad j = 1, 2, \ldots, p \qquad \text{if } p^* \leqslant p$$
$$e_j = a_j, \qquad j = 1, 2, \ldots, p \qquad \text{if } p^* > p$$
$$= 0, \qquad j = p + 1, \ldots, p^* \qquad \text{if } p^* > p$$

Thus it follows that no finite order autoregressive process other than (3.4.1) can have autocorrelations ρ_τ, for if (3.4.2) were such a process it would be possible to write

$$\rho_\tau = \sum_{j=1}^{\max(p,\,p^*)} a_j^* \rho_{\tau-j}, \qquad \tau = 1, 2, \ldots, \max(p, p^*)$$

with $a_j^* = 0$ for $j > p^*$ if $p > p^*$, such that at least one a_j^* was different from a_j for $j = 1, 2, \ldots, p$ or different from zero for $j > p$. It has just been shown that this is impossible.

Now consider the ARMA(p, q) process

$$a(B)X_t = b(B)\epsilon_t \qquad (3.4.4)$$

whose autocorrelations are ρ_τ. Let an alternative process of order (p^*, q^*) and possessing the same autocorrelation structure be denoted as

$$a^*(B)X_t = b^*(B)\epsilon_t^* \qquad (3.4.5)$$

It follows from (1.3.8) and (1.7.18) that the autocorrelation generating function of the process (3.4.4) is given by

$$\rho(z) = \frac{\sigma_\epsilon^2}{\lambda_0} \frac{b(z)b(z^{-1})}{a(z)a(z^{-1})}$$

and that of (3.4.5) by

$$\rho(z) = \frac{\sigma_\epsilon^{*2}}{\lambda_0^*} \frac{b^*(z)b^*(z^{-1})}{a^*(z)a^*(z^{-1})}$$

where λ_0 and λ_0^* denote the variances of the two processes, and it is assumed that the operators $a(B)$ and $a^*(B)$ are stationary. If the two processes have identical autocorrelation structures, it follows that

$$\frac{\sigma_\epsilon^2}{\lambda_0} \frac{1}{a(z)b^*(z)a(z^{-1})b^*(z^{-1})} \tag{3.4.6}$$

and

$$\frac{\sigma_\epsilon^{*2}}{\lambda_0^*} \frac{1}{a^*(z)b(z)a^*(z^{-1})b(z^{-1})} \tag{3.4.7}$$

are equal. But (3.4.6) and (3.4.7) represent respectively the autocorrelation generating functions of the processes

$$a(B)b^*(B)Y_t = \eta_t \quad \text{and} \quad a^*(B)b(B)Y_t = \eta_t^*$$

provided that the roots of $b^*(B)$ and $b(B)$ all lie outside the unit circle, i.e., given invertibility (and where η_t and η_t^* are white noise processes). But it has already been shown that autoregressive operators are uniquely determined by their autocorrelation functions. Hence it follows that

$$a(B)b^*(B) = a^*(B)b(B)$$

and hence $a^*(B)/a(B) = b^*(B)/b(B)$. Thus, for a given autocorrelation structure, the representation (3.4.4) is unique in the class of invertible processes up to multiplication by a common polynomial function of B on either side of the equation. As a simple illustration, consider the process $(1 - aB)X_t = \epsilon_t$. Multiplying through by $1 - eB$ yields

$$(1 - eB)(1 - aB)X_t = (1 - eB)\epsilon_t$$

which for any $-1 < e < 1$ will clearly have the same autocorrelation structure.

The requirement of invertibility has been stressed in the above proof. It is a simple matter to demonstrate that such a requirement is necessary to ensure uniqueness of representation. Consider the two processes

$$X_t = (1 + 0.5B)\epsilon_t, \qquad X_t = (1 + 2B)\epsilon_t^* \tag{3.4.8}$$

where ϵ_t and ϵ_t^* are white noise processes. It follows from (1.6.3) and (1.6.4) that for both processes

$$\rho_\tau = 0.4 \quad \text{for} \quad \tau = 1$$
$$= 0 \quad \text{for} \quad \tau > 1$$

Thus both processes have the same autocorrelation function, although of course only the first process satisfies the invertibility requirement.

The above discussion suggests two points of some practical importance in model identification.

(i)   The possibility of multiple solutions arising from the multiplication of both sides of (3.4.4) by a common factor should caution against the selection of overelaborate models at the identification stage. The aim of model identification should be to choose the simplest (in terms of fewest coefficients) model compatible with the particular autocorrelation structure exhibited by the data.

(ii)   Since multiple solutions do occur when the model contains moving average terms, care should be taken to ensure that the initial parameter estimates calculated are those appropriate to the (unique) invertible process.

It has been shown that, if a model of the class (3.4.4) possesses a particular autocorrelation structure, then it will be the only model in that class to do so. However, as hinted in Section 1.6, it is not true that given a particular autocorrelation structure there must be a model in the class (3.4.4) possessing such a structure. For example, consider the case

$$\rho_1 = \rho, \qquad \rho_\tau = 0, \quad \tau > 1$$

If $|\rho| \leqslant 0.5$, then there exists a first-order moving average process $X_t = (1 + bB)\epsilon_t$, with these particular autocorrelations. However, for $|\rho| > 0.5$ it is not possible to find an autoregressive moving average model with such a correlogram. If it should happen that the sample autocorrelations are such that r_1 is much greater in magnitude than 0.5, while the remaining values are close to zero, the best strategy is probably to fit a higher order moving average model.

3.5 Estimation

We now assume that a specific model of the form

$$\left(1 - a_1 B - a_2 B^2 - \cdots - a_p B^p\right) Y_t = \left(1 + b_1 B + b_2 B^2 + \cdots + b_q B^q\right)\epsilon_t$$

$$(3.5.1)$$

where $Y_t = (1 - B)^d X_t$, has been chosen. Given n observations, on $Y_1, Y_2, \ldots, Y_n$, the next step is to estimate the parameters $a_1, a_2, \ldots, a_p$; $b_1, b_2, \ldots, b_q$ of (3.5.1). (For expositional convenience, it will be assumed that the process Y_t has zero mean. The estimation of an an additional parameter for the mean can easily be incorporated into what follows.)

Given an assumption that the Y_t are jointly normal, the exact likelihood function for the ARMA(p, q) model has been derived by a number of authors, including Newbold [1974], Dent [1977], Ansley [1979], and Ljung and Box [1979]. Here we follow Ansley.

First, consider the transformation from $Y_1, Y_2, \ldots, Y_n$ to $Z_1, Z_2, \ldots, Z_n$, defined by

$$Z_t = Y_t, \qquad\qquad\qquad t = 1, \ldots, m$$
$$ = Y_t - a_1 Y_{t-1} - \cdots - a_p Y_{t-p}, \qquad t = m+1, \ldots, n \qquad (3.5.2)$$

where $m = \max(p, q)$. The advantage of using this transformation is that the covariance matrix of the Z_t takes a very special, and easily handled, form since

$$\operatorname{cov}(Z_t, Z_{t+s}) = 0 \qquad \text{for} \quad |s| > m$$

(Indeed, this covariance is zero for all $|s| > q$ when $\min(t, t+s) > m$.) Therefore, writing $Z' = (Z_1, Z_2, \ldots, Z_n)$, it follows that the covariance matrix

$$E(ZZ') = \sigma_\epsilon^2 \Omega$$

is a band matrix, with bandwidth m for the first m rows, and q thereafter. The nonzero elements of the matrix Ω can be readily found as functions of the autoregressive and moving average parameters, using the methods discussed in Chapter 1.

Now, the matrix Ω has Cholesky decomposition

$$\Omega = LL'$$

where L is a lower triangular band matrix, whose bandwidths are the same as those of Ω. An efficient algorithm for computing this decomposition is given by Martin and Wilkinson (1965). Consider now the transformation

$$e = L^{-1}Z \qquad\qquad\qquad (3.5.3)$$

It follows that the random variables e have covariance matrix

$$E(ee') = L^{-1}E(ZZ')L^{-1\prime} = \sigma_\epsilon^2 L^{-1}LL'L^{-1\prime} = \sigma_\epsilon^2 I$$

so that, given our normality assumption, the members e_t of e are independently normally distributed, each with mean zero and variance σ_ϵ^2. Given that the transformation (3.5.2) has Jacobian unity and (3.5.3) Jacobian $|L|^{-1}$, it follows that the joint density function of $Y' = (Y_1, Y_2, \ldots, Y_n)$ can be written as

$$p(Y|\beta, \sigma_\epsilon^2) = (2\pi\sigma_\epsilon^2)^{-n/2} |L|^{-1} \exp\left(-\sum_{t=1}^{n} \frac{e_t^2}{2\sigma_\epsilon^2}\right) \qquad (3.5.4)$$

where $\beta' = (a_1, \ldots, a_p, b_1, \ldots, b_q)$.

The maximum likelihood estimates of the autoregressive and moving average parameters are then those values for which (3.5.4) is a maximum. These can be most conveniently found by minimizing the sum of squares

$$S^* = \sum_{t=1}^{n} e_t^{*2}$$

where

$$e_t^* = |L|^{1/n} e_t$$

noting that the determinant of the matrix L is simply the product of its diagonal elements.

Having expressed the maximum likelihood problem as one requiring the minimization of a sum of squares, we can find point estimates of the autoregressive and moving average parameters using a standard nonlinear regression algorithm based, for example, on a procedure proposed by Marquardt [1963]. A fuller account of nonlinear regression estimation is given in Draper and Smith [1981].

Many of the computer programs in current use for the estimation of ARMA models are based, not on full maximum likelihood estimation, but on one or another of two least squares procedures proposed by Box and Jenkins [1970]. These can be regarded as approximations to a full maximum likelihood estimation and are generally satisfactory for large sample sizes. However, when only a relatively modest amount of sample observations are available, simulation evidence in Ansley and Newbold [1980] suggests, in general, a preference for full maximum likelihood estimation.

So far we have discussed only point estimation of the model parameters. Interval estimates can be derived from a result of Whittle [1953], who shows that the maximum likelihood estimators are consistent and asymptotically normally distributed. Their asymptotic covariance matrix is V/n, where, partitioning the estimators as $\hat{\boldsymbol{\beta}}' = (\hat{a}_1, \ldots, \hat{a}_p : \hat{b}_1, \ldots, \hat{b}_q)$,

$$V^{-1} = \begin{bmatrix} A & \vdots & B \\ \cdots & & \cdots \\ B' & \vdots & D \end{bmatrix} \tag{3.5.5}$$

In (3.5.5)

   (i) A is a $p \times p$ matrix whose (i, j)th element is

$$E(v_t v_{t-i+j})$$

where $a(B)v_t = \epsilon_t^*$ and ϵ_t^* is zero-mean white noise with unit variance.

   (ii) D is a $q \times q$ matrix whose (i, j)th element is

$$E(u_t u_{t-i+j})$$

where $b(B)u_t = -\epsilon_t^*$.

   (iii) B is a $p \times q$ matrix whose (i, j)th element is

$$E(u_t v_{t-i+j})$$

This result is established in Hannan [1970, p. 392]. Notice that the covariance matrix of the parameter estimators depends on $a_1, \ldots, a_p, b_1, \ldots, b_q$, but not on the error variance σ_ϵ^2.

To illustrate, suppose that the ARMA(1, 1) model

$$Y_t - aY_{t-1} = \epsilon_t + b\epsilon_{t-1} \tag{3.5.6}$$

is estimated by maximum likelihood, the point estimators being denoted $\hat{a}$, $\hat{b}$. Then, the quantities A, B, and D in (3.5.5) will be scalars, with

$$A = E(u_t^2)$$

where $u_t - au_{t-1} = \epsilon_t^*$, so that $A = (1 - a^2)^{-1}$. Similarly,

$$D = E(v_t^2)$$

where $v_t + bv_{t-1} = -\epsilon_t^*$, so that $D = (1 - b^2)^{-1}$.

Finally,

$$C = E(u_t v_t)$$

which, after a little algebra, we find to be

$$C = -(1 + ab)^{-1}$$

By substituting in (3.5.5), we then find that the variance–covariance matrix for $\hat{\beta}' = (\hat{a}', \hat{b}')$ is

$$\operatorname{var}(\hat{\beta}) = n^{-1} \begin{bmatrix} (1 - a^2)^{-1} & -(1 + ab)^{-1} \\ -(1 + ab)^{-1} & (1 - b^2)^{-1} \end{bmatrix}^{-1}$$

$$= n^{-1} \frac{(1 + ab)}{(a + b)^2} \begin{bmatrix} (1 - a^2)(1 + ab) & (1 - a^2)(1 - b^2) \\ (1 - a^2)(1 - b^2) & (1 - b^2)(1 + ab) \end{bmatrix}$$

Notice that this implies infinite variance for the point estimators when $a + b = 0$. This is not surprising since in that case, as we see from (3.5.6), the autoregressive and moving average operators cancel, and Y_t is white noise. This could be represented by *any* pair of values a and b satisfying $a + b = 0$.

Now, the matrix V^{-1} of (3.5.5) involves the unknown true autoregressive and moving average parameters. However, in practice these can be replaced by the maximum likelihood estimates, so that the estimated covariance $\hat{V}/n$ is then employed. The square roots of the diagonal elements of this matrix provide the estimated standard errors of the maximum likelihood parameter estimators. The approximate normality of the estimators then allows interval estimation.

The procedure just described for finding the asymptotic covariance matrix of the parameter estimators can be algebraically extremely tedious unless p and q are small. Fortunately, Godolphin and Unwin [1983] have derived an efficient algorithm through which this matrix can readily be obtained.

We return now to three series whose identification was discussed in Section 3.2; the estimates of the coefficients of the tentatively identified models are given below (together with estimated standard errors in brackets).

(i) For the data on the ratio of consumer installment debt to personal income, the fitted model was

$$(1 - 0.74B)(1 - B)X_t = 0.021 + \epsilon_t$$
$$[0.06]$$

(ii)   For the data on the U.S.–U.K. exchange rate, the estimated model was

$$(1 - 0.26B)(1 - B)X_t = (1 + 0.28B)\epsilon_t$$
$$\quad [0.17] \qquad\qquad\qquad [0.17]$$

(iii)   For the series of observations on 30-day commercial paper yield, we decided in Section 3.2 to proceed with three possible model forms— ARIMA(1, 1, 1), ARIMA(2, 1, 0), and ARIMA(2, 1, 1), which includes the other two as special cases. The fitted equations for the first two models were

$$(1 + 0.10B)(1 - B)X_t = (1 + 0.57B)\epsilon_t \qquad (3.5.7)$$
$$\quad [0.18] \qquad\qquad\qquad [0.14]$$

and

$$(1 - 0.44B + 0.27B^2)(1 - B)X_t = \epsilon_t \qquad (3.5.8)$$
$$\quad [0.08] \qquad [0.08]$$

The respective estimated error variances for the two fitted models were 0.8969 and 0.8877, indicating a preference for the ARIMA(2, 1, 0) model. This is borne out by the fit obtained for the ARIMA(2, 1, 1) model, which was

$$(1 - 0.55B + 0.31B^2)(1 - B)X_t = (1 - 0.13B)\epsilon_t$$
$$\quad [0.25] \qquad [0.10] \qquad\qquad\qquad [0.26]$$

The estimate of the moving average parameter is very small compared with its estimated standard error, while the autoregressive parameter estimates are not terribly different from those of (3.5.8). The evidence therefore suggests a clear preference for the ARIMA(2, 1, 0) formulation.

The reader might find it perplexing that, at the identification stage, we were so unsure as to whether ARIMA(1, 1, 1) or ARIMA(2, 1, 0) was the appropriate model for the 30-day commercial paper yield series. After all, the fitted models (3.5.7) and (3.5.8) look, on the surface, very different from one another, and, with as many as 131 observations, it would be hoped that such apparently distinct formulations could be readily distinguished at the selection stage of the model building cycle. The resolution of this puzzle lies in the fact that the two models are, in fact, not as different as they seem to be at first sight. To see this, we note that the ARIMA(1, 1, 1) model (3.5.7) can be written as

$$(1 + 0.57B)^{-1}(1 + 0.10B)(1 - B)X_t = \epsilon_t$$

or

$$\left(1 - 0.57B + (0.57)^2B^2 - (0.57)^3B^3 + (0.57)^4B^4 - \cdots \right)$$
$$\times (1 + 0.10B)(1 - B)X_t = \epsilon_t$$

Multiplying out the polynomials in B in the first two terms on the left-hand side of this expression yields

$$(1 - 0.47B + 0.27B^2 - 0.15B^3 + 0.09B^4 - \cdots)(1 - B)X_t = \epsilon_t$$

which is not so terribly different from the model (3.5.8). In consequence, these two models would yield quite similar forecasts, so that in practice relatively little would be lost by proceeding with one rather than the other.

3.6 Diagnostic Checking

It is very often the case, as the reader who attempts to follow the model building procedure just described will quickly discover, that in practice model identification is fraught with uncertainties. One might feel able to select a particular model as a "best bet," but would be unhappy about the prospect of making inference from such a model without reassurance as to its validity. Accordingly, in this section a number of diagnostic checks on the adequacy of representation of the chosen model to the given data set are described. As will be seen, any inadequacies that are revealed may well suggest an alternative model as being more appropriate.

Fitting Extra Coefficients

In identifying, possibly after suitable differencing, a particular mixed autoregressive moving average model of order (p, q), it is of course implicitly assumed that in the more general model

$$\left(1 - a_1 B - a_2 B^2 - \cdots - a_p B^p - a_{p+1} B^{p+1} - \cdots - a_{p+p^*} B^{p+p^*}\right) Y_t$$
$$= \left(1 + b_1 B + b_2 B^2 + \cdots + b_q B^q + b_{q+1} B^{q+1} + \cdots + b_{q+q^*} B^{q+q^*}\right) \epsilon_t$$

the coefficients a_{p+j}, $j = 1, 2, \ldots, p^*$, and b_{q+j}, $j = 1, 2, \ldots, q^*$, are effectively zero. To a certain extent, this assumption is testable and where it is thought desirable to do so one can extend the identified model by adding extra coefficients. The augmented model can then be estimated, as described in Section 3.5, and the standard deviations of the estimates of the added coefficients will indicate whether or not the true values differ significantly from zero.

A good deal of computation time can be saved by basing tests of model adequacy, against the alternative that a particular more elaborate model is appropriate, on the Lagrange multiplier test of Rao [1948] and Silvey [1959]. In carrying out this test, it is not necessary to estimate the more elaborate model. The use of Lagrange multiplier tests in the present context has been discussed by Godfrey [1979].

The Lagrange multiplier test is based on the derivatives of the log likelihood function, with respect to the additional parameters, evaluated at the parameter estimates under the null hypothesis that the original model is correctly specified. It can be shown that, under this null hypothesis, these derivatives have asymptotic normal distributions. Now, for an ARMA(p, q) process, generated by innovations ϵ_t, the log likelihood function can be written approximately as

$$\log L = \text{const} - \frac{n}{2} \log \sigma_\epsilon^2 - \frac{\sum\limits_{t=1}^{n} \epsilon_t^2}{2\sigma_\epsilon^2}$$

$$= \text{const} - \frac{n}{2} \log \sigma_\epsilon^2$$

$$- \frac{\sum\limits_{t=1}^{n} \left[(1 + b_1 B + \cdots + b_q B^q)^{-1} (1 - a_1 B - \cdots - a_p B^p) Y_t \right]^2}{2\sigma_\epsilon^2}$$

The partial derivatives of this function with respect to the autoregressive and moving average parameters are

$$\frac{\partial \log L}{\partial a_i} = \frac{\sum\limits_{t=1}^{n} (1 + b_1 B + \cdots + b_q B^q)^{-1} Y_{t-i} \epsilon_t}{\sigma_\epsilon^2}$$

and

$$\frac{\partial \log L}{\partial b_j} = \frac{\sum\limits_{t=1}^{n} (1 + b_1 B + \cdots + b_q B^q)^{-2} (1 - a_1 B - \cdots - a_p B^p) Y_{t-j} \epsilon_t}{\sigma_\epsilon^2}$$

$$= \frac{\sum\limits_{t=1}^{n} (1 + b_1 B + \cdots + b_q B^q)^{-1} \epsilon_{t-j} \epsilon_t}{\sigma_\epsilon^2}$$

The Lagrange multiplier test statistic is based on these derivatives.

Suppose that, if necessary, the data have been differenced and that n observations on the stationary process Y_t are available. We will again assume for ease of exposition that Y_t has zero mean. The initially identified model for this process will be denoted ARMA(p, q), so that the model to be estimated is

$$Y_t - a_1 Y_{t-1} - \cdots - a_p Y_{t-p} = \epsilon_t + b_1 \epsilon_{t-1} + \cdots + b_q \epsilon_{t-q}$$

or

$$a(B) Y_t = b(B) \epsilon_t$$

Denote the maximum likelihood parameter estimates by $\hat{a}_i$ and $\hat{b}_i$ and the residuals by

$$\hat{\epsilon}_t = \hat{b}^{-1}(B) \hat{a}(B) y_t$$

where y_t are the observed values of the process Y_t. We now construct two new series, w_t and z_t, from

$$\hat{b}(B) w_t = y_t \qquad \text{or} \qquad w_t = y_t - \hat{b}_1 w_{t-1} - \cdots - \hat{b}_q w_{t-q} \qquad (3.6.1)$$

and

$$\hat{b}(B)z_t = \hat{\epsilon}_t \quad \text{or} \quad z_t = \hat{\epsilon}_t - \hat{b}_1 z_{t-1} - \cdots - \hat{b}_q z_{t-q} \quad (3.6.2)$$

In practice the computations in (3.6.1) and (3.6.2) can be initiated by setting w_t and z_t, to zero for $t = (1 - q), \ldots, -1, 0$.

Consider, now, the problem of testing that our model is correctly specified against the alternative that m additional moving average parameters are needed. Thus, the null hypotheses of an ARMA(p, q) specification for Y_t is to be tested against the alternative of ARMA($p, q + m$). Godfrey shows that the Lagrange multiplier test can be carried out by estimating by least squares the regression model

$$\hat{\epsilon}_t = \alpha_1 w_{t-1} + \cdots + \alpha_p w_{t-p} + \beta_1 z_{t-1} + \cdots + \beta_{q+m} z_{t-q-m} + u_t, \quad (3.6.3)$$

where the α_i and β_j are parameters and u_t an error term. Let $\hat{u}_t$ denote the residuals from the estimated regression equation. Then, under the null hypothesis that the ARMA(p, q) model is correct, the statistic

$$G = n\left[1 - \frac{\Sigma \hat{u}_t^2}{\Sigma \hat{\epsilon}_t^2}\right] \quad (3.6.4)$$

has an asymptotic χ^2 distribution with m degrees of freedom. The null hypothesis is rejected against the alternative of a more elaborate model for large values of this test statistic.

Godfrey also develops a Lagrange multiplier test against the alternative that the true model is ARMA($p + m, q$). However, Poskitt and Treymayne [1980] show that the two tests are essentially identical. These authors further show that this equivalence extends to any admissible ARMA($p + K_1$, $q + K_2$) alternative where m is equal to the greater of K_1 and K_2.

To illustrate this test, consider the ARIMA(1, 1, 1) model fitted to the data on U.S.–U.K. exchange rates. If we denote by y_t the observed first differences of this series, the residuals are

$$\hat{\epsilon}_t = (1 + 0.28B)^{-1}(1 - 0.26B)y_t$$

Hence, the w_t of (3.6.1) are obtained from

$$w_t = y_t - 0.28w_{t-1}$$

where we initialize the calculations by setting $w_0 = 0$. Similarly, the z_t of (3.6.2) can be calculated from

$$z_t = \hat{\epsilon}_t - 0.28z_{t-1}$$

Following from (3.6.3), to test against the possibility of m additional moving average terms, we estimate by least squares the regression

$$\hat{\epsilon}_t = \alpha_1 w_{t-1} + \beta_1 z_{t-1} + \cdots + \beta_{1+m} z_{t-1-m} + u_t$$

The statistic (3.6.4) was calculated for values of $m = 1, 2, 3$, giving 0.03, 0.04, and 0.20, respectively. Comparison with tabulated values of the χ^2 distribution for 1, 2, and 3 degrees of freedom does not suggest strong grounds for suspecting the adequacy of representation of the fitted model.

Use of Autocorrelations of the Residuals

If the time series model is correctly specified, then the innovations ϵ_t will constitute a white-noise process. If the innovation series $\epsilon_1, \epsilon_2, \ldots, \epsilon_n$ were available, then natural checks on model adequacy could be based on the sample autocorrelations of this series. Anderson [1942] has shown that the sample autocorrelations of white noise are asymptotically independently normally distributed with zero means and standard deviations $n^{-1/2}$. Thus, if the true ϵ_t were known, readily carried out checks of model adequacy could be based on their sample autocorrelations.

Unfortunately, in practice, the true innovations will be unknown, and we must rely instead on their estimates, the residuals $\hat{\epsilon}_t$ from the fitted model. It seems reasonable, given the discussion of the previous paragraph, to expect the sample autocorrelations of the residuals

$$r_\tau(\hat{\epsilon}) = \sum_{t=\tau+1}^{n} \hat{\epsilon}_t \hat{\epsilon}_{t-\tau} \Big/ \sum_{t=1}^{n} \hat{\epsilon}_t^2$$

to yield valuable information about model inadequacies. Indeed, it is useful to calculate these quantities. However, their value is somewhat limited since, as noted by Durbin [1970], the asymptotic standard deviations of the residual sample autocorrelations can be a good deal lower than $n^{-1/2}$, particularly for low values of τ. Intuitively this is so because, in estimating a linear time series model, one is in effect choosing as parameter estimates those values that render the residuals from the fitted equation as much like white noise as possible, at least with regard to their first few autocorrelations. Thus, the estimation procedure itself by its very nature ensures that the first few autocorrelations of the residuals will be quite close to zero.

The asymptotic distribution of the residual autocorrelations from fitted autoregressive–moving average models has been derived by Box and Pierce [1970] and McLeod [1978], while simulation evidence for moderate sample sizes is available from Ansley and Newbold [1979a]. It emerges that the standard deviations of the residual sample autocorrelations can indeed be a good deal smaller than $n^{-1/2}$ for low lags τ. The actual asymptotic standard deviations are rather complicated functions of the model parameters. Nevertheless, we feel that comparison of the sample autocorrelations of the residuals with bounds $\pm 2n^{-1/2}$ will provide at least a crude check on model adequacy, and that examination of these quantities can suggest the direction of any inadequacy, provided that it is remembered that for small τ this will understate the significance of any discrepancies.

Table 3.4 shows the sample autocorrelations of the residuals from the ARIMA(1, 1, 1) model fitted to the U.S.–U.K. exchange rate series. Since there are $n = 121$ observations on the first differences, we have $2/\sqrt{n} \simeq 0.18$. Judged by this standard, the residual autocorrelations in Table 3.4 do not seem excessively large and provide little grounds for questioning the adequacy of the fitted model.

Table 3.4   *Residual autocorrelations from ARIMA(1, 1, 1) model fitted to U.S.–U.K. exchange rate series*

τ:	1	2	3	4	5	6	7	8	9	10
$r_\tau(\hat{\epsilon})$:	$-.01$	.01	$-.01$	.01	.04	.06	$-.06$	$-.04$	.05	.03
τ:	11	12	13	14	15	16	17	18	19	20
$r_\tau(\hat{\epsilon})$:	.08	.06	$-.02$	.02	$-.11$	.05	$-.10$	.23	$-.06$	$-.11$

In addition to the examination of individual residual autocorrelations, one can examine them jointly, asking if they are generally too high in magnitude to allow the contention that the model innovations are white noise. The procedure is to compare the so-called "portmanteau" statistic

$$Q = n(n + 2) \sum_{\tau=1}^{M} (n - \tau)^{-1} r_\tau^2(\hat{\epsilon}) \qquad (3.6.5)$$

with tabulated values of the χ^2 distribution with $M - p - q$ degrees of freedom, the hypothesis of model adequacy being rejected for high values of Q. The test rests for its validity on the number M of autocorrelations being moderately large (generally at least 10 to 20). In fact, the statistic (3.6.5) is a modification, due to Ljung and Box [1978], of an earlier proposal of Box and Pierce [1970]. This modification is desirable since, as noted by Davies, Triggs, and Newbold [1977], the null distribution of the Box–Pierce statistic, in moderate-sized samples, can be very different from χ^2. The portmanteau test may, as demonstrated by Davies and Newbold [1979], have very low power in the detection of specific important departures from the assumed model. It is, therefore, unwise to rely *exclusively* on this test in checking for model adequacy. It can, however, be valuable when used in conjunction with other checks.

For the series on U.S.–U.K. exchange rates, the portmanteau statistic (3.6.5) was calculated from the residual autocorrelations from the fitted model for values of $M = 10, 15$, and 20. The corresponding Q statistics were 1.73, 4.73, and 15.93. Comparing these with tabulated values of the χ^2 statistic for 8, 13, and 18 degrees of freedom, we find little evidence of model inadequacy.

We have now considered two apparently different approaches to checking the adequacy of representation to the given data of an assumed ARIMA specification. We can either consider the possibility of an alternative model with additional parameters or base checks on the residual autocorrelations from the fitted model. In fact, however, viewed in one light, these two approaches are not really distinct. Newbold [1980] has shown that the Lagrange multiplier test against the alternative of m additional parameters is identical to the appropriate test based on the first m residual autocorrelations. There is, then, no point in carrying out both tests. In addition, Hosking [1980a] has shown how the portmanteau test can be derived as a Lagrange multiplier test.

The Lagrange multiplier test, if model specification is found to be inadequate, may suggest an alternative model, though it will not help us distinguish between the desirability of additional autoregressive and additional moving average parameters. The autocorrelations of the residuals can also be used to suggest an alternative specification if they appear not to exhibit white noise behavior. Suppose that the residual autocorrelations from the assumed model

$$a(B)(1 - B)^d X_t = b(B)\epsilon_t \qquad (3.6.6)$$

suggest that the ϵ_t are not white noise, but rather follow the ARIMA(p^*, d^*, q^*) process

$$a^*(B)(1 - B)^{d^*}\epsilon_t = b^*(B)\eta_t \qquad (3.6.7)$$

where η_t is white noise. Combining (3.6.6) and (3.6.7) then yields for the process X_t the ARIMA($p + p^*, d + d^*, q + q^*$) model

$$a(B)a^*(B)(1 - B)^{d+d^*} X_t = b(B)b^*(B)\eta_t$$

so that a model of this order could be estimated at the next iteration of the model building cycle. The process of identification, estimation, and checking is then continued until a satisfactory model is found.

Although we have on occasion found this approach to model modification useful, the situation is not quite so straightforward as it may at first sight appear. For example, suppose the process

$$(1 - 0.6B)(1 + 0.3B)Y_t = \eta_t \qquad (3.6.8)$$

is wrongly identified as first-order autoregressive. Would the residuals from the fitted model be first-order autoregressive and hence lead directly to the correct identification? Even ignoring sampling variability, such would not be the case, since for the process (3.6.8) $\rho_1 \simeq 0.37$. Hence, for large samples, the fitted model would be close to

$$(1 - 0.37B)Y_t = \epsilon_t \qquad (3.6.9)$$

Thus the residuals from the fitted model obey

$$(1 - 0.6B)(1 + 0.3B)\epsilon_t = (1 - 0.37B)\eta_t \qquad (3.6.10)$$

and this process is even more complicated than the one that was not identified in the first place. The position is rendered even more difficult by sampling errors that could make the cancellation involved in combining (3.6.9) and (3.6.10)—that is, the occurrence of the term $1 - 0.37B$ on both sides of the amalgamated equation—very difficult in practice to detect on the basis of just the residual autocorrelations.

3.7 Model Building for Seasonal Time Series
In Section 1.14 the model

$$a(B)a_s(B^s)(1 - B)^d(1 - B^s)^D X_t = b(B)b_s(B^s)\epsilon_t \qquad (3.7.1)$$

where

$$a(B) = 1 - a_1 B - a_2 B^2 - \cdots - a_p B^p$$

$$a_s(B^s) = 1 - a_{1,s} B^s - a_{2,s} B^{2s} - \cdots - a_{P,s} B^{Ps}$$

$$b(B) = 1 + b_1 B + b_2 B^2 + \cdots + b_q B^q$$

$$b_s(B^s) = 1 + b_{1,s} B^s + b_{2,s} B^{2s} + \cdots + b_{Q,s} B^{Qs}$$

was introduced for the representation of seasonal time series of period s—that is, $s = 4$ for quarterly data and $s = 12$ for monthly data. It has been found that models of the form (3.7.1) are capable of well describing a wide range of practically occurring seasonal time series. Such models are fitted to a given set of data by employing essentially the same principles as were described for the nonseasonal case. The approach to model building again is composed of an iterative cycle of identification, estimation, and diagnostic checking. These elements of the model building cycle will be briefly described and their application to seasonal series discussed in this section.

Identification

At the identification stage, the objective is to choose suitable values for d, D, p, P, q, and Q, the degrees of the polynomial operators in (3.7.1). The identification procedure is, as before, in two steps. At the first step, the degree of differencing required to produce stationarity is determined. This is achieved by applying the two operators $1 - B$ and $1 - B^s$ until the sample autocorrelations of the differenced series die out quickly at high lags.

At the second step the sample autocorrelations and partial autocorrelations of the appropriately differenced series $Y_t = (1 - B)^d (1 - B^s)^D X_t$ are employed to suggest appropriate degrees for the four polynomial operators $a(B)$, $a_s(B^s)$, $b(B)$, and $b_s(B^s)$. In principle, the patterns followed by the autocorrelation function for various members of the class (3.7.1) can be determined from the autocovariance generating function for Y_t

$$\gamma(z) = \sigma_\epsilon^2 \frac{b(z) b_s(z^s) b(z^{-1}) b_s(z^{-s})}{a(z) a_s(z^s) a(z^{-1}) a_s(z^{-s})}$$

Furthermore, the results of Section 3.2, which characterized the nonseasonal process, carry over in an obvious way, so that

(i) If Y_t is a multiplicative autoregressive process of order p, P, i.e., $q, Q = 0$, its autocorrelations will die out according to the difference equation

$$a(B) a_s(B^s) \rho_\tau = 0 \qquad \text{for all} \quad \tau > 0$$

where the operator B is on the index τ; and its partial autocorrelations will obey

$$a_{KK} = 0 \qquad \text{for all} \quad K > p + sP$$

(ii) If Y_t is a multiplicative moving average process of order q, Q, i.e., $p, P = 0$, its autocorrelations will obey

$$\rho_\tau = 0 \quad \text{for} \quad q < \tau < s - q$$

$$s + q < \tau < 2s - q$$

$$\vdots$$

$$(Q - 1)s + q < \tau < Qs - q$$

$$Qs + q < \tau$$

(iii) If Y_t is a multiplicative mixed autoregressive moving average process of order (p, P, q, Q), its autocorrelations will obey

$$a(B)a_s(B^s)\rho_\tau = 0 \quad \text{for all} \quad \tau > q + sQ$$

In fact, for many members of the class (3.7.1) more comprehensive conditions than these can be derived. These are best illustrated by consideration of three fairly general cases which might be expected to include the vast majority of models that occur in practice, and which can be expanded in an obvious fashion to cover many other potentially useful models.

As a first case, consider the multiplicative moving average process

$$Y_t = (1 + b_1 B + b_2 B^2)(1 + b_{1,s} B^s + b_{2,s} B^{2s})\epsilon_t \qquad (3.7.2)$$

As noted above, for this process

$$\rho_\tau = 0 \quad \text{for} \quad 2 < \tau < s - 2, \quad s + 2 < \tau < 2s - 2, \quad 2s + 2 < \tau \quad (3.7.3)$$

It is also straightforward to verify that

$$\rho_{s-2} = \rho_{s+2}, \quad \rho_{s-1} = \rho_{s+1}, \quad \rho_{2s-2} = \rho_{2s+2}, \quad \rho_{2s-1} = \rho_{2s+1} \quad (3.7.4)$$

By setting some of the coefficients of (3.7.2) equal to zero, a number of special cases can be examined. The general conditions (3.7.4) continue to hold, while modifying (3.7.3) it is straightforward to show for the various cases:

(i) If $b_2 = 0$: $\rho_\tau = 0$ for $1 < \tau < s - 1, s + 1 < \tau < 2s - 1, 2s + 1 < \tau$.
(ii) If $b_1 = b_2 = 0$: $\rho_\tau = 0$ for all τ except $\tau = s, 2s$.
(iii) If $b_2 = b_{2,s} = 0$: $\rho_\tau = 0$ for $1 < \tau < s - 1, s + 1 < \tau$.
(iv) If $b_{2,s} = 0$: $\rho_\tau = 0$ for $2 < \tau < s - 2, s + 2 < \tau$.
(v) If $b_1 = b_2 = b_{2,s} = 0$: $\rho_\tau = 0$ for all τ except $\tau = s$.

The second important case is the model

$$(1 - a_1 B)(1 - a_{1,s} B^s)Y_t = (1 + b_1 B)(1 + b_{1,s} B^s)\epsilon_t \qquad (3.7.5)$$

The autocorrelations of this process obey the difference equation

$$\rho_\tau = a_1 \rho_{\tau-1} + a_{1,s}\rho_{\tau-s} - a_1 a_{1,s}\rho_{\tau-s-1} \quad \text{for all} \quad \tau > s + 1 \quad (3.7.6)$$

In practice, behavior of this kind can be recognized in the following way. Suppose that, in general, the difference equation in (3.7.6) is obeyed for all τ bigger than some number T. Then

$$\rho_\tau - a_1\rho_{\tau-1} = a_{1,s}(\rho_{\tau-s} - a_1\rho_{\tau-s-1}) \qquad \text{for all} \quad \tau > T \quad (3.7.7)$$

and

$$\rho_\tau - a_{1,s}\rho_{\tau-s} = a_1(\rho_{\tau-1} - a_{1,s}\rho_{\tau-s-1}) \qquad \text{for all} \quad \tau > T \quad (3.7.8)$$

It follows, then, that for some number k, from (3.7.8)

$$\rho_\tau - a_{1,s}\rho_{\tau-s} = ka_1^{\tau-T} \qquad \text{for all} \quad \tau > T$$

Thus, in particular,

$$\rho_{T+1} - a_{1,s}\rho_{T+1-s} = ka_1 \qquad \text{and} \qquad \rho_{T+1+K} - a_{1,s}\rho_{T+1+K-s} = ka_1^{K+1}$$

Hence it follows that

$$\rho_{T+1+K} - a_{1,s}\rho_{T+1+K-s} = a_1^K(\rho_{T+1} - a_{1,s}\rho_{T+1-s}) \qquad (3.7.9)$$

Now if K is moderately large, it follows from the stationarity requirement $|a_1| < 1$, that the right-hand side of (3.7.9) will be close to zero, and

$$\rho_{T+1+K} \approx a_{1,s}\rho_{T+1+K-s}$$

In words, this implies that for high lags the effects of the operator a_1 will become negligible. Hence behavior of the type (3.7.8) will be typified by the ratios $\rho_{T+1+K}/\rho_{T+1+K-s}$ being roughly constant for all moderately large K (say $K \geqslant 10$). Now suppose that this is so, and that the ratio is approximately equal to $\hat{a}_{1,s}$, which should be close to the value $a_{1,s}$. Then, from (3.7.8) it follows that the ratios

$$(\rho_\tau - \hat{a}_{1,s}\rho_{\tau-s})/(\rho_{\tau-1} - \hat{a}_{1,s}\rho_{\tau-1}) \qquad \text{for all} \quad \tau > T$$

should also be roughly constant, approximating a_1.

By setting some of the coefficients of (3.7.5) equal to zero, it is possible to consider a number of special cases and typify their behavior:

(i)   If $b_1 = 0$: the difference equation in (3.7.6) holds for all $\tau > s$.

(ii) If $b_{1,s} = 0$: the difference equation in (3.7.6) holds for all $\tau > 1$.

(iii) If $b_1 = b_{1,s} = 0$: the difference equation in (3.7.6) holds for all $\tau > 0$. Furthermore the partial autocorrelations obey

$$a_{KK} = 0 \qquad \text{for all} \quad K > s + 1$$

(iv) If $a_{1,s} = 0$: the autocorrelations obey

$$\rho_\tau = a_1\rho_{\tau-1} \qquad \text{for all} \quad \tau > s + 1$$

(v)   If $a_{1,s} = b_1 = 0$: the autocorrelations obey

$$\rho_\tau = a_1\rho_{\tau-1} \qquad \text{for all} \quad \tau > s$$

(vi) If $a_1 = 0$: the autocorrelations obey

$$\rho_\tau = 0 \qquad \text{for all} \quad 1 < \tau < s - 1$$

and

$$\rho_\tau = a_{1,s}\rho_{\tau-s} \qquad \text{for all} \quad \tau > s + 1$$

Also $\rho_{s-1} = \rho_{s+1}$.

(vii) If $a_1 = b_1 = 0$: the only nonzero autocorrelations are ρ_{js}, $j = 1, 2, 3, \ldots$, and $\rho_\tau = a_{1,s}\rho_{\tau-s}$ for all $\tau > s$.

(viii) If $a_1 = b_{1,s} = 0$: the autocorrelations obey the same conditions as in (vi) except that now

$$\rho_\tau = a_{1,s}\rho_{\tau-s} \qquad \text{for all} \quad \tau > 1$$

(ix) If $a_1 = b_1 = b_{1,s} = 0$: the only nonzero autocorrelations are ρ_{js}, $j = 1, 2, 3, \ldots$ and $\rho_\tau = a_{1,s}\rho_{\tau-s}$ for all $\tau > 0$. Further, the partial autocorrelations obey $a_{KK} = 0$ for all $K > s$.

The third case of interest concerns situations in which the multiplicativity assumed in (3.7.1) is no longer tenable. To illustrate, consider the moving average process

$$Y_t = (1 + b_1 B)(1 + b_{1,s} B^s)\epsilon_t \tag{3.7.10}$$

It has been noted that the only nonzero autocorrelations of such a process are ρ_1, ρ_{s-1}, ρ_s, and ρ_{s+1} and that

$$\rho_{s-1} = \rho_{s+1} \tag{3.7.11}$$

Consider now the alternative process

$$Y_t = (1 + b_1 B + b_s B^s + b_{s+1} B^{s+1})\epsilon_t \tag{3.7.12}$$

This differs from the process (3.7.10) if $b_{s+1} \neq b_1 b_s$. The process (3.7.12) again has only $\rho_1, \rho_{s-1}, \rho_s, \rho_{s+1}$ as nonzero autocorrelations, but can be distinguished from (3.7.10) by noting that now the condition (3.7.11) fails in general to hold. The process

$$(1 - a_1 B)Y_t = (1 + b_1 B + b_s B^s + b_{s+1} B^{s+1})\epsilon_t$$

can be distinguished from the corresponding multiplicative process in exactly the same way. It appears to be true, in general, that for most practically occurring seasonal time series, multiplicative models provide a good representation. However, it should be remembered that the restriction of multiplicativity can always be dropped if this is thought necessary from examination of the sample autocorrelations. Some of the principles involved in the identification of seasonal models are now illustrated with some specific examples.

EXAMPLE 1 First consider a series of 122 monthly observations on the currency held by the public element of the U.S. money supply. Table 3.5 shows the sample autocorrelations r_K and partial autocorrelations $\hat{a}_{KK}$ for the series and some of its differences.

Table 3.5 *Sample autocorrelations and partial autocorrelations for currency held by the public series*

	K	1	2	3	4	5	6	7	8	9	10	11	12
	r_K	.98	.95	.93	.91	.88	.86	.84	.81	.79	.76	.74	.72
	$\hat{a}_{KK}$	.98	−.03	−.04	.02	−.00	−.02	−.02	−.03	−.01	−.01	.01	.01
	K	13	14	15	16	17	18	19	20	21	22	23	24
X_t	r_K	.69	.67	.64	.62	.59	.57	.54	.52	.49	.47	.45	.43
	$\hat{a}_{KK}$	−.06	−.03	−.05	.01	−.00	−.01	−.02	−.02	−.01	−.00	.01	−.00
	K	25	26	27	28	29	30	31	32	33	34	35	36
	r_K	.40	.38	.36	.33	.31	.29	.27	.24	.22	.20	.18	.16
	$\hat{a}_{KK}$	−.05	−.02	−.03	.01	−.01	−.02	−.01	−.01	−.01	.00	.00	−.00

	K	1	2	3	4	5	6	7	8	9	10	11	12
	r_K	.01	−.40	−.17	.15	.15	−.14	.11	.16	−.13	−.38	−.01	.81
	$\hat{a}_{KK}$	.01	−.40	−.19	−.03	.01	−.15	.23	.13	−.06	−.30	−.10	.72
	K	13	14	15	16	17	18	19	20	21	22	23	24
$(1-B)X_t$	r_K	.03	−.33	−.16	.12	.12	−.11	.07	.12	−.13	−.33	.00	.68
	$\hat{a}_{KK}$	−.03	.20	.11	−.00	−.09	.09	−.11	−.14	−.14	−.03	−.04	.09
	K	25	26	27	28	29	30	31	32	33	34	35	36
	r_K	.01	−.31	−.13	.09	.11	−.10	.06	.11	−.14	−.30	−.01	.61
	$\hat{a}_{KK}$	−.04	−.05	.03	−.05	.02	−.03	.06	.01	.03	−.00	−.08	.05

	K	1	2	3	4	5	6	7	8	9	10	11	12
	r_K	.96	.92	.89	.86	.84	.81	.78	.76	.73	.69	.66	.62
	$\hat{a}_{KK}$	.96	−.08	.05	.09	.02	−.04	.02	.03	−.07	−.18	.03	−.01
	K	13	14	15	16	17	18	19	20	21	22	23	24
$(1-B^{12})X_t$	r_K	.60	.58	.55	.53	.50	.47	.45	.42	.39	.36	.34	.31
	$\hat{a}_{KK}$	.08	.01	−.07	.02	−.01	−.04	−.01	.03	−.13	.00	.07	−.10
	K	25	26	27	28	29	30	31	32	33	34	35	36
	r_K	.29	.26	.23	.20	.18	.15	.13	.11	.08	.06	.03	.01
	$\hat{a}_{KK}$	.01	−.04	−.00	−.08	.05	.04	−.02	−.05	−.07	.02	.00	−.10

	K	1	2	3	4	5	6	7	8	9	10	11	12
	r_K	.06	−.10	−.08	−.08	.11	−.06	−.08	.06	.26	−.06	−.06	−.25
	$\hat{a}_{KK}$	.06	−.10	−.06	−.08	.11	−.10	−.06	.06	.26	−.14	.01	−.25
	K	13	14	15	16	17	18	19	20	21	22	23	24
$(1-B)(1-B^{12})X_t$	r_K	−.00	.18	−.06	.02	.03	.00	.02	.13	−.04	−.03	.11	−.06
	$\hat{a}_{KK}$	.07	.05	−.03	.02	.06	−.10	.04	.21	.07	−.13	.11	−.10
	K	25	26	27	28	29	30	31	32	33	34	35	36
	r_K	−.02	−.01	−.08	−.02	.02	−.00	−.00	.04	−.09	−.02	.05	−.00
	$\hat{a}_{KK}$	−.04	.06	−.05	−.11	.01	−.02	.01	.13	−.08	−.12	.19	−.04

The sample autocorrelations of the undifferenced series die out only slowly at high lags, suggesting nonstationary behavior. In passing, it is worth noticing that this series provides a nice illustration of the advantages of differencing. For time series that exhibit this typical nonstationary behavior it is, as noted earlier, very often the case that, when looking at the raw data alone, all other characteristics will be swamped by the evidence of non-stationarity. Thus, looking only at the sample autocorrelations and partial autocorrelations of the original series, one would be hard pressed indeed to detect seasonality. For the series of first differences $(1 - B)X_t$, we find high sample autocorrelations at lags that are multiples of 12, and these seem to be dying out very slowly. This indicates the desirability of seasonal differencing. The series $(1 - B)^{12}X_t$ has sample autocorrelations that do appear eventually to die out to quite small values. However, they do so only very slowly and smoothly.

These considerations suggest examination of the doubly differenced series $(1 - B)(1 - B^{12})X_t$, for which the sample autocorrelation pattern presents no evidence of remaining nonstationarity. Since there are 109 observations on this series, the magnitudes of the sample autocorrelations and partial autocorrelations are compared with $2/\sqrt{109} \simeq 0.19$. There is a large sample autocorrelation at lag 12, suggesting a seasonal moving average term. There is also a large value at lag 9. However, since it is difficult to think of any reasonable explanation for an important correlation at such a lag, we will put this down to sampling error. The model to be fitted to these data, then, is

$$(1 - B)(1 - B^{12})X_t = (1 + b_{1,s}B^{12})\epsilon_t$$

EXAMPLE 2   The second example is a time series of 108 monthly values of unemployment in Belgium. Relevant sample autocorrelations are given in Table 3.6, and the series is graphed in Fig. 3.1.

The sample autocorrelations of the original series exhibit typical nonstationary behavior, suggesting that differencing is required. The series $(1 - B)X_t$ has high and persistent autocorrelations at lags around multiples of 12, while the series $(1 - B^{12})X_t$ has autocorrelations that suggest the need for further differencing. On the other hand, there is very little evidence to suggest that the series $(1 - B)(1 - B^{12})X_t$ is anything other than white noise. (As in the previous example, approximate 95% significance levels for sample autocorre-lations under the hypothesis of white noise are given by ± 0.21.) Perhaps the first autocorrelation, which is moderate in size, may be of importance, and therefore the model

$$(1 - B)(1 - B^{12})X_t = (1 + b_1 B)\epsilon_t$$

will be carried forward for estimation.

Table 3.6   *Sample autocorrelations and partial autocorrelations for data on unemployment in Belgium*

	K	1	2	3	4	5	6	7	8	9	10	11	12
	r_K	.92	.80	.70	.62	.58	.56	.55	.57	.61	.64	.66	.64
	$\hat{a}_{KK}$	.92	−.27	.07	.07	.11	.08	.11	.16	.14	.10	.03	−.18
	K	13	14	15	16	17	18	19	20	21	22	23	24
X_t	r_K	.56	.47	.39	.33	.28	.26	.24	.25	.28	.30	.31	.27
	$\hat{a}_{KK}$	−.19	−.05	−.08	−.08	−.04	−.05	−.06	.02	.07	.05	.03	−.06
	K	25	26	27	28	29	30	31	32	33	34	35	36
	r_K	.20	.12	.06	.00	−.04	−.06	−.07	−.07	−.05	−.03	−.03	−.05
	$\hat{a}_{KK}$	−.09	−.02	−.02	−.06	−.04	−.04	−.06	−.06	.01	.07	.03	.02
	K	1	2	3	4	5	6	7	8	9	10	11	12
	r_K	.65	.24	−.06	−.26	−.32	−.33	−.36	−.34	−.17	.19	.55	.68
	$\hat{a}_{KK}$	.65	−.32	−.11	−.17	−.04	−.18	−.20	−.16	.09	.33	.33	.17
	K	13	14	15	16	17	18	19	20	21	22	23	24
$(1 - B)X_t$	r_K	.47	.16	−.06	−.20	−.23	−.29	−.31	−.28	−.14	.14	.43	.52
	$\hat{a}_{KK}$	−.17	−.07	.01	.01	.07	−.06	.16	.00	−.06	−.10	.09	.11
	K	25	26	27	28	29	30	31	32	33	34	35	36
	r_K	.37	.16	−.02	−.13	−.17	−.20	−.22	−.21	−.12	.09	.28	.38
	$\hat{a}_{KK}$	−.00	.06	−.04	.04	.02	.03	.09	−.00	.01	−.08	−.02	.07
	K	1	2	3	4	5	6	7	8	9	10	11	12
	r_K	.94	.87	.80	.75	.71	.67	.63	.59	.55	.52	.49	.46
	$\hat{a}_{KK}$	.94	−.18	.09	.05	−.01	.07	−.04	−.02	.01	.03	−.02	−.00
	K	13	14	15	16	17	18	19	20	21	22	23	24
$(1 - B^{12})X_t$	r_K	.44	.42	.40	.38	.37	.36	.35	.36	.36	.35	.34	.31
	$\hat{a}_{KK}$	.04	−.01	.02	.02	.02	−.01	.09	.02	.01	−.02	−.04	−.13
	K	25	26	27	28	29	30	31	32	33	34	35	36
	r_K	.27	.24	.20	.17	.14	.11	.09	.06	.03	.00	−.03	−.07
	$\hat{a}_{KK}$	−.06	−.02	−.04	−.03	−.01	−.02	−.01	−.01	−.03	−.07	−.07	−.05
	K	1	2	3	4	5	6	7	8	9	10	11	12
	r_K	.17	−.10	.02	.00	−.21	−.01	.07	−.12	−.15	.13	.08	−.14
	$\hat{a}_{KK}$	.17	−.14	.07	−.03	−.20	.08	.01	−.13	−.09	.12	.02	−.13
	K	13	14	15	16	17	18	19	20	21	22	23	24
$(1 - B)(1 - B^{12})X_t$	r_K	.01	−.03	−.09	−.08	−.02	−.21	−.20	−.02	.04	.07	.22	.14
	$\hat{a}_{KK}$	.03	−.13	.01	−.07	−.11	−.22	−.13	−.07	−.08	.06	.10	.03
	K	25	26	27	28	29	30	31	32	33	34	35	36
	r_K	.06	.06	.05	−.03	−.05	.05	−.00	.05	.03	.13	.01	−.04
	$\hat{a}_{KK}$	.10	.02	.01	.01	.00	.03	−.02	.08	−.08	.15	−.01	−.08

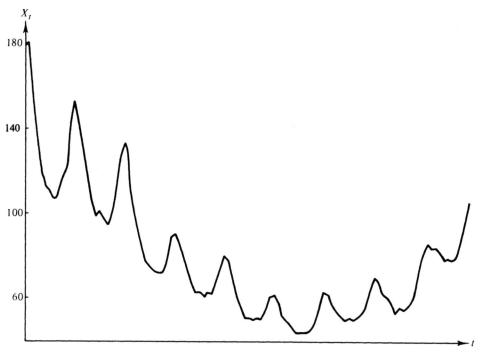

FIG. 3.1   *Monthly unemployment in Belgium.*

EXAMPLE 3   The final example, a series of 64 quarterly values of construction begun in England and Wales, presents rather more difficulties, particularly with regard to the choice of an appropriate difference operator.

Examination of the sample autocorrelations of the raw data in Table 3.7 is not terribly suggestive. There is some evidence of seasonality, as can be seen from the relatively high values at lags 4 and 8. Nevertheless the overall picture is rather unclear, and it must be admitted that the evidence in favor of differencing is less than overwhelming. (Perhaps the seasonal effect— occuring as it does every four lags—is clouding the picture.) On the other hand, it can be seen that the series $(1 - B)X_t$ has very persistently high autocorrelations at lags that are multiples of 4, suggesting that the operator $1 - B^4$ should be employed. Now, for the series $(1 - B^4)X_t$, the autocorrelations are not terribly high for longer lags, but the *pattern* of these autocorrelations is rather smooth—typical of the behavior of an underdifferenced series. Rather surprisingly, in view of what has preceded, when one comes to look at the series $(1 - B)(1 - B^4)X_t$ the autocorrelations suggest very strongly the multiplicative first-order moving average model since these values are to be compared in magnitude with $2/\sqrt{59} \approx 0.26$. (It seems that, if nothing else, differencing has finally produced an autocorrelation pattern

Table 3.7   *Sample autocorrelations and partial autocorrelations for construction begun data*

	K	1	2	3	4	5	6	7	8	9	10
	r_K	.69	.52	.52	.60	.36	.17	.12	.26	.07	−.08
	$\hat{a}_{KK}$	.69	.09	.24	.32	−.42	−.17	−.07	.29	−.21	−.02
X_t											
	K	11	12	13	14	15	16	17	18	19	20
	r_K	−.07	.05	−.09	−.17	−.14	.00	−.09	−.13	−.09	.05
	$\hat{a}_{KK}$	.06	−.05	−.11	.06	.10	−.04	−.03	.11	−.09	.01
	K	1	2	3	4	5	6	7	8	9	10
	r_K	−.27	−.34	−.15	.65	−.14	−.28	−.19	.57	−.09	−.31
	$\hat{a}_{KK}$	−.27	−.44	−.55	.35	.14	.08	−.19	.10	.04	−.11
$(1-B)X_t$											
	K	11	12	13	14	15	16	17	18	19	20
	r_K	−.19	.55	−.12	−.26	−.15	.47	−.10	−.21	−.13	.44
	$\hat{a}_{KK}$	−.18	.06	−.10	−.06	−.04	.02	−.06	.00	.03	.07
	K	1	2	3	4	5	6	7	8	9	10
	r_K	.52	.38	.30	−.02	.12	.08	−.05	−.08	−.12	−.17
	$\hat{a}_{KK}$	.52	.15	.08	−.33	.28	−.02	−.10	−.22	.14	−.10
$(1-B^4)X_t$											
	K	11	12	13	14	15	16	17	18	19	20
	r_K	−.18	−.14	−.16	−.15	−.10	−.09	−.02	.05	−.02	−.03
	$\hat{a}_{KK}$	−.10	−.04	.07	−.08	−.03	.03	.10	.01	−.18	−.01
	K	1	2	3	4	5	6	7	8	9	10
	r_K	−.34	−.07	.21	−.46	.21	.08	−.06	−.01	.02	−.03
	$\hat{a}_{KK}$	−.34	−.16	.00	−.08	−.10	−.17	−.04	.10	−.04	.02
$(1-B)(1-B^4)X_t$											
	K	11	12	13	14	15	16	17	18	19	20
	r_K	−.06	−.06	−.05	−.04	.03	−.06	.01	.14	.07	.06
	$\hat{a}_{KK}$	−.04	−.16	.00	−.08	−.10	.17	.04	.10	.04	.02

that is easy to interpret!) Accordingly the model

$$(1 - B)(1 - B^4) X_t = (1 + b_1 B)(1 + b_{1,s} B^4)\epsilon_t$$

will be tentatively entertained.

It must be admitted that the degree of differencing proposed for this series is not based solely on the evidence of the data. Generally speaking two other considerations are of importance. First, all other things being equal, we would favor differencing any time series when in doubt. Otherwise one is tying the series to a fixed mean, which will not be estimable with any great precision if the series in question is highly autocorrelated. Further, forecasts based on the model will of necessity be highly dependent on this imprecisely estimated mean, and hence potentially unreliable. Finally, our experience in analyzing a large number of economic time series has convinced us that, in those situations where the degree of differencing has been in doubt, it is generally the case that superior forecasts are obtained when the difference operator in question is included in the model.

Estimation

As in the case of nonseasonal models, seasonal time series models can be estimated through the numerical maximization of the exact likelihood functions, derived on an assumption of a Gaussian distribution for the innovations. Ansley [1979] shows how the special structure of the multiplicative seasonal model (3.7.1) can be exploited in the derivation of an efficient algorithm for the evaluation of the likelihood function. In the case of seasonal models, simulation evidence, reported in Ansley and Newbold [1980], indicates a stronger advantage for full maximum likelihood, over alternative least squares methods, than for simple nonseasonal models.

For the three series discussed earlier in this section, estimates of the coefficients of the identified models are given below (together with estimated standard errors in brackets):

(i) For the series on the currency held by the public element of the United States money supply, the estimated model was

$$(1 - B)(1 - B^{12})X_t = (1 - 0.38B^{12})\epsilon_t$$
$$[0.09]$$

(ii) For the data on unemployment in Belgium, the fitted model was

$$(1 - B)(1 - B^{12})X_t = (1 + 0.25B)\epsilon_t$$
$$[0.10]$$

(iii) For the quarterly series of construction begun in England and Wales the fitted model was

$$(1 - B)(1 - B^4)X_t = (1 - 0.37B)(1 - 0.68B^4)\epsilon_t \qquad (3.7.13)$$
$$[0.13] \qquad [0.10]$$

Diagnostic Checking

For seasonal time series, the range of reasonable alternatives to the originally chosen model is likely to be even greater than in the nonseasonal case. Therefore, the implementation of diagnostic checks takes on even greater importance here. As before, the two most useful approaches involve the consideration of alternative models containing additional parameters and examination of the autocorrelations of the residuals from the fitted model.

The application of Lagrange multiplier tests to seasonal models is discussed by Newbold [1983]. We assume that an appropriate degree of differencing has been determined and that n observations on the differenced process Y_t are available. The multiplicative seasonal autoregressive–moving average model

$$a(B)a_s(B^s)Y_t = b(B)b_s(B^s)\epsilon_t$$

will be denoted ARMA(p, q)(P, Q)$_s$. We assume that a model of this form has been estimated by maximum likelihood, and use $\hat{}$ to denote the estimates. In order to carry out the tests, we construct four auxiliary series, w_t, z_t, $w_t^{(s)}$, and $z_t^{(s)}$, defined by

$$\hat{a}(B)w_t = -\hat{\epsilon}_t \qquad (3.7.14)$$

$$\hat{b}(B)z_t = -\hat{\epsilon}_t \qquad (3.7.15)$$

$$\hat{a}_s(B^s)w_t^{(s)} = -\hat{\epsilon}_t \qquad (3.7.16)$$

and

$$\hat{b}_s(B^s)z_t^{(s)} = -\hat{\epsilon}_t \qquad (3.7.17)$$

A test that the specification is appropriate against the ARMA($p, q + m$) $(P, Q)_s$ alternative of m additional nonseasonal moving average parameters can be carried out through the least squares estimation of

$$\hat{\epsilon}_t = \alpha_1 w_{t-1} + \cdots + \alpha_p w_{t-p} + \beta_1 z_{t-1} + \cdots + \beta_{q+m} z_{t-q-m}$$
$$+ \gamma_1 w_{t-s}^{(s)} + \cdots + \gamma_P w_{t-Ps}^{(s)} + \delta_1 z_{t-s}^{(s)} + \cdots + \delta_Q z_{t-Qs}^{(s)} + u_t \qquad (3.7.18)$$

where u_t is an error term. The statistic (3.6.4), which again has an asymptotic χ^2 distribution with m degrees of freedom under the null hypothesis that the original model is adequate, is then calculated. It can be shown that the same test results if the alternative is of m additional nonseasonal autoregressive parameters.

We can also check the possibility that further seasonal parameters are required. A test against the ARMA($p, q)(P, Q + m)_s$ alternative of m additional seasonal moving average parameters is carried out through estimating by least squares

$$\hat{\epsilon}_t = \alpha_1 w_{t-1} + \cdots + \alpha_p w_{t-p} + \beta_1 z_{t-1} + \cdots + \beta_q z_{t-q}$$
$$+ \gamma_1 w_{t-s}^{(s)} + \cdots + \gamma_P w_{t-Ps}^{(s)} + \delta_1 z_{t-s}^{(s)} + \cdots + \delta_{Q+m} z_{t-(Q+m)s}^{(s)} + u_t$$
$$(3.7.19)$$

The test statistic is of the same form and has the same asymptotic null distribution as before. It can further be shown that the same test results if the alternative is of m additional seasonal autoregressive parameters.

For the series on currency held by the public, the estimated model was

$$Y_t = (1 - 0.38B^{12})\epsilon_t$$

where

$$Y_t = (1 - B)(1 - B^{12})X_t$$

The four auxiliary series of (3.7.14)–(3.7.17) are then obtained from

$$w_t = -\hat{\epsilon}_t, \qquad z_t = -\hat{\epsilon}_t, \qquad w_t^{(s)} = -\hat{\epsilon}_t, \qquad \text{and} \qquad z_t^{(s)} = -\hat{\epsilon}_t + 0.38z_{t-12}^{(s)}$$

To test for m nonseasonal moving average terms, we then fit, following from (3.7.18),

$$\hat{\epsilon}_t = \alpha_1 z_{t-1} + \cdots + \alpha_m z_{t-m} + \delta_1 z_{t-12}^{(s)} + u_t$$

For $m = 1, 2$, the values obtained for the test statistic (3.6.4) were 0.69 and 1.25, respectively, which do not suggest the desirability of extending the model in this way.

To test for m additional seasonal moving average terms, following (3.7.19), we estimate by least squares

$$\epsilon_t = \delta_1 z^{(s)}_{t-12} + \cdots + \delta_{1+m} z^{(s)}_{t-12(1+m)} + u_t$$

For $m = 1, 2$, the values obtained for the statistic (3.6.4) were 0.34 and 1.11. Again, comparison with tabulated values of the χ^2 distribution does not lead us to suspect the adequacy of the originally chosen model.

In addition to these possibilities, it is often worthwhile to check the assumption of multiplicativity in the chosen model by the addition of extra coefficients. One should be prepared to drop the multiplicativity assumption if such a course is suggested by this check.

For the series on construction begun in England and Wales, the fitted model (3.7.13) can be written

$$(1 - B)(1 - B^4) X_t = (1 - 0.37B - 0.68B^4 + 0.2516B^5)\epsilon_t$$

To check the assumption of multiplicativity the model

$$(1 - B)(1 - B^4) X_t = (1 + b_1 B + b_4 B^4 + b_5 B^5)\epsilon_t$$

was fitted to this series. The estimated equation which resulted was

$$(1 - B)(1 - B^4) X_t = (1 - 0.33B - 0.65B^4 + 0.29B^5)\epsilon_t$$
$$\quad\quad\quad\quad\quad [0.13] \quad\quad [0.10] \quad\quad\quad [0.13]$$

The estimated coefficients differ very little from those predicted by the multiplicative model, providing no grounds on which to question the adequacy of representation of that model.

It is also useful to compute the residual autocorrelations from the fitted model. The asymptotic distribution of these statistics, under the assumption that the model is correctly specified, is derived by McLeod [1978]. Once again, a crude comparison of these quantities with bounds $\pm 2n^{-1/2}$ can be made.

An assessment of the magnitude of the residual autocorrelations, taken as a group, can again be based on the portmanteau statistic (3.6.5). However, simulation results reported by Ansley and Newbold [1979a] suggest that the null distribution of the test statistic in moderate sized samples can differ substantially from the corresponding asymptotic distribution. In particular, these authors noticed a tendency for a correctly specified model to be rejected far more frequently than the asymptotic distribution theory would suggest.

For the model fitted to the data on currency held by the public, the first 36 residual autocorrelations are shown in Table 3.8. Since there are 109 observa-

Table 3.8   *Residual autocorrelations from model fitted to series on the currency held by the public element of United States money supply*

τ:	1	2	3	4	5	6	7	8	9	10	11	12
$r_\tau(\hat{\varepsilon})$:	.08	$-.05$	$-.01$	$-.03$	.17	$-.05$	$-.00$	.13	.28	$-.08$	$-.02$	$-.03$
τ:	13	14	15	16	17	18	19	20	21	22	23	24
$r_\tau(\hat{\varepsilon})$:	.03	.19	$-.06$	.04	.07	$-.01$	.01	.18	.01	.01	.14	$-.03$
τ:	25	26	27	28	29	30	31	32	33	34	35	36
$r_\tau(\hat{\varepsilon})$:	.01	$-.02$	$-.08$	.07	.07	.00	.03	.08	$-.08$	$-.04$	.04	.01

tions on the differenced series, these residual autocorrelations can be compared with ± 0.19. Judged by this criterion, only the value at lag 9 looks particularly large. Since this does not suggest any intuitively appealing modification to our model, our instinct is to attribute this large value to chance. Also, for this fitted model, we calculated the portmanteau statistic (3.6.5) for values of m of 12, 24, and 36, obtaining 17.59, 30.71, and 35.72, respectively. Since there is just one estimated parameter in the fitted model, the appropriate standards for comparison are tabulated values of the χ^2 distribution for 11, 23, and 35 degrees of freedom. In the latter two cases, the test statistics are not significant at the usual levels. However, the statistic based on the first twelve residual autocorrelations is just significant at the 10% level. This does not cause us undue alarm and is in the main a reflection of the single large residual autocorrelation at lag 9. As we have already stated, our preference is to discount this value and retain the original model.

As in the nonseasonal case, checks based on the Lagrange multiplier tests and on residual autocorrelations are related. It can be shown that the test based on (3.7.18) is equivalent to a test based on the first m residual autocorrelations. Furthermore, the Lagrange multiplier test following from the fitting of (3.7.19) is equivalent to a test based on the residual autocorrelations at lags $s, 2s, \ldots, ms$.

In principle, the residual autocorrelations can be used to suggest an alternative model, in a manner similar to that outlined in Section 3.6. However, the practical drawbacks noted there continue to apply, and it may be preferable to base any modification of the model on the results of the Lagrange multiplier tests.

3.8 Time Series Model Building—An Overview

The time series model building procedure just described constitutes an attempt to construct, from a given set of data, the underlying stochastic process that might have generated the given observations. Such a task is, of course, extremely formidable and, indeed, would remain so even if the samples generally available were very large indeed. A good deal of progress can be made, however, if only linear processes are considered—the hope being that in most practical situations there can be found a linear model that approximates well in all relevant aspects the properties of the true underlying process. Accordingly, a class of linear processes is examined and the objective is to select from this class a single process to describe a particular given time series. (Nonlinear models are considered in Chapter 10.)

A further restriction is imposed by the assumption that the series under consideration can be well represented, after appropriate differencing, by a stationary stochastic process, and the validity of this assumption will undoubtedly influence to some degree the validity of any inference made from the fitted model. However, the facility to remove certain kinds of nonstationarity by suitable differencing is of considerable importance in the study of economic time series. In our experience, differencing of such series is almost always required to produce stationarity and models based on the differenced series generally provide superior representation to the low-order autoregressive processes traditionally favored by econometricians. Further evidence for this contention is provided by the typical spectral shape of economic time series (see, for example, Granger [1966].) Of course other types of nonstationarity may also be important, and this topic is discussed in Chapter 10.

The model building procedure introduced in this chapter consists of an iterative cycle of identification, estimation, and diagnostic checking. Not surprisingly, the stage that causes the most difficulties in practical attempts at time series model building is identification. Here one is required to choose from a wide class of models a single process that might adequately describe a given time series. While some objective criteria are available on which a rational choice can be based, it remains the case that there does not exist a clearly defined procedure leading in any given situation to a unique identification. Rather, it is necessary to exercise a good deal of judgment at this stage. To some extent, experience with the procedures involved will increase the chances of successful identification, but nevertheless it must be expected that occasional difficulties will crop up. Before discussing particular problems, it is perhaps worth reiterating that in selecting a particular model for subsequent estimation one is not irrevocably committed to retaining it. The model chosen is subjected to checks on its validity, and the iterative nature of the model building process allows one the possibility of making appropriate modifications.

Two particular problems in model identification are worth mentioning. First, it is at times extremely difficult from a given set of data to identify any particular model from the general class in which one has a great deal of confidence. Up to a point, one finds this happening less frequently the more experience one has in using the techniques. Nevertheless, difficulties of this nature do on occasion still arise. It would be extremely rash, for example, to claim that on the basis of sample autocorrelations and partial autocorrelations from a series of a length that is likely to occur in practice one could immediately identify complex models such as

$$(1 - a_1 B - a_2 B^2 - a_3 B^3 - a_4 B^4) X_t = (1 + b_1 B + b_2 B^2 + b_3 B^3) \epsilon_t$$

$$(3.8.1)$$

In situations where one suspects a complex structure, the best strategy might be to begin by constructing a fairly simple model which one may then be able to modify on the basis of the autocorrelation structure of the residuals from the fitted equation or by suitable overfitting. Thus the construction of models like (3.8.1) might require as many as three or four iterations of the cycle of identification, estimation, and diagnostic checking. It should also be added that, in our experience, such complex models occur very rarely in practice (or, at least, if they do we do not succeed in detecting them very often.) It may also be profitable to look for extensions of the identification procedure outlined in Section 3.2 as a further aid in the detection of more complex models.

We already noted in Section 3.2 that for nonseasonal series we find it useful to look, in addition to the sample autocorrelations and partial autocorrelations, at statistics derived from the procedure proposed by Hannan and Rissanen [1982]. We regard these quantities as providing valuable additional information as to what might be an appropriate specification and not as infallible guides to be blindly followed. A number of further aids to model selection have been proposed in the literature.

Several authors have considered using as identification tools the inverse autocorrelations of a process. These were introduced, in the frequency domain, by Cleveland [1972] but are perhaps easier to interpret in the time domain—the equivalence is established by Chatfield [1979]. Essentially, the inverse autocorrelations of the process $a(B)Y_t = b(B)\epsilon_t$ are the same as the autocorrelations of $b(B)Y_t = a(B)\epsilon_t$.

For seasonal time series, Hamilton and Watts [1978] discuss and illustrate how the pattern of the sample partial autocorrelations can be used to aid in model selection.

A number of articles, including Gray, Kelley, and McIntire [1978], Beguin, Goúrieroux, and Monfort [1980], Woodward and Gray [1981], and Glasbey [1982], have contained related proposals for statistics to help discriminate among different nonseasonal mixed models. All are essentially based on the fact that, for an ARMA(p, q) process, the autocorrelations obey

$$\rho_\tau = a_1 \rho_{\tau-1} + \cdots + a_p \rho_{\tau-p}, \qquad \tau = q + 1, q + 2, \ldots$$

There is very little empirical evidence available on the usefulness of these and other proposed aids to model selection. The accumulation of practical experience will have to determine which, if any, are of value. Still, it has to be admitted that the state of the art is such that it sometimes happens that one finds it difficult at the outset to embrace with much confidence any particular model from the general ARIMA class.

A related point has been made by Chatfield and Prothero [1973]. It is sometimes the case that multiple identifications are thought possible; that is, the identification procedure might suggest two or more models from the general class that could well represent a particular set of data. It is further contended that, on the basis of available data, it might prove impossible to distinguish at acceptable levels of statistical significance between the alternatives. One solution to this dilemma is to construct a general model that incorporates as subsets the possibilities being entertained. As a simple illustration, suppose for a time series of length 80 the first two sample autocorrelations were $r_1 = 0.32$, $r_2 = 0.07$ and that the remaining sample autocorrelations were small. Does one regard r_2 as being close to zero (in which case the appropriate identification is $X_t = \epsilon_t + b_1\epsilon_{t-1}$) or should r_2 be taken as being approximately equal to r_1^2, and $r_j \approx r_1^j$ for $j = 3, 4, 5, \ldots$ (in which case the appropriate identification is $X_t - a_1 X_{t-1} = \epsilon_t$)? Perhaps the best solution to this difficulty would be to fit the more general model $X_t - a_1 X_{t-1} = \epsilon_t + b_1\epsilon_{t-1}$. As well as providing a diagnostic check by fitting an extra coefficient, the statistical significance of the estimated coefficients of the more general model can help determine which (if any) of the simple models is appropriate. Of course, as noted by Box and Jenkins [1973], it may well be the case that the "different" models are in fact very similar to one another. If this is so, they will yield very similar forecasts and it is not terribly important to distinguish between them.

As a final point on model identification, it should be repeated that in order to have any reasonable hopes of success a moderately long series of observations is necessary. This should be obvious by now, for it is required of the procedure that it select a particular stochastic model from a wide class of models. In order to do this with a fair amount of objectivity, one must have a considerable amount of evidence on which a rational choice of model can be based. It would be foolish to expect a series of, say, 30 observations to supply sufficient evidence for such a task. That is not to say that the applied time series analyst ought to refuse to handle such data, but rather that his analysis ought to be less ambitious than that outlined earlier in this chapter. In such situations it is still possible to fit two or three fairly simple models, test the estimated coefficients for statistical significance, and compare the resulting error variance estimates. In this way one might well arrive at a model in whose forecasting ability it is possible to have at least a fair amount of confidence.

Since identification contains so many difficulties, it is tempting to seek a procedure that circumvents the need for this stage entirely. Why not, for example, simply fit a model that contains a large number of both autoregressive and moving average coefficients and thus includes as subsets any models that are likely to arise in practice? As has been seen, such a procedure is unworkable since it will in general lead to coefficient estimates with extremely high standard deviations due to multiple solutions. A more viable alternative might be to fit a very high order autoregressive process since this could capture the essential characteristics of simple mixed processes. However, the model building philosophy outlined in this chapter is predicated on the belief that in most practical situations the underlying process is likely to be a very simple one; that is, few coefficients will be required to provide an adequate description of the behavior of the particular time series. It follows that if such is the case, the fitting of high-order autoregressive processes will lead to the estimation of models in which most of the coefficients are redundant, with the consequence that the few nonredundant coefficients will be estimated with unnecessary imprecision. In Chapter 5 it is shown that a useful compromise can be achieved by fitting high-order autoregressive equations not directly but by stepwise regression techniques.

A further possibility is to circumvent the identification stage of the model building cycle by employing some automatic order selection criterion, such as those whose asymptotic properties are analyzed by Hannan [1982]. Here it is necessary to estimate models for all possible values of p and q that the analyst wishes to consider. Let $\hat{\sigma}_{p,q}^2$ denote the maximum likelihood error variance estimates for the fitted models. Then, the AIC criterion of Akaike [1969] selects that model for which $\log \hat{\sigma}_{p,q}^2 + 2(p + q)/n$ is smallest. Experience with this criterion confirms theoretical findings that the procedure is inconsistent, tending to yield overly elaborate models. A consistent procedure can be based on the BIC criterion, where the model for which $\log \hat{\sigma}_{p,q}^2 + (p + q)\log n/n$ is smallest is chosen. However, the difficulty remains that full maximum likelihood estimation of a large number of alternative models is computationally quite expensive.

The models discussed in this chapter are restrictive in the sense that they assume linearity and stationarity (possibly after suitable differencing). We conclude this chapter by noting two readily made modifications that can be made to the models to take account of specific types of nonlinearity and nonstationarity.

Following Chatfield and Prothero [1973] and the discussion of that paper by Box and Jenkins [1973], considerable interest was generated in the possibility of fitting an ARIMA model not necessarily to the observed series X_t but to some instantaneous transformed version $X_t^{(\lambda)}$. In particular, a number of authors considered the class of power transformations

$$X_t^{(\lambda)} = (X_t^\lambda - 1)/\lambda, \qquad \lambda \neq 0$$
$$= \log X_t, \qquad \lambda = 0$$

of Box and Cox [1964]. The parameter λ is then regarded as an additional coefficient to be estimated, together with the autoregressive and moving average parameters of the model. The question of parameter estimation in this framework has been considered by Ansley, Spivey, and Wrobleski [1977]. Granger and Newbold [1976] have shown that allowing for the possibility of this type of transformation introduces an additional difficulty into the model selection process. Essentially this is so because the autocorrelation structure of $X_t^{(\lambda)}$ in general depends on the value of λ, which, of course, at the outset will be unknown. An elaboration of the usual model selection procedure, designed to get around this difficulty, has been proposed and implemented by Hopwood, McKeown, and Newbold [1984].

Granger and Newbold [1976] also discuss the problem of deriving optimal forecasts when instantaneous transformations are employed. The contemplation of the possibility of incorporating power transformations into the model certainly adds to the practical difficulties of univariate time series analysis. Whether the additional effort is likely to lead to much reward in terms of superior forecast performance is not clear. The evidence to date is sparse and rather mixed. Nelson and Granger [1979], analyzing a collection of macro-economic time series, found little gain in forecast quality. On the other hand, Hopwood, McKeown, and Newbold [1981], who examined a set of series on corporate earnings per share, found that for these particular data, on the whole, worthwhile improvements in forecast quality did result when power transformations were incorporated in the ARIMA model structure.

One specific type of nonstationarity is also rather easily incorporated within the ARIMA model structure we have described in this chapter. Suppose that the evolutionary pattern of a time series is suspected to have been altered or disrupted through the occurrence of an outside event *at some known point in time.* Box and Tiao [1975] have developed a procedure, known as intervention analysis, for analyzing such data. Essentially, intervention analysis is the time series analog of introducing dummy variables into a regression model. The particular model structure employed by Box and Tiao has the same form as the transfer function–noise model, to be discussed in Chapter 8.

CHAPTER FOUR

THE THEORY OF FORECASTING

Time present and time past are both perhaps present in time future and time future contained in time past.

T. S. ELIOT

4.1 Some Basic Concepts

Information Set

Let X_t be some discrete-time stochastic process, which for the time being will be assumed to be stationary. Suppose that one is at time n ($\equiv$ now) and one wishes to forecast[1] h time units ahead to time $n + h$ ($h \equiv$ hence), so that attention is directed to the random variable X_{n+h}. Thus for $h = 1$, a one-step ahead forecasting situation arises. Any forecast procedure will have to be based on some *information set*, consisting of data together with knowledge, theories, or assumptions about the properties of the process *as available at time n*. For example, the information set could consist of a sample of previous values of the series X_{n-j}, $j = 0, 1, \ldots, N$, together with the knowledge that the series has zero mean and an assumption that the series is stationary. A different information set may contain past and present values of several series. It is often important to be precise about the information set being used, particularly when comparing different forecasting procedures. For the time being it will be assumed merely that a specific information set is to be used, and this will be denoted by I_n.

---

[1] The words *forecast* and *prediction* will be used interchangeably. In many situations a better description is *extrapolation*.

Conditional Variables

Since the variable to be forecast X_{n+h} is a random variable, it can be fully characterized only in terms of a probability density function or some equivalent function. However, since the information set I_n is to be utilized one needs to use a *conditional* density function, i.e.,

$$\text{Prob}(x < X_{n+h} \leqslant x + dx | I_n) = g_c(x)\, dx \qquad (4.1.1)$$

where the subscript c denotes "conditional." If $g_c(x)$ were available, then all other properties of X_{n+h}, such as the conditional mean $E_c(X_{n+h})$, could be immediately determined. However, in practice, it is generally rather too ambitious to hope to be able to characterize fully X_{n+h}, and so one attempts the less ambitious task of finding some confidence band for X_{n+h} or some single value, called a *point forecast*, that in some way "best" represents the random variable X_{n+h}. The forecast picture is depicted in Fig. 4.1, which illustrates a possible conditional density function for X_{n+h} given information available at time n, together with interval and point estimates based on that density function.

Cost Function

To obtain any kind of best value for a point forecast, one requires a criterion against which various alternatives can be judged. An intellectually satisfying way to proceed is to introduce the idea of a *cost function*. Suppose that one is not just forecasting in some vacuous situation, but rather that someone, such as a production manager of a firm whose product demand is

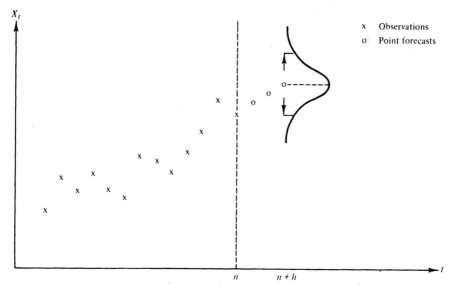

FIG. 4.1 *Conditional density of X_{n+h}, given information up to time n, point and interval forecasts.*

being forecast, will actually wish to base decisions upon the forecasts one makes. Since forecast errors are virtually certain to occur in connection with a random process, suppose that one can cost the effect of an error of size e to be $C(e)$, with $C(0) = 0$. If in some fashion a point forecast $f_{n,h}$ is made of X_{n+h}, based on I_n, with resulting error

$$e_{n,h} = X_{n+h} - f_{n,h} \qquad (4.1.2)$$

then because the user has not made the optimal decision a cost $C(e_{n,h})$ will arise. It is now a fairly natural criterion, given such a cost function, to choose the point forecast $f_{n,h}$ so that the expected cost $E_c\{C(e_{n,h})\}$ is minimized, the expectation being conditional on the information set I_n being used. One particular cost function gives a rather tidy and easily used solution, and that is the function

$$C(e) = ae^2 \qquad (4.1.3)$$

where a is some positive constant. Classical statistical theory tells us that the point forecast that minimizes this cost function, which corresponds to a least-squares criterion, is just the conditional mean of X_{n+h}, i.e.,

$$f_{n,h} = E_c\{X_{n+h}\} \qquad (4.1.4)$$

As will be seen, this is a particularly useful result, but it does depend on the cost function being of the form (4.1.3). More general cost functions are considered in Section 4.2.

Linear Forecasts

The procedure just outlined, with whatever cost function is used, may well lead to a point forecast $f_{n,h}$ that is a nonlinear function of the data within the information set I_n. However, in practice one will rarely know the conditional density function sufficiently well for a complete solution to be possible. In these circumstances, the problem of choosing the best point forecast is greatly eased by putting restrictions on the form of forecast to be considered; in particular by assuming that $f_{n,h}$ is a linear function of the data available in I_n. If this restriction is made, only *linear forecasts* are considered. Since the benefits in ease of procedure are so considerable from this restriction, it will generally be taken to apply, although some consideration will be given to nonlinear forecasts in Chapter 10. Alternatively, theory may suggest certain specific nonlinear functional forms by which the available data might enter the forecasting mechanism. This is often the case in econometric forecasting, which will be discussed in Chapter 6.

If one assumes that all subsets of variables have normal distributions, called a Gaussian assumption, then it may be shown that only linear forecasts need be considered. However, linear forecasts can also be optimal in nonnormal situations. An example is when a series X_t is generated by a linear model, such as an AR(1) model, but with an error series of independent nonnormally distributed deviates.

Deterministic Processes

Suppose for the moment that a satisfactory measure of the quality of a forecast procedure is the mean square of the one-step error, i.e., $V(1) = E_c\{e_{n,1}^2\}$. The size of this quantity will depend both upon the properties of the series X_t being forecast and also on the contents of the information set I_n being used. If, for example, the information set was $I_n = \{x_{n-j}, j = 0, 1, \ldots, N, \text{model}\}$, i.e., a finite sample of past and present values of the series one is interested in, together with a knowledge of the generating process for the series, then $V(1)$ can vary between variance of x_t if X_t is a white noise series,[1] down to zero if $X_t = a \cos \lambda t$ for example, with a and λ known. In the first case X_t might be said to be *unpredictable* and in the second case X_t is *self-deterministic*. A more conventional definition of deterministic considers $\lim_{N \to \infty} V_N(1)$, where $V_N(1)$ is the mean squared error of one-step forecasts based on the previous N terms of the series. If this limit is zero, X_t is usually said to be deterministic. Thus, given an infinite amount of past values of the series, so that presumably a generating process or model can be determined without error, the next value of the series X_{n+1} can be forecast without error if it is deterministic. However, we prefer the expression "self-deterministic." It follows by iterative reasoning that if one can forecast one step ahead perfectly, then it is possible to forecast perfectly any number of steps ahead. The expression self-deterministic is used here because a series need not be deterministic for one information set yet can be deterministic with respect to a larger information set. Consider the example $X_t = Y_{t-1}$, where Y_t is a zero mean, white noise series. Then X_t is not self-deterministic since given past values of X_t one cannot predict future values at all, but if the information set is expanded to include past and present values of the Y_t series, then X_{n+1} is known without error. If, for some set I_n, X_t is perfectly predictable, it will be said to be deterministic with respect to I_n.

The concept of a series being deterministic need not be phrased in terms of the mean squared errors $V(1)$ but could be defined as the series being predictable with zero cost of error for any given cost function or, almost equivalently in practice, by saying that the conditional distribution function $G_c(x)$, corresponding to the density function $g_c(x)$ of (4.1.1), is a single-step function. This broadening of definition has little or no practical significance.

As a *statement of belief* we would suggest that virtually no series of any importance within the field of economics is deterministic for *any* information set I_n, however widely defined. Thus one would *always* expect to produce forecasts with error, however sophisticated one's forecasting procedure. This belief has implications when the problem of the evaluation of forecasts is discussed in Chapter 9. This statement does not exclude the possibility that a *component* of the series X_t is deterministic, so that Wold's decomposition (see Section 1.11) can apply.

---

[1] This variance is assumed to be finite.

4.2 Generalized Cost Functions

Suppose that one wishes to form an optimal point forecast $f_{n,h}$ of X_{n+h} using the information set I_n and a cost function $C(e)$. The cost function will be assumed to have the properties that $C(0) = 0$, $C(e)$ is monotonic nondecreasing for $e > 0$ (i.e., $C(e_1) \geqslant C(e_2)$ for every $e_1 > e_2 > 0$) and monotonic nonincreasing for $e < 0$. Thus, if one forecasts without error, then no cost arises; but if there is an error, then the larger it is the greater will be the cost. However, $C(e)$ need not be symmetrical, so that $C(e)$ and $C(-e)$ need not be equal. Let $g_{c,h}(x)$ be the conditional probability density function (pdf) of X_{n+h} given I_n, then the required optimal forecast $f_{n,h}$, which will be a function only of I_n, will be found by choosing $f_{n,h}$ so that the expected cost is a minimum, i.e., minimizing

$$J = \int_{-\infty}^{\infty} C(x - f_{n,h}) g_{c,h}(x)\, dx \qquad (4.2.1)$$

In the case when the error function is a quadratic, so that $C(e) = ae^2$ with $a > 0$, J becomes

$$J = \int_{-\infty}^{\infty} a(x - f_{n,h})^2 g_{c,h}(x)\, dx \qquad (4.2.2)$$

Define M_h to be the conditional mean of X_{n+h} given I_n, so that

$$M_h = \int_{-\infty}^{\infty} x g_{c,h}(x)\, dx \qquad (4.2.3)$$

Then some simple algebraic manipulation, combined with the fact that $\int_{-\infty}^{\infty} g_{c,h}(x)\, dx = 1$ as $g_{c,h}(x)$ is a pdf, shows that (4.2.2) may be written

$$J = a(M_h - f_{n,h})^2 + a \int_{-\infty}^{\infty} (x - M_h)^2 g_{c,h}(x)\, dx \qquad (4.2.4)$$

The quantity $f_{n,h}$ appears only in the first term of (4.2.4) and so J is minimized by taking

$$f_{n,h} = M_h = E_c\{X_{n+h}|I_n\} \qquad (4.2.5)$$

In the Gaussian situation, where every finite subset of variables in the set $\{I_n, X_{n+h}\}$ is normally distributed, this leads to the important result that the optimal least-squares prediction of X_{n+h} is a linear sum of the terms in I_n. It should also be noted that in this case $g_{c,h}(x)$ is a normal distribution with mean M_h and variance that does not depend on I_n, so that the expected or average cost is a constant if the optimal predictor (4.2.5) is used. In non-Gaussian situations, M_h need not be a linear function of the terms in I_n, and the expected cost may vary through time depending on the values actually found in I_n. Thus, without an assumption of normality, the usual restriction of prediction theory to linear predictors may be suboptimal. However, the restriction to linear predictors does ensure considerable computational simplicity and is generally thought to be a reasonable one unless specific information is available as to the kind of nonlinear form that should be used. This problem is discussed further in Chapter 10.

It is interesting to ask whether the predictor given by (4.2.5) is optimal for a wider class of cost functions than just the quadratic function. Two theorems proved by Granger [1969a] show that in fact it is. These theorems may be summarized as follows:

THEOREM   The optimal predictor of X_{n+h} given I_n is $f_{n,h} = M_h$ if

(i) $C(e)$ is symmetric about $e = 0$, the derivative $C'(e)$ exists almost everywhere and is strictly monotonically increasing on the whole range $-\infty < e < \infty$, and also $g_{c,h}(x)$ is symmetric about $x = M_h$; or

(ii) $C(e)$ is symmetric about $e = 0$ and $g_{c,h}(x)$, symmetric about $x = M_h$, is continuous and unimodal.

For proofs, readers are referred to the original article. An example may also be found there showing that both $C(e)$ and $g_{c,h}(x)$ can be symmetric but the optimal $f_{n,h}$ need not be equal to M_h.

In practice, one rarely has any direct evidence about the properties of the conditional pdf $g_{c,h}(x)$, so an assumption of symmetry about the conditional mean M_h is likely to be an easy one to accept. It is not difficult to then go further and assume $g_{c,h}(x)$ to be a normal density function, although there is surprisingly little evidence for or against such an assumption in data originating either in industry or in many branches of economics. To a statistician, a Gaussian assumption is an extremely useful one since it leads to considerable simplification in techniques, tests, and interpretation. Such an assumption will underlie much of what follows, although this will not always be stated explicitly.

An assumption of symmetry for the cost function is much less acceptable. As examples of situations where nonsymmetric cost functions arise, consider two cases:

(i)   A bank intends to purchase a computer to handle its current accounts. To determine the size of computer to buy, a prediction of future business is made. If this prediction is too high, the result will be that the computer will be underutilized and a cheaper machine could have been bought. If the prediction is too low, the result will be that part of the accounts will have to be handled by other means. There is no reason to suppose that cost of errors will be symmetric in these circumstances.

(ii)   A firm is about to issue shares on a stock exchange for the first time. It approaches a bank to act as issuing agent. The bank guarantees to buy all shares not taken by the public but is allowed to choose the price at which the shares are offered. The problem is to predict public demand for each price and then pick the best price. If too low a price is chosen, the original firm makes less money than would otherwise have been possible. If the price is too high, the issuing bank will be left with many unsold stocks and could lose more than its commission. The cost to the bank, which makes the prediction, is clearly not symmetric. The result, in the U.K. at least, is usually that the price chosen is subsequently found to be too low.

In just a few cases, the optimal predictor can be found for specific nonsymmetric cost functions. Consider the linear cost function

$$C(e) = ae, \qquad e > 0, \quad a > 0$$
$$= 0, \qquad e = 0$$
$$= be, \qquad e < 0, \quad b < 0 \qquad (4.2.6)$$

Then, from (4.2.1), the expected cost with predictor $f \equiv f_{n,h}$ is

$$J = E_c\{C(X_{n+h} - f)|I_n\} = a\int_f^{\infty}(x - f)g_{c,h}(x)\,dx$$
$$+ b\int_{-\infty}^{f}(x - f)g_{c,h}(x)\,dx \qquad (4.2.7)$$

Differentiating this with respect to f and equating to zero to find the minimum expected cost gives

$$G_{c,h}(f) = a/(a - b) \qquad (4.2.8)$$

where $G_{c,h}(x)$ is the conditional cumulative distribution function of X_{n+h} given I_n, i.e.,

$$G_{c,h}(x') = \int_{-\infty}^{x'} g_{c,h}(x)\,dx \qquad (4.2.9)$$

The second derivative of J is $(a - b)g_{c,h}(f)$, which will always be positive, so the predictor f found from solving (4.2.8) will correspond to a minimization of the expected cost. In the symmetric case $a = -b$, and so the optimal predictor $f \equiv f_{n,h}$ will be given by $G_{c,h}(f) = \frac{1}{2}$, so that f is the median of $g_{c,h}(x)$.

The linear cost function may well provide a good approximation to nonsymmetric cost functions that arise in practice. Consider the production of some highly perishable commodity, such as creamcakes. A producer decides to predict tomorrow's demand for his cakes, which cannot be stored from one day to another, and then to produce as many cakes as is predicted will be demanded. A low prediction of demand $(e > 0)$ will result in an underproduction and the cost will equal the lost profits, which might be approximately equal to the marginal profit (a) times the number of cakes that could have been sold if available. A high prediction $(e < 0)$ will result in a loss due to unsold cakes, this loss may be approximated by the marginal production cost $(-b)$ times the number of cakes unsold. There is no reason to suppose that marginal costs and marginal profits are equal, so a nonsymmetric cost function will arise.

Results such as (4.2.8) are of little practical importance since only very rarely will one have sufficient knowledge of the conditional distribution for solutions to be available. If the conditional distribution is assumed to be normal, so that the distribution of $X_{n+h} - M_h$ is independent of I_n, then it is easily shown that the optimal predictor is given by $f_{n,h} = M_h + \alpha$ where α depends only on the cost function being used and not on I_n. This may be seen as follows. Consider the expected cost J given by (4.2.1), but assume a Gaussian situation, so that $\bar{g}_{c,h}(x)$, the conditional pdf of $X_{n+h} - M_h$, is in fact independent of I_n. Then J may be written $J = \int_{-\infty}^{\infty} C(x - \alpha) \bar{g}_{c,h}(x) \, dx$ and α has to be chosen so that J is minimized. If the linear cost function (4.2.6) is used, α will be given by $\bar{G}_{c,h}(\alpha) = a/(a - b)$ where $\bar{G}_{c,h}(x)$ is the cumulative distribution function of $X_{n+h} - M_h$, that is of a normally distributed variable, but with zero mean. The optimal forecast is then $M_h + \alpha$.

The practical relevance of these results seems to be that a least-squares approach, corresponding to a quadratic cost function, is both more general and more defensible than might originally have been thought. With a normality assumption about one's data, the optimal least-squares predictor will also be optimal for all symmetric cost functions that are likely to arise in practice. If the cost function is not symmetric, then a generally acceptable procedure is to form the best least-squares predictor and then, at the decision stages, to allow for the cost function being used by adding the appropriate bias term. This is somewhat reassuring, since actual cost functions are unlikely to be quadratic, but nevertheless the classical least-squares prediction theory to be presented in later sections will still be usable.

It might also be noted that with the cost function $C(e) = ae^2$, $a > 0$, the actual value of the parameter a is unimportant. This is also a useful property since otherwise one would need to know the cost function at time $n + h$, which is the time at which the error will occur. For this, one would need to predict the cost function, and a circular situation would result, as well as throwing a difficult and undesirable prediction problem on the reluctant accountants who would need to produce the future cost function.

4.3 Properties of Optimal, Single-Series Forecasts

Let X_t be a zero-mean, stationary, and purely nondeterministic series with finite variance, therefore necessarily having an MA(∞) representation

$$X_t = \sum_{j=0}^{\infty} c_j \epsilon_{t-j}, \qquad c_0 = 1 \tag{4.3.1}$$

where ϵ_t is a zero-mean, white noise process with variance $\sigma_\epsilon^2 < \infty$. Thus,

$$E\{X_t\} = 0 \quad \text{and} \quad \text{var}(X_t) = \sigma_\epsilon^2 \sum_{j=0}^{\infty} c_j^2 < \infty$$

It was noted in Section 1.11 that any stationary series could be represented in this fashion, possibly after removal of its deterministic components.

A further assumption about X_t is also required for the following theory, that the MA(∞) representation is invertible, so that a model of the form

$$X_t = \sum_{j=1}^{\infty} a_j X_{t-j} + \epsilon_t$$

also exists, i.e., if $a_N(z) = 1 - \sum_{j=1}^{N} a_j z^j$, then $\lim_{N \to \infty} a_N(z)$ exists. A necessary and sufficient condition for this to hold is that the roots of $c(z) = 0$ all lie outside the unit circle $|z| = 1$, where $c(z) = \sum_{j=0}^{\infty} c_j z^j$. The reason for requiring this invertibility condition should become clear within this section and is further discussed in Section 4.8.

The information set to be considered in this section is $I_n = \{x_{n-j}, \ j \geq 0,$ model$\}$ so that all past and present values of the series are known together with the generating model, which is equivalent to knowing the values $c_j, \ j \geq 0$, in the above formulation. In practice this second assumption is an unreasonable one but it does provide an obvious and important starting point for a theory of forecasting. Given that the model is known, knowledge of the complete past of the series could be replaced by knowledge of a finite sample prior to time n, provided the length of this sample is greater than the backward ϵ-memory for small enough ϵ. However, since an inherently unreal situation is being considered, there is little point in examining the slightly more difficult finite sample case.

With I_n as given above, the problem is to find a linear forecast for X_{n+h} of the form

$$f_{n,h} = \sum_{j=0}^{\infty} w_{j,h} X_{n-j} \tag{4.3.2}$$

using a least-squares criterion. Thus, the $w_{j,h}$ need to be chosen so that

$$J = E\left\{\left(X_{n+h} - \sum w_{j,h} X_{n-j}\right)^2\right\} \tag{4.3.3}$$

is minimized. In the Gaussian case, it is clear that the resulting $f_{n,h}$ will be the conditional mean M_h defined in the previous section.

In operator terms, (4.3.1) becomes

$$X_t = c(B)\epsilon_t \tag{4.3.4}$$

where

$$c(B) = \sum_{j=0}^{\infty} c_j B^j \tag{4.3.5}$$

and (4.3.2) gives

$$f_{n,h} = w_h(B) X_n \tag{4.3.6}$$

where

$$w_h(B) = \sum_{j=0}^{\infty} w_{j,h} B^j \tag{4.3.7}$$

Letting t take the value n in (4.3.4) and substituting into (4.3.6) gives

$$f_{n,h} = \phi_h(B)\epsilon_n \tag{4.3.8}$$

where

$$\phi_h(B) = \sum_{j=0}^{\infty} \phi_{j,h} B^j \tag{4.3.9}$$

and

$$\phi_h(B) = w_h(B)c(B) \tag{4.3.10}$$

Thus the forecast $f_{n,h}$ is expressed in terms of the white noise, or innovation, process ϵ_t.

By letting t take the value $n + h$ in (4.3.1) and using (4.3.8), it is seen that J of (4.3.3) may be expressed as

$$J = E\left\{ \left(\sum_{j=0}^{h-1} c_j \epsilon_{n+h-j} + \sum_{j=0}^{\infty} (c_{j+h} - \phi_{j,h})\epsilon_{n-j} \right)^2 \right\} \tag{4.3.11}$$

which gives

$$J = \sigma_\epsilon^2 \sum_{j=0}^{h-1} c_j^2 + \sigma_\epsilon^2 \sum_{j=0}^{\infty} (c_{j+h} - \phi_{j,h})^2 \tag{4.3.12}$$

by using the fact that $E\{\epsilon_s \epsilon_t\} = 0$, $s \neq t$, since ϵ_t is a white noise series. Since the $w_{j,h}$ in (4.3.2) are at our choice, it follows that the $\phi_{j,h}$ are similarly at our choice. It is immediately clear that J in (4.3.12) is minimized by taking

$$\phi_{j,h} = c_{j+h} \tag{4.3.13}$$

so that

$$\phi_h(B) = \sum_{j=0}^{\infty} c_{j+h} B^j \tag{4.3.14}$$

and the optimal h-step forecast may then be written as

$$f_{n,h} = \sum_{j=0}^{\infty} c_{j+h}\epsilon_{n-j} \tag{4.3.15}$$

An occasionally useful notation may be introduced here as follows: consider a function $A(z) = \sum_j A_j z^j$, where j ranges over positive and negative values; then the notation $[A(z)]_+$ will be used to denote the sum over nonnegative values of j, i.e., $[A(z)]_+ = \sum_{j \geq 0} A_j z^j$. Using this notation,

$\phi_h(z)$ may be expressed as

$$\phi_h(z) = [c(z)/z^h]_+ \tag{4.3.16}$$

However, the problem as originally posed was to find the parameters $w_{j,h}$ in (4.3.2). In theory at least, they can be found by equating coefficients of powers of z in the expression $\phi_h(z) = w_h(z)c(z)$ with $\phi_h(z)$ given by (4.3.16). Since $w_h(z)$ is now expressed in terms of the known function $c(z)$, a full solution has been reached. Before considering the form of the optimal predictor for some particular models, a number of general properties of considerable importance will be derived.

The h-step error when using an optimal predictor will be

$$e_{n,h} = X_{n-h} - f_{n,h} \tag{4.3.17}$$

but from (4.3.1), with t taking the value $n + h$, and from (4.3.13) it is immediately seen that

$$e_{n,h} = \sum_{j=0}^{h-1} c_j \epsilon_{n+h-j} \tag{4.3.18}$$

so that $e_{n,h}$ is an MA($h - 1$) process. In particular, the one-step error resulting from an optimal predictor is

$$e_{n,1} = \epsilon_{n+1} \tag{4.3.19}$$

and so is a white noise series. Alternatively, this result can be reversed, giving

$$\epsilon_n = X_n - f_{n-1,1} \tag{4.3.20}$$

so that the innovation process ϵ_n can be expressed in terms of the observed series X_n and the previous one-step optimal predictor, which is itself a linear function of X_{n-j}, $j \geq 1$.

From (4.3.18) it follows that the errors have mean zero and variances given by

$$V(h) = E\{e_{n,h}^2\} = \sigma_\epsilon^2 \sum_{j=0}^{h-1} c_j^2 \tag{4.3.21}$$

Further $\lim_{h \to \infty} V(h) = \text{var}(X_t)$. The sequence of error variances is seen to be monotonically nondecreasing since

$$V(h + 1) - V(h) = \sigma_\epsilon^2 c_h^2 \geq 0 \tag{4.3.22}$$

It thus follows that, when using optimal forecasts, the further ahead one forecasts the worse one does, on average. An apparent counterexample to this is to consider the sequence of daily figures for car production in the U.K. There are certain days in the year for which car production can be predicted exactly, for example Christmas Day will certainly have zero production. However, this feature occurs because of a (multiplicative) deterministic component in the series and such components were assumed to have been removed before the above analysis was applied.

From (4.3.18) it is seen that

$$e_{n,h} = e_{n-1,h+1} - c_h \epsilon_n \tag{4.3.23}$$

Subtracting both sides of this expression from X_{n+h} and substituting for ϵ_n from (4.3.20), one gets a formula known as the *updating formula*:

$$f_{n,h} = f_{n-1,h+1} + c_h(X_n - f_{n-1,1}) \tag{4.3.24}$$

Clearly, given the sequence of forecasts made at time $n-1$ and the most recent value of the observed series, X_n, one can generate all of the new h-step forecasts. It will be seen in Chapter 5 that use of (4.3.24) can result in considerable computational saving in the calculation of forecasts.

Consider now the pair of forecasts $f_{n,h}$ and $f_{n,h+k}$ $(k > 0)$ of X_{n+h} and X_{n+h+k} made at time n. It follows immediately from (4.3.18) that

$$E(e_{n,h}e_{n,h+k}) = \sigma_\epsilon^2 \sum_{j=0}^{h-1} c_j c_{j+k} \tag{4.3.25}$$

Hence forecast errors from the same base n are typically correlated with one another.

Further properties of optimal forecasts and their errors that follow easily from (4.3.15), (4.3.17), and (4.3.18) are that

$$\mathrm{var}(X_{n+h}) = \mathrm{var}(f_{n,h}) + \mathrm{var}(e_{n,h})$$

so that $\mathrm{var}(X_{n+h}) > \mathrm{var}(f_{n,h})$ unless the series X_t is deterministic, and

$$\mathrm{cov}(f_{n,h}, e_{n,h}) = 0$$

so that $\mathrm{cov}(X_{n+h}, f_{n,h}) = \mathrm{var}(f_{n,h})$.

Throughout this section it has been assumed that the correctly specified model is being used to form the forecasts. When the wrong model is used most of the results obtained here are lost; for example, the variance of the h-step forecast error does not necessarily increase monotonically as h increases. However, the updating formula (4.3.24) continues to hold. The model misspecification case is analyzed in some detail in Davies and Newbold [1980b].

Most of the theory of this section also assumes that an infinite record of the series being forecast is available to form forecasts. If, in fact, only k previous values are known, then if $X_t \sim \mathrm{ARMA}(p, q)$ with either $p > k$ or $q > 0$ it will be necessary to use an approximation to the true optimal forecast. Newton and Pagano [1983] provide an algorithm to form these approximations. One obvious method is to use the form

$$f_{n,1}(k) = \sum_{j=0}^{k} \alpha_j(k) X_{n-j}$$

with the α's obtained from a least squares criterion, to minimize

$$\sigma_k^2 = E\left[(X_{n+1} - f_{n,1}(k))^2\right]$$

It can be shown that the minimum of this quantity is

$$\sigma_k^2 = D_{k+1}/D_k$$

where D_s is the $s \times s$ determinant whose entry in the ith row and jth column is corr$(X_{t-i}, X_{t-j}) = \rho_{i-j}$.

Provided k is large enough, the difference between σ_k^2 and σ_∞^2 is small, of the order of ρ_k.

4.4 Optimal Forecasts for Particular Models

In this section, the optimal single-series forecasts derived above will be applied to the models considered in the first chapter.

A series X_t is a moving average of order q, MA(q), if it is generated by

$$X_t = \sum_{j=0}^{q} b_j \epsilon_{t-j}, \qquad b_0 = 1 \tag{4.4.1}$$

where ϵ_t is a zero-mean white noise series. It immediately follows from the theory of the previous section that the optimal h-step forecast is given by

$$f_{n,h} = \sum_{j=0}^{q-h} b_{j+h} \epsilon_{n-j} \tag{4.4.2}$$

which may be expressed as

$$f_{n,h} = \sum_{j=0}^{q-h} b_{j+h}(X_{n-j} - f_{n-j-1,1}) \tag{4.4.3}$$

Given the infinite past of the series, (4.4.3) can be used to generate the forecasts. In practice, there will be a problem in "starting-up" the iterative procedure. This problem will be discussed in Chapter 5. It should be noted that $f_{n,h} = 0$, $h > q$, and thus for a white noise series with zero mean, which is MA(0), the optimal forecast is always zero when the forecast is based just on the past of the series. This reflects the basic property of a white noise series that earlier terms contain no information about later terms.

If X_t is a first-order autoregressive process AR(1) generated by

$$X_t = aX_{t-1} + \epsilon_t, \qquad |a| < 1 \tag{4.4.4}$$

then it may be written

$$X_t = \sum_{j=0}^{\infty} a^j \epsilon_{t-j} \tag{4.4.5}$$

and so applying (4.3.13) one gets as the optimal h-step forecast

$$f_{n,h} = \sum_{j=0}^{\infty} a^{j+h} \epsilon_{n-j} \tag{4.4.6}$$

Thus

$$f_{n,h} = a^h \sum_{j=0}^{\infty} a^j \epsilon_{n-j} = a^h X_n \qquad (4.4.7)$$

The same formula can, of course, also be derived directly from (4.3.16) by noting that $c(z) = 1/(1 - az)$. The variance of the h-step forecast error is immediately seen from (4.3.21) to be

$$V(h) = \frac{(1 - a^{2h})}{1 - a^2} \sigma_\epsilon^2 \qquad (4.4.8)$$

Note that, as h tends to infinity, (4.4.8) tends to $\sigma_\epsilon^2/(1 - a^2)$, the variance of the process X_t.

Consider now the mixed ARMA(p, q) process X_t generated by

$$a(B)X_t = b(B)\epsilon_t \qquad (4.4.9)$$

where

$$a(B) = 1 - \sum_{j=1}^{p} a_j B^j \quad \text{and} \quad b(B) = \sum_{j=0}^{q} b_j B^j, \quad b_0 = 1$$

The corresponding MA(∞) representation will be

$$X_t = c(B)\epsilon_t \qquad (4.4.10)$$

where

$$b(z)/a(z) = c(z) \qquad (4.4.11)$$

Thus

$$a(z)c(z) = b(z) \qquad (4.4.12)$$

Equating coefficients of z^k gives

$$c_k - \sum_{j=1}^{p} a_j c_{k-j} = b_k \quad \text{with} \quad c_j \equiv 0, \quad j < 0, \quad k = 0, 1, 2, \ldots \qquad (4.4.13)$$

Recall that

$$f_{n,h} = \sum_{i=0}^{\infty} c_{i+h} \epsilon_{n-i} \qquad (4.4.14)$$

and, taking $f_{n,k}$ to be X_{n+k} for $k \leqslant 0$, consider

$$f_{n,h} - \sum_{j=1}^{p} a_j f_{n,h-j} = \sum_{i=0}^{\infty} \left\{ c_{i+h} \epsilon_{n-i} - \sum_{j=1}^{p} a_j c_{i+h-j} \epsilon_{n-i} \right\}$$

$$= \sum_{i=0}^{\infty} b_{i+h} \epsilon_{n-i}, \quad b_i \equiv 0, \, i > q \qquad (4.4.15)$$

as follows from (4.4.13). This is an important formula since it allows one to form the sequence of optimal forecasts for given n and increasing h. To illustrate this, suppose that X_t is an AR(p) process given by

$$X_t = \sum_{j=1}^{p} a_j X_{t-j} + \epsilon_t \qquad (4.4.16)$$

Then (4.4.15) gives

$$f_{n,h} = \sum_{j=1}^{p} a_j f_{n,h-j} \qquad (4.4.17)$$

with $f_{n,k} = X_{n+k}$ for $k \leqslant 0$. In particular, for $h = 1$,

$$f_{n,1} = \sum_{j=1}^{p} a_j X_{n-j+1} \qquad (4.4.18)$$

Equation (4.4.18) gives the optimal one-step forecast in terms of known values and (4.4.17) gives an iterative formula for $f_{n,h}$, $h > 1$.

The more general formula (4.4.15) is similar in nature, but with the addition of terms involving ϵ_{n-i}, which may be replaced by $X_{n-i} - f_{n-i-1,1}$ by (4.3.20). A useful interpretation of (4.4.15) may be derived as follows: consider the generating formula (4.4.9) for the observed series, with t taking the value $n + h$, i.e.,

$$X_{n+h} = \sum_{j=1}^{p} a_j X_{n+h-j} + \sum_{j=0}^{q} b_j \epsilon_{n+h-j} \qquad (4.4.19)$$

If one is at time n, replace every term in this expression either by its known value at time n or its optimal forecast made at time n. Thus X_{n+k} is replaced by $f_{n,k}$ for $k > 0$ or by X_{n+k} if $k \leqslant 0$, and ϵ_{n+k} is replaced by zero, its optimal forecast for $k > 0$, and by itself, or equivalently, by $X_{n+k} - f_{n+k-1,1}$, for $k \leqslant 0$. This procedure gives (4.4.15), and so this formula is seen to be completely reasonable in commonsense terms.

So far attention has been restricted to stationary processes, but prediction of integrated processes with a known model is equally straightforward. Suppose X_t is ARIMA($p, 1, q$), so that $Y_t = X_t - X_{t-1}$ is ARMA(p, q). The preceding methods provide forecasts of Y_{n+h}, denoted by $f_{n,h}^Y$. The optimal forecast of X_{n+h}, denoted by $f_{n,h}^X$, is given simply by

$$f_{n,h}^X = f_{n,h-1}^X + f_{n,h}^Y$$

with, in the particular case $h = 1$,

$$f_{n,1}^X = X_n + f_{n,1}^Y$$

Extension to processes that require a higher degree of differencing follows immediately.

All of the above theory has assumed that the series to be forecast are purely nondeterministic. Suppose that X_t does have deterministic components, and may be written $X_t = T_t + Y_t$ where T_t is deterministic and Y_t is purely nondeterministic. If T_t is known exactly, the optimal forecast of X_{n+h} is obviously given by

$$f_{n,h}^X = T_{n+h} + f_{n,h}^Y$$

Since T_t is deterministic and known it follows that T_{n+h} will also be known exactly. In practice things are not necessarily this simple since, although a series may have a deterministic component, the form of this component is rarely precisely known.

One property of the optimal forecast derived in these past two sections is worth noting particularly, and that is that the generating equations of $f_{n,h}$, the optimal forecast, and X_{n+h}, the series being forecast, are usually quite different and so the time series properties, and the plots through time, will be far from identical. Put another way, the spectrum of $f_{n,h}$ and X_{n+h} will not be the same. This property is particularly relevant when considering the evaluation of forecasts. This will be discussed in Chapter 9.

4.5 A Frequency-Domain Approach

The theory outlined in the previous two sections has involved analysis only in the time domain, and is largely due to Wold [1954] and Kolmogorov [1939, 1941a]. The finding of the MA(∞) representation

$$X_t = \sum_{j=0}^{\infty} c_j \epsilon_{t-j}, \qquad c_0 = 1 \qquad (4.5.1)$$

is clearly of major importance in this approach. In the frequency domain this representation may be written

$$\lambda_x(z) = c(z^{-1}) c(z) \lambda_\epsilon(z) \qquad (4.5.2)$$

where $\lambda_x(z)/2\pi \equiv s_x(\omega)$, $z = e^{-i\omega}$, is the spectrum of X_t, $\lambda_\epsilon(z)/2\pi \equiv s_\epsilon(\omega)$ is the spectrum of ϵ_t, and $c(z) = \sum_{j=0}^{\infty} c_j z^j$. Equation (4.5.2) follows from the fact that X_t may be regarded as a filtered version of the series ϵ_t. Since ϵ_t is white noise, with variance σ_ϵ^2, (4.5.2) becomes

$$\lambda_x(z) = \sigma_\epsilon^2 c(z) c(z^{-1}) \qquad (4.5.3)$$

Considerable theoretical work has been concerned with the prediction problem given merely the spectrum of X_t rather than the generating model. However, since in practice it is most unusual for the spectrum to be known exactly, this work does not as it stands have a great deal of practical relevance. If one is given a spectral function, it is usually very difficult in practice to find a function $c(z)$ so that the decomposition (4.5.3) holds. As an example the reader might consider a series X_t that is the sum of two independent MA(∞) components with known parameters. In theory a decomposition can be achieved as follows. Suppose that $\log \lambda_x(z)$ has a power series expansion in z, with both negative and positive powers, of the form

$$\log \lambda_x(z) = \sum_{j=-\infty}^{\infty} d_j z^j \qquad (4.5.4)$$

This is known as a Laurent expansion and is assumed to be valid in some annulus $\rho < |z| < \rho^{-1}$, $\rho < 1$. Thus

$$\lambda_x(z) = \exp\left\{ \sum_{j=-\infty}^{\infty} d_j z^j \right\} \qquad (4.5.5)$$

and

$$c(z) = \exp\left\{ \sum_{j=1}^{\infty} d_j z^j \right\} \qquad (4.5.6)$$

will then be an obvious choice for $c(z)$ since it will have a Taylor series expansion in nonnegative powers of z. By equating coefficients of z^0 in (4.5.5) one sees that

$$\sigma_\epsilon^2 = e^{d_0} = \exp\left\{ \frac{1}{2\pi} \int_{-\pi}^{\pi} \log 2\pi s_x(\omega) \, d\omega \right\} \qquad (4.5.7)$$

It was shown in Section 4.3 that σ_ϵ^2 is the variance of the one-step prediction error when an optimal predictor is used. Thus (4.5.7) gives a general expression in terms of the spectrum of X_t for the minimum achievable one-step error variance when X_t is predicted from its own past and has a known spectrum. It follows directly that a necessary condition that X_t be nondeterministic is that

$$\int_{-\pi}^{\pi} \log 2\pi s_x(\omega) \, d\omega > -\infty \qquad (4.5.8)$$

otherwise X_t is deterministic. This condition may also be shown to be a sufficient one. It further follows that if $s_x(\omega) = 0$ on a set of nonzero measure, for example if $s_x(\omega) = 0$ for all ω in (ω_0, ω_1), then X_t will be deterministic. Rosenblatt [1957] has discussed how one would form the optimal predictor in such cases. A practical use for Eq. (4.5.7) is discussed in Chapter 9.

A class of processes for which the decomposition (4.5.3) is particularly simple is the mixed ARMA class. If X_t is generated by

$$X_t = \sum_{j=1}^{p} a_j X_{t-j} + \sum_{j=0}^{q} b_j \epsilon_{t-j}$$

i.e., $a(B)X_t = b(B)\epsilon_t$, then it was shown in Chapter 2 that the spectrum of X_t is given by

$$\frac{\lambda_x(z)}{2\pi} \equiv s_x(\omega) = \frac{b(z)b(z^{-1})}{a(z)a(z^{-1})} \frac{\sigma_\epsilon^2}{2\pi}$$

and so, immediately $c(z) = b(z)/a(z)$. Further, writing $c(z)$ as

$$c(z) = \prod_{j=1}^{p} (1 - \gamma_j z) \Big/ \prod_{j=1}^{q} (1 - \theta_j z), \qquad |\gamma_j| < 1, \quad |\theta_j| < 1$$

which will always be possible, then since

$$\int_{-\pi}^{\pi} \log(1 - \gamma z)\, d\omega = 0, \qquad z = e^{-i\omega}, \quad |\gamma| < 1$$

as may be seen by expanding $\log(1 - \gamma z)$ as a power series in z, the truth of (4.5.7) is easily verified in this case by substitution for $s_x(\omega)$ in that equation.

These results indicate why the mixed ARMA model is of particular importance when considering the formation of optimal single series forecasts.

The formula for the optimal predictor (4.3.16), previously obtained by a time-domain analysis, can also be achieved by an argument in the frequency domain. Since this derivation, known as the Wiener-Hopf technique, has some considerable power, in the sense that a variety of situations can be handled by it, a brief outline of the approach will be given. (We follow Whittle [1963, p. 67].) One may start with the more general problem of how to best "explain" a series Y_t by a linear sum of past and present terms of a series X_t, both series being stationary and having zero means. Consider a representation

$$\hat{Y}_t = \sum_{j=0}^{\infty} w_j X_{t-j} \tag{4.5.9}$$

Strictly, one should consider the sum over the range $j = 0, \ldots, N$ and then consider the limit as $N \to \infty$, but such subtleties will be ignored and all infinite sums will be assumed to exist. Using a least-squares criterion, the w_j have to be chosen so that

$$J = E\{(Y_t - \hat{Y}_t)^2\} \tag{4.5.10}$$

is minimized. By considering $\partial J/\partial w_j = 0$, one gets

$$\sum_{k=0}^{\infty} \lambda_{j-k}^{(xx)} w_k = \lambda_j^{(yx)}, \qquad j = 0, 1, 2, \ldots \tag{4.5.11}$$

where

$$\lambda_k^{(xx)} = E\{X_t X_{t-k}\}, \qquad \lambda_k^{(yx)} = E\{Y_t X_{t-k}\} \tag{4.5.12}$$

Multiplying (4.5.11) by z^j and summing over all integers j, both positive and negative, gives

$$\lambda_x(z) w(z) = \lambda_{yx}(z) + h(z) \tag{4.5.13}$$

where $\lambda_x(z)/2\pi \equiv s_x(\omega)$, $z = e^{-i\omega}$, is the spectrum of X_t, $\lambda_{yx}(z)/2\pi \equiv s_{yx}(\omega)$ is the cross spectrum between Y_t and X_t, $w(z) = \sum_{j=0}^{\infty} w_j z^j$, and $h(z)$ is some unknown series in negative powers of z. The left-hand side term of

(4.5.13) arises because the left-hand side of (4.5.11) is a convolution, as discussed in Section 1.3. The function $h(z)$ is necessary because (4.5.11) holds only for positive j. Equation (4.5.11) can be derived from (4.5.13) by noting that

$$\lambda_x(z) = \sum_{j=-\infty}^{\infty} \lambda_j^{(xx)} z^j \qquad (4.5.14)$$

and

$$\lambda_{yx}(z) = \sum_{j=-\infty}^{\infty} \lambda_j^{(yx)} z^j \qquad (4.5.15)$$

and then equating coefficients of positive powers of z.

Assume now that X_t is purely nondeterministic and so its spectrum has the decomposition (4.5.3), then dividing both sides of (4.5.13) by $c(z^{-1})$ gives

$$\sigma_\epsilon^2 c(z)w(z) = \frac{\lambda_{yx}(z)}{c(z^{-1})} + \frac{h(z)}{c(z^{-1})} \qquad (4.5.16)$$

The term on the left-hand side of (4.5.16) contains no negative powers of z and the second term on the right-hand side contains only negative powers. It follows therefore that

$$\sigma_\epsilon^2 c(z)w(z) = \left[\frac{\lambda_{yx}(z)}{c(z^{-1})} \right]_+ \qquad (4.5.17)$$

using the notation introduced in Section 4.3.

Two particular cases will now be considered. First, suppose that Y_t, the series to be "explained," is just X_{t+h}, so that the problem considered is the prediction of X_{n+h} by X_{n-j}, $j \geq 0$, which is the single-series forecast problem considered in Section 4.3. Then

$$\lambda_k^{(yx)} = E\{ X_{t+h} X_{t-k} \} = \lambda_{k+h}^{(xx)} \qquad (4.5.18)$$

and so

$$\lambda_{yx}(z) = z^{-h} \lambda_x(z) \qquad (4.5.19)$$

Further, since $\lambda_x(z) = \sigma_\epsilon^2 c(z)c(z^{-1})$, Eq. (4.5.17) becomes

$$c(z)w_h(z) = [c(z)/z^h]_+ \qquad (4.5.20)$$

which is identical to formula (4.3.16). Hence the optimal forecast has been derived through a frequency-domain approach.

As a second example, consider the case where one wishes to forecast Y_{n+h} by the information set $I_n = \{ X_{n-j},\ j \geq 0,\ \text{model} \}$, so that one series Y_t is to be forecast in terms of past and present values of another series X_t. If the cross spectrum between Y_t and X_t is $\lambda_{yx}^{(1)}(z)/2\pi$, then the optimal terms w_j

in (4.5.9) are given by

$$w(z) = \frac{1}{\sigma_\epsilon^2 c(z)} \left[\frac{\lambda_{yx}^{(1)}(z)}{z^h c(z^{-1})} \right]_+ \tag{4.5.21}$$

as follows from (4.5.17) by noting that $\lambda_{yx}^{(1)}(z) = z^h \lambda_{yx}(z)$ since, by definition, $\lambda_{yx}(z)/2\pi$ is the cross spectrum between Y_{t+h} and X_t.

Suppose now that the two series are actually related by an equation of the form

$$Y_t = \sum_{j=0}^{\infty} \delta_j X_{t-j} + U_t \tag{4.5.22}$$

where U_t is some stationary series independent of X_t, while X_t is generated as before by the process $X_t = c(B)\epsilon_t$. Then

$$\lambda_{yx}^{(1)}(z) = \delta(z)\lambda_x(z)$$

where

$$\delta(z) = \sum_{j=0}^{\infty} \delta_j z^j \tag{4.5.23}$$

The optimal prediction of Y_{n+h} in terms of X_{n-j}, $j \geqslant 0$ is then given by

$$f_{n,h}^{(y)} = \sum_{j=0}^{\infty} w_{j,h} X_{n-j} \tag{4.5.24}$$

where

$$w_h(z) = \frac{1}{\sigma_\epsilon^2 c(z)} \left[\frac{\delta(z)\lambda_x(z)}{z^h c(z^{-1})} \right]_+ \tag{4.5.25}$$

from (4.5.21). Noting that $\lambda_x(z) = \sigma_\epsilon^2 c(z)c(z^{-1})$ this becomes

$$w_h(z) = \frac{1}{c(z)} \left[\frac{c(z)\delta(z)}{z^h} \right]_+ \tag{4.5.26}$$

and expanding $\delta(z)$ in the form (4.5.23), the expression for $w_h(z)$ may be written

$$w_h(z) = \sum_{j=0}^{h-1} \frac{\delta_j}{c(z)} \left[\frac{c(z)}{z^{h-j}} \right]_+ + \sum_{j=h}^{\infty} \delta_j z^{j-h} \tag{4.5.27}$$

In operator form (4.5.24) is $f_{n,h}^{(y)} = w_h(B)X_n$. Thus by noting from (4.5.20) that

$$\frac{1}{c(B)} \left[\frac{c(B)}{B^{h-j}} \right]_+ X_n = f_{n,h-j}^{(x)}, \qquad h > j$$

where $f_{n,h}^{(x)}$ is the optimal forecast of X_{n+h} made at time n and B now operates on the index n of X_n, one finds that the optimal forecast of Y_{n+h}

based on X_{n-j}, $j \geq 0$, may be written

$$f_{n,h}^{(y)} = \sum_{j=0}^{h-1} \delta_j f_{n,h-j}^{(x)} + \sum_{j=h}^{\infty} \delta_j X_{n+h-j} \qquad (4.5.28)$$

Comparing this to (4.5.22) with t given the value $n + h$, the optimal forecast is seen to be the commonsense one, with all future X_t values replaced by their optimal forecasts made at time n, using past and present values of X_t and with U_{n+h} given the value zero, which is the optimal prediction if one only has information on the X_t series, which is independent of U_t. The model (4.5.22) is one frequently used in economics, known as the distributed lag model (see Dhrymes [1971]).[1] The optimal forecast of Y_{n+h} using just past and present X values may be rather a poor one if the U_t component of Y_t is of greater importance than the component involving values of X_t. It is clear that a much improved forecast can be achieved in this case when the information set contains both X_{n-j}, $j \geq 0$, *and* Y_{n-j}, $j \geq 0$, or, equivalently, U_{n-j}, $j \geq 0$. It is particularly worth noting that the form of U_t does not at all affect the forecast (4.5.28). This could be taken as a criticism of the distributed lag approach. Put another way if, as is frequently done, it is assumed that the error term in a distributed lag model is white noise, this is equivalent to postulating a situation in which forecasts of future Y are based only on current and past X. It would seem more reasonable to expect that current and past values of Y would also be relevant, and these can be accounted for by incorporating into the model a more general time series structure for the error series. Procedures of this kind will be discussed further in Chapter 8.

4.6 Expectations and Forecasts

Economists frequently encounter expectations in their theories, that is, values of some economic variable that are thought likely to occur in the future, the expectations being made either by individuals or, implicitly by their actions, by some group of individuals, such as those making a market. An expectation may vary from a very naïve guess about the future based on little data and no analysis to a full-scale forecast. If the individuals involved are sufficiently sophisticated, it seems reasonable to consider the possibility that their expectations are, in fact, optimal forecasts based on a wide enough information set. This set need not consist merely of past and present numerical data but could also include subjective information, so that the forecasts will reflect concepts such as "experience" and "prejudices" which are difficult to quantify. Such information sets cannot be fitted into the foregoing theory without adopting a Bayesian viewpoint of some kind, and

---

[1] Strictly, the distributed lag formulation writes $\delta(z) = \beta(z)/\alpha(z)$, where $\alpha(z)$ and $\beta(z)$ are finite order polynomials in z.

so attention will be limited here to numerical information sets. To ease exposition, the only case to be considered will be the single-series one, so that the information set will consist only of the past and present of the series to be forecast.[1]

The first example to be presented, showing how forecast theory can be used in economics, involves the term structure of interest rates. At any moment of time there exists not just one interest rate but many rates, depending on how long one wishes to borrow the money. Denote by $R_{k,t}$ the rate quoted at time t for a loan made at that time and to be repaid at the end of the kth year of the loan, so that $R_{1,t}$ represents the rate on a one-year loan and $R_{2,t}$ the rate on a two-year loan, both loans to be made at time t. At each time t one may also get quotes for loans to be made in the future, at least in theory. Let $r_{t,h}$ be the rate quoted at time t for a one year loan to start at time $t + h$. This will be a forward rate and one would naturally expect there to be a relationship between the two-year rate $R_{2,t}$ and the pair of one-year rates $R_{1,t}$ and $r_{t,1}$ since a two-year loan is equivalent to borrowing for one year now and for a further year in a year's time. The required formula is in fact

$$r_{t,1} = \frac{(1 + R_{2,t})^2}{1 + R_{1,t}} - 1 \tag{4.6.1}$$

These forward rates may not actually be quoted in the market but can be taken as implied or expected rates and can be estimated from (4.6.1), using the values of $R_{1,t}$ and $R_{2,t}$ actually observed in the money market.

A particular form of expectations hypothesis proposed by Meiselman [1962] is an error-learning model of the form

$$r_{t,h} - r_{t-1,h+1} = g_h(E_t) \tag{4.6.2}$$

where E_t is the error made in forecasting the current one-year rate, so that

$$E_t = R_{1,t} - r_{t-1,1} \tag{4.6.3}$$

Both $r_{t,h}$ and $r_{t-1,h+1}$ are expectations of the one-year rate to prevail in year $t + h$, but made in years t and $t - 1$, respectively. The function $g(x)$ is assumed to be linear, of the form

$$g_h(E_t) = A_h + D_h E_t \tag{4.6.4}$$

The resulting formula, obtained from (4.6.4) and (4.6.2), should be compared to the updating formula (4.3.24), which states that if $r_{n,h}$ is the optimal forecast of $R_{1,n+h}$ based on the information set $I_n = \{ R_{1,n-j}, j \geq 0 \}$ then

$$r_{n,h} - r_{n-1,h+1} = c_h(R_{1,n} - r_{n-1,1}) \tag{4.6.5}$$

---

[1] Results to be presented in Chapter 7 will show that no considerable changes result from using multiseries information sets.

where

$$R_{1,t} = \sum_{j=0}^{\infty} c_j \epsilon_{t-j}, \qquad c_0 = 1 \qquad\qquad (4.6.6)$$

and ϵ_t is a white noise process. Thus the model suggested by Meiselman as a working hypothesis is seen to follow from the theory of optimal forecasting, assuming the market to be using optimal forecasts for its expectations, but with specific values for A_h and D_h in (4.6.4), namely $A_h = 0$, $D_h = c_h$ where c_h is given by (4.6.6).

Meiselman fitted his model to some U.S. data for the period 1901–1954 and estimated A_h and D_h. The values for A_h, $h = 1, 2, \ldots, 8$ were all very small, and none were significantly different from zero, in agreement with the optimal forecasting theory. The estimated D_h values were well fitted by the equation

$$D_h = \beta \alpha^h \qquad\qquad (4.6.7)$$

with $\beta = 0.72$, $\alpha = 0.84$. Setting c_h in (4.6.6) equal to D_h of (4.6.7) this suggests the model for the one-year rates

$$R_{1,t} = \epsilon_t + \beta \sum_{h=1}^{\infty} \alpha^h B^h \epsilon_t \qquad\qquad (4.6.8)$$

where B is the backward operator. This may be written as

$$R_{1,t} = \frac{1 - \alpha(1 - \beta)B}{1 - \alpha B} \epsilon_t \qquad\qquad (4.6.9)$$

Hence, if the forward rates constitute optimal forecasts of future one-year rates based on the information set consisting of just current and past one-year rates, and if the relation (4.6.7) is taken to hold exactly, the series $R_{1,t}$ must be generated by the ARMA(1,1) process

$$(1 - 0.84B)R_{1,t} = (1 - 0.24B)\epsilon_t \qquad\qquad (4.6.10)$$

as follows by substituting for α and β in (4.6.9). In fact, Nelson [1972a] has fitted several models to the series $R_{1,t}$. For the ARMA process he obtained (with standard errors in brackets)

$$R_{1,t} - \underset{[0.05]}{0.94} R_{1,t-1} = 0.20 + \epsilon_t - \underset{[0.13]}{0.13} \epsilon_{t-1}$$

which is in reasonable agreement with the predicted form (4.6.10). A slightly better fit in terms of error variance was given by the IMA(1, 1) process

$$R_{1,t} - R_{1,t-1} = \epsilon_t - \underset{[0.12]}{0.16} \epsilon_{t-1}$$

which differs insignificantly from a random walk. Nelson concludes that the simple error-learning theory of forward rates is in itself an insufficient explanation of their behavior and that the level of interest rates and an index of business confidence should be incorporated in the model (4.6.5).

A second example of the use of expectations in economics is provided by what is known as the current valuation formula. Suppose a company has, or is contemplating, an investment in some asset from which it is reasonable to expect a flow of returns or dividends. An example would be an investment in a new machine or in a particular portfolio of stocks. A frequently used method of valuing the investment at time n is by the formula

$$V_n = \sum_{h=1}^{\infty} \frac{D_{n,h}^*}{(1+r)^h} \qquad (4.6.11)$$

where V_n is the current value, at time n, $D_{n,h}^*$ is the expected dividend to be paid in year $n+h$, and r is a positive discount factor, used to reflect a preference for dividends in the near future rather than those in the more distant future. The valuation formula merely says that current value is a discounted sum of all expected dividends.

This formula is much used by accountants and by financial economists. An account of its uses may be found in Van Horne [1971]. A problem of considerable importance and difficulty in practice is the choice of r, the discount factor. One suggested method is to put r equal to a "normally expected" rate plus a term reflecting a belief about the degree of risk involved with the investment. In the following analysis, r will be taken to be a known constant.

Suppose that one has available a flow of past dividends from the investment, $I_n = \{ D_{n-j}, j \geqslant 0 \}$, and that the company's expectations are optimal forecasts based on this information set. Suppose that the series D_t is stationary and has an $MA(\infty)$ representation

$$D_t = \sum_{j=0}^{\infty} c_j \epsilon_{t-j} \equiv c(B) \epsilon_t \qquad (4.6.12)$$

where ϵ_t is a white noise series. From (4.6.11) one can write

$$V_{n+1} + D_{n+1} - (1+r)V_n = D_{n+1} - D_{n,1}^* + \sum_{h=1}^{\infty} \frac{D_{n+1,h}^* - D_{n,h+1}^*}{(1+r)^h} \qquad (4.6.13)$$

From (4.3.19) and the updating formula (4.3.24) it follows that

$$V_{n+1} + D_{n+1} - (1+r)V_n = \sum_{h=0}^{\infty} \frac{c_h}{(1+r)^h} \epsilon_{n+1} \qquad (4.6.14)$$

$$= c(\mu)\epsilon_{n+1}, \qquad \mu = 1/(1+r) \quad (4.6.15)$$

The rate of return in the year $n+1$ may be taken to be the change in the capital value of the investment $V_{n+1} - V_n$ plus the direct monetary return D_{n+1} divided by the value of the capital involved in the investment at the start of the period. This value may be taken to be V_n since, if other people agreed with the company's valuation, in theory the investment or asset could be sold at price V_n, so that V_n is the value of the investment in terms of alternative costs. The accounting rate of return is thus

$$R_{n+1} = \frac{V_{n+1} + D_{n+1} - V_n}{V_n}$$

and from (4.6.15), it is seen that $R_{n+1} = r + c(\mu)(\epsilon_{n+1}/V_n)$. Thus, the sequence of accounting returns R_{n+1} will be the sum of a constant r plus a white noise term since ϵ_{n+1} is white noise and is uncorrelated with V_n. The variance of the white noise term also depends on the value of r through the term $c(\mu)$ since $\mu = 1/(1 + r)$. The use of forecasting theory in conjunction with the valuation formula casts some doubt on the usefulness of this formula since the average return that results is equal to the discount factor inserted and so the argument becomes circular. Further discussion of this formula with a more general forecasting formulation can be found in Granger [1975].

4.7 Unbiased Forecasts

A forecast $f_{n,h}$ may be thought of as being an estimate of the random variable being forecast X_{n+h}; and, as elsewhere in statistics, it seems reasonable to require that the estimate be unbiased. If $f_{n,h}$ is based on the information set I_n, then $f_{n,h}$ will be said to be "completely unbiased" if

$$E_c\{e_{n,h}|I_n\} = 0 \qquad (4.7.1)$$

where E_c denotes conditional expectation and

$$e_{n,h} = X_{n+h} - f_{n,h} \qquad (4.7.2)$$

is the forecast error. When using a least squares criterion, the only forecast that is completely unbiased is the optimal forecast since

$$f_{n,h} = E_c\{X_{n+h}|I_n\} \qquad (4.7.3)$$

The forecast $f_{n,h}$ will be said to be "unbiased on average" (henceforth just "unbiased") if

$$E\{e_{n,h}\} = 0 \qquad (4.7.4)$$

To illustrate these definitions, consider the AR(1) model $X_t = aX_{t-1} + \epsilon_t$ where ϵ_t is a white noise series, but with mean $E\{\epsilon_t\} = m$. Then $E\{X_t\} = \mu$ where $\mu = m/(1 - a)$. Using $I_n = \{X_{n-j}, j \geq 0\}$, consider the two forecasts $f_{n,1} = aX_n + m$ with error $e_{n,1}$, and $g_{n,1} = \mu$ with error $e'_{n,1}$. Then

$$e_{n,1} = (X_{n+1} - aX_n - m) \quad \text{and} \quad E_c(e_{n,1}) = E_c(\epsilon_{n+1} - m) = 0$$

since ϵ_{n+1} has mean m and is independent of I_n. When using $g_{n,1}$, one has

$$e'_{n,1} = X_{n+1} - \mu = aX_n + \epsilon_{n+1} - \mu$$

and so

$$E_c\{e'_{n,1}\} = aX_n + m - \mu = a(X_n - \mu)$$

Thus, $g_{n,1}$ is not a completely unbiased forecast, but since $E\{e'_{n,1}\} = 0$, it *is* unbiased on average.

The example illustrates the fact that the completely unbiased property is a very strong one, but that the other definition of unbiasedness is rather a weak one, although it is the only one generally applied or considered. With model misspecification, which will be the rule rather than the exception, the resulting forecasts will generally not be completely unbiased.

4.8 Invertibility

In this section, the discussion of Section 3.4, in which it was noted that moving average representation is not generally unique, is elaborated. Consider a zero-mean, stationary series X_t with theoretical autocovariances $\lambda_\tau = E\{X_t X_{t-\tau}\}$ such that

$$\lambda_\tau = 0, \qquad \tau \geq q + 1 \tag{4.8.1}$$

It follows from Section 1.6 that provided the λ_τ obey certain restrictions X_t will be a moving average process, which may be represented by

$$X_t = b(B)\epsilon_t = \left(\sum_{j=0}^{q} b_j B^j \right)\epsilon_t, \qquad b_0 = 1 \tag{4.8.2}$$

It was also shown in Section 1.6 that if $\lambda(z)$ is the autocovariance generating function

$$\lambda(z) = \sum_{j=-q}^{q} \lambda_j z^j \tag{4.8.3}$$

then

$$\lambda(z) = \sigma_\epsilon^2 b(z) b(z^{-1}) \tag{4.8.4}$$

The model-building problem can be thought of as being given the λ_τ and being required to find the b_j. In theory at least one could proceed as follows: find the roots of

$$\lambda(z) = 0 \tag{4.8.5}$$

noting that as $\lambda_j = \lambda_{-j}$, and hence $\lambda(z) = \lambda(z^{-1})$, then if z_j is a root it follows that z_j^{-1} must also be a root. Denote those roots of (4.8.5) that lie outside the unit circle by z_j, $j = 1, \ldots, q$, so that $|z_j| > 1$; and it is assumed that no roots have modulus one. Then the $2q$ roots of (4.8.5) may be denoted

$$z_j, \quad j = 1, \ldots, 2q, \qquad \text{where} \quad z_{j+q} = z_j^{-1}, \quad j = 1, \ldots, q$$

Let z_j', $j = 1, \ldots, q$ be a subset of size q of these roots, such that if z_j is contained in it, then z_j^{-1} is not. Then a possible solution for $b(z)$ is

$$b'(z) = \sigma_\epsilon^{-1/2} \prod_{j=1}^{q} (z - z_j') \tag{4.8.6}$$

and by expanding this as a power series in z and equating coefficients in (4.8.2), some possible values for the b_j result. Since there are at most[1] $M_q = 2^q$ ways of choosing the subset z_j', it follows that there are this many possible moving average MA(q) processes all with the same autocovariance sequence. However, only one of these models has the invertibility property, so that ϵ_t may be written as a convergent sum of past and present values of X_t. To see this, transform (4.8.2) to

$$\epsilon_t = \frac{1}{b(B)} X_t = \frac{1}{\prod_{j=1}^{q} (B - z_j')} \sigma_\epsilon X_t \tag{4.8.7}$$

Expanding the reciprocal of the product into partial fractions gives terms such as

$$\frac{A_j}{B - z_j'} = -\frac{A_j}{z_j'} \sum_{k=0}^{\infty} \frac{B^k}{(z_j')^k} \tag{4.8.8}$$

and for convergence one requires $|z_j'| > 1$. Thus, the only moving average model of those considered that is invertible is the one corresponding to the set of roots $z_j' = z_j$, $j = 1, \ldots, q$, such that all have modulus greater than one. Clearly this is unique since, by definition, if z_j is not in the subset, then z_j^{-1} must be in it.

To show the considerable importance of this invertibility condition consider an MA(1) process with

$$\lambda_0 = 1, \qquad \lambda_1 = \rho \leqslant \tfrac{1}{2}, \qquad \lambda_\tau = 0, \quad \tau > 1 \tag{4.8.9}$$

The foregoing theory suggests that there are two alternative MA(1) representations, of the form

$$X_t = \epsilon_t - \beta \epsilon_{t-1}, \qquad |\beta| < 1 \tag{4.8.10}$$

and

$$X_t = e_t - \beta^{-1} e_{t-1} \tag{4.8.11}$$

where ϵ_t and e_t are both white noise series, only the first being invertible. By considering $E\{X_t X_{t-1}\}$ for both models one gets

$$\beta \sigma_\epsilon^2 = \beta^{-1} \sigma_e^2$$

---

[1] The qualification "at most" is required since the b_j of (4.8.2) are required to be real. Hence, any complex roots must be taken in conjugate pairs.

so that

$$\sigma_e^2 = \beta^2\sigma_\epsilon^2 < \sigma_\epsilon^2 \qquad (4.8.12)$$

This suggests the rather surprising result that if one could find an optimal forecast using the noninvertible form (4.8.11), *then* the variance of the one-step forecast error σ_e^2 would be less than the corresponding variance σ_ϵ^2 using the invertible model (4.8.10). However, it is quite impossible to form an optimal forecast based on just past and present X_t using (4.8.11) since the e_t are not observable given this information set, just because the model is not invertible. That is to say, the optimal forecast theory of Section 4.3 suggests, based on (4.8.11), the forecast of X_{n+1}

$$g_{n,1} = -\beta^{-1}e_n$$

However, because of noninvertibility, e_n cannot be determined in terms of current and previous values of the series X. It is therefore seen that if one had the slightly larger information set $I_n' = \{ X_{n-j}, j \geq 0, e_{n-k}, \text{any } k \geq 0\}$ then one could forecast X_t one step ahead very much better than with the information set $I_n = \{ X_{n-j}, j \geq 0\}$. But the set I_n' is impossible to realize in any practical situation. One is therefore forced always to use invertible models, and, given only I_n, one cannot be better off using a noninvertible form.

This can be shown more formally as follows, using $p(X)$ to represent the pdf of the random variable X and $\mathbf{X}_n$ to denote the vector $X_{n-j}, j \geq 0$. Then, using a least squares criterion, the optimal one-step forecast is known to be

$$f_{n,1} = E\{ X_{n+1}|\mathbf{X}_n\}$$

and an expression for this can be derived from

$$p(X_{n+1}|\mathbf{X}_n) = \int p(X_{n+1}, \epsilon_n|\mathbf{X}_n) \, d\epsilon_n = \int p(X_{n+1}|\epsilon_n, \mathbf{X}_n) p(\epsilon_n|\mathbf{X}_n) \, d\epsilon_n$$

Hence

$$f_{n,1} = E\{ X_{n+1}|\mathbf{X}_n\} = \int \int X_{n+1} p(X_{n+1}|\epsilon_n, \mathbf{X}_n) p(\epsilon_n|\mathbf{X}_n) \, d\epsilon_n \, dX_{n+1}$$

$$= \int E\{ X_{n+1}|\epsilon_n, \mathbf{X}_n\} p(\epsilon_n|\mathbf{X}_n) \, d\epsilon_n \qquad (4.8.13)$$

But from (4.8.10)

$$E\{ X_{n+1}|\epsilon_n, \mathbf{X}_n\} = -\beta\epsilon_n \qquad (4.8.14)$$

and for the invertible form, ϵ_n is assumed to be known exactly given $\mathbf{X}_n$, so that (4.8.13) becomes

$$f_{n,1} = E\{ X_{n+1}|\mathbf{X}_n\} = -\beta\epsilon_n$$

where ϵ_n is some known function of $\mathbf{X}_n$. Similarly using the noninvertible form, one gets

$$E\{X_{n+1}|\mathbf{X}_n\} = \int E\{X_{n+1}|e_n,\mathbf{X}_n\} p(e_n|\mathbf{X}_n)\, de_n$$

and from (4.8.11)

$$E\{X_{n+1}|e_n,\mathbf{X}_n\} = -\beta^{-1}e_n$$

But, for the noninvertible form, e_n is not known exactly given $\mathbf{X}_n$, so that $p(e_n|\mathbf{X}_n)$ takes a form such that

$$-\beta^{-1}\int e_n p(e_n|\mathbf{X}_n)\, de_n = -\beta\epsilon_n = f_{n,1}$$

To illustrate this in a special case, suppose that the distributions are multivariate normal, so that $p(\epsilon_n,\mathbf{X}_n) \sim N(0,\Sigma)$ where the covariance matrix Σ takes the form

$$\Sigma = \begin{bmatrix} \sigma_\epsilon^2 & \sigma_\epsilon^2 & 0 & 0 & 0 & \cdots \\ \sigma_\epsilon^2 & & & & & \\ 0 & & & \Sigma_x & & \\ 0 & & & & & \end{bmatrix}$$

where Σ_x is the covariance matrix of $\mathbf{X}_n$. Then from classical multivariate normal regression theory $p(\epsilon_n|\mathbf{X}_n)$ is normal with mean $\sigma_\epsilon^2(\Sigma_x)_1^{-1}\mathbf{X}_n$, where $(\Sigma_x)_1^{-1}$ denotes the first row of Σ_x^{-1}. Thus, from (4.8.13) and (4.8.14)

$$f_{n,1} = -\beta\sigma_\epsilon^2(\Sigma_x)_1^{-1}\mathbf{X}_n$$

In the same way, using the noninvertible form and considering $p(e_n,\mathbf{X}_n)$, one gets

$$f'_{n,1} = -\beta^{-1}\sigma_e^2(\Sigma_x)_1^{-1}\mathbf{X}_n$$

but, as $\sigma_e^2 = \beta^2\sigma_\epsilon^2$, these two forecasts are seen to be identical.

Thus, in terms of forecasting ability, nothing can be gained from employing a noninvertible form. The invertible form is inevitably used in practice since the computation of coefficient estimates and of forecasts from the fitted model is considerably easier for invertible than for noninvertible models.

In non-Gaussian situations, a nonlinear forecast, based on I_n, can sometimes be found for noninvertible MA models, at least in theory. Shepp, Slepian, and Wyner [1980] provide optimum, nonlinear forecasts for the MA(1) model with a few specific distributions for the innovations.

The definition of invertibility used above, and in previous sections, is not capable of use with the more general models to be introduced in Chapter 10. Consider a very general univariate time series model of the form

$$X_t = f(t; X_{t-1}, X_{t-2},\ldots, X_{t-p}, \epsilon_{t-1}, \epsilon_{t-2},\ldots, \epsilon_{t-q}) + \epsilon_t$$

so that X_t is generated by a possibly nonlinear, time-varying function of the previous pX's and previous q innovations ϵ_{i-j}, plus a current innovation ϵ_t. If the process is observed from time $a - p$, and one has q initial, arbitrarily chosen innovation values $\hat{\epsilon}_{a-1}, \hat{\epsilon}_{a-2}, \ldots, \hat{\epsilon}_{a-q}$, then a sequence of estimates of the innovations can be constructed by

$$\hat{\epsilon}_t = X_t - f(t, X_{t-1}, X_{t-2}, \ldots, X_{t-p}, \hat{\epsilon}_{t-1}, \ldots, \hat{\epsilon}_{t-q})$$

Granger and Andersen [1978a] say that the model is invertible if $\lim_{t \to \infty} (\hat{\epsilon}_t - \epsilon_t) = 0$ so that, regardless of the choice of the initial innovation values, the innovation estimates eventually converge to the true values. Hallin [1980] suggests that a somewhat better definition is that the model is invertible if

$$\lim_{a \to -\infty} (\hat{\epsilon}_t - \epsilon_t) = 0$$

These two generalized definitions have no practical differences and are particularly useful for forecasting purposes from general models; see Chapter 10 for examples. They coincide with the previous definition for linear, time-invariant models.

4.9 Types of Forecasts

The only kind of forecast to have been considered in any detail in the earlier sections has been the point forecast, where a best estimate is made of the future value of some variable. It would often be very much better if a more sophisticated type of forecast were available, such as a confidence interval with the property that the probability that the true value would fall into this interval takes some specified value. However, unless one has a very long series of forecast errors or one is able to make a realistic assumption about the distribution of the errors, such confidence intervals are impossible to provide. An assumption of normality for the error distribution is an easy one to make and to use but it is less easy to justify. Frequently one does, in fact, resort to a normality assumption in order to produce confidence intervals, the hope being that the distribution of the forecast errors is sufficiently close to normal for the probability content of the intervals to be but little affected. Occasionally the decision maker or forecast consumer wants some other quantity to be forecast rather than the conditional mean. One may, for example, be considering returns on a portfolio of risky investments and be asked to forecast the probability that the return will be negative since this probability is associated with an interesting definition of risk, known as safety-first risk. It is not clear how one would do this without knowing the conditional distribution of future return given one's information set.

An apparently different type of forecasting situation is that for which forecasts are required, not for a single point in the future, but for a whole trace of future points. Thus, one may require a vector of point forecasts $f'_{n,j}$, $j = 1, \ldots, h$, for the variables X_{n+j}, $j = 1, \ldots, h$, based on some information set I_n. In fact it may be shown that if expected cost is of the form

$$C = E\left(\sum_{k, j} C_{kj}(X_{n+k} - f_{n, k})(X_{n+j} - f_{n, j}) \right)$$

where $\sum_{k, j} C_{kj} x_k x_j > 0$ for all x_k, x_j when not all x_j are zero, then the optimal vector or trace of forecasts is just the sequence of optimal forecasts $f_{n, k}$, $k = 1, \ldots, h$, derived in Section 4.3. It is important to have such a trace of forecasts when making a decision about when to take some action. An example would be a buyer of some commodity such as cocoa. He would need to have forecasts of future cocoa prices over some period so that he could decide when to make a purchase on the commodity market. Further, it is straightforward to show that if a forecast of a linear combination of future values $L = \sum_{h=1}^{H} l_h X_{n+h}$ is required, the optimal least-squares forecast is given by $\hat{L} = \sum_{h=1}^{H} l_h f_{n, h}$.

A much more difficult forecasting situation occurs when one attempts to answer a question of the form, When, if ever, will some event occur? Examples are, When will a competitor announce a new product or new advertising campaign? When will the Government change the official interest rate? or When will a specific household buy a new car? A question of this type, of particular importance to economists, is, When will the next turning point in the economy occur? Apart from the purely definitional problem of what exactly constitutes a real turning point, it is also rather difficult to invent a cost function that emphasizes a particular feature of the series rather than some other feature. These types of forecasts may be called timing forecasts and might be tackled using the theory of point processes (see Lewis [1972]).

A further type of forecast, which may be called an event forecast, occurs when one knows that an event will occur in the future but the outcome of the event needs forecasting. For example, a baby is to be born, but what will its sex be, or an election is to occur, but which candidate will win? The obvious problem with this situation is that the future event may be unique, so that the usually assumed flow of past information need not be available. Clearly some information has to be collected for a forecast to be made, such as chemical tests on the pregnant wife or an opinion poll on the voting public.

The existence of these types of forecasting situations, and many others that can be constructed, merely indicates the very particular case considered by the classical statistical forecasting theory, as outlined in this chapter. At least there is comfort in the fact that the classical theory deals with what is generally recognized as being the most important type of forecasting problem.

CHAPTER FIVE

PRACTICAL METHODS FOR UNIVARIATE TIME SERIES FORECASTING

Chief Witch *Yes, that's right.*
MacBeth *I understand you can foretell the future.*

BBC RADIO PROGRAM
June 1968

5.1 Introduction

In this chapter, the problem of analyzing the information yielded in a given realization $x_1, x_2, \ldots, x_n$ of a particular time series is further considered, with attention now focused on the problem of predicting future values of the series. In forming the forecasts, only current and past values of the series to be predicted will be employed and so, in the terminology of Chapter 4, the information set used is a rather restricted one. Forecasts based on this information set will be termed *univariate forecasts*. It may surprise the reader that we should devote so much space to univariate forecasting methods. After all, the quantity of available information in the universe is vast, and it would be reasonable to expect the forecaster to make use of all relevant information in assessing the future. Nevertheless, we feel that univariate time series forecasting methods deserve consideration for a number of reasons:

(i) They are quick and inexpensive to apply, and may well produce forecasts of sufficient quality for the purposes at hand. The cost of making particular forecasting errors should always be balanced against the cost of *producing* forecasts, for it is hardly worth expanding large resources to obtain a relatively small increase in forecast accuracy if the payoff, in terms of improved decision making, is likely to be only marginally beneficial.

(ii) Relevant extraneous information may be unavailable or available only at a prohibitively high cost.

(iii)   Univariate forecasting procedures can be useful as a yardstick against which the success or otherwise of more elaborate forecasting exercises can be judged. This point will be amplified in Chapter 9.

(iv)   Forecasts obtained in this manner can often be usefully combined with other forecasts in the production of a superior overall forecast, as will be seen in Chapter 9.

(v)   Having produced univariate forecasts, one is in a position to assess how much of the variation in a particular quantity can be explained in terms of its own past behavior, and so form a clearer picture of what particular behavior patterns require consideration of extraneous factors for their explanation. This point will be discussed further in Chapter 8, where multivariate time series forecasting methods are considered.

(vi)   For the vast majority of economic time series, the information considered here, while restrictive, *is* of great importance—a point all too often neglected in more traditional approaches to economic forecasting.

There exist a number of procedures, of varying degrees of complexity, whereby a time series can be forecast from its own current and past values. The more complex procedures do not produce forecasts either as quickly or as cheaply as do the simple ones, but it is to be expected that some compensation in terms of increased accuracy would obtain through their use since they allow for a more detailed investigation of the properties of the particular series under investigation. In the remainder of this chapter methods for univariate time series forecasting are outlined under three main headings: Box–Jenkins methods, exponential smoothing procedures, and stepwise autoregression. These procedures will be compared and contrasted and situations in which a particular approach is likely to prove valuable will be indicated.

5.2 Box–Jenkins Forecasting Methods

In Chapter 3 procedures for the fitting of autoregressive integrated moving average (ARIMA) models, and their seasonal variants, to a particular time series were described. It will be recalled that the fitting procedures consisted of an iterative cycle of identification, estimation, and diagnostic checking. Essentially a particular model is chosen from the general ARIMA class, its coefficients estimated, and its adequacy of representation checked, possibly leading to the choice of an alternative form and a repeat of the model building cycle. In this section, it will be shown how forecasts can be generated from the fitted models, using some of the theory developed in Chapter 4. The whole process of constructing an ARIMA model and the generation of forecasts from that model will be referred to as the Box–Jenkins forecasting method since, although a number of elements in the methodology were well known before these authors wrote, it is their contribution that has allowed an integrated and well-defined approach to time series forecasting via model building stimulating a good deal of practical application over a wide range of actual time series.

As a first step, a number of results derived in Chapter 4 are summarized.

(i)   Let X_t follow the stationary, invertible ARMA(p, q) process

$$X_t = \sum_{j=1}^{p} a_j X_{t-j} + \sum_{j=0}^{q} b_j \epsilon_{t-j}, \qquad b_0 = 1$$

Standing at time n, let $f_{n,h}$ be the forecast of X_{n+h} which has smallest expected squared error among the set of all possible forecasts which are linear in X_{n-j}, $j \geq 0$. Now write

$$X_{n+h} = \sum_{j=1}^{p} a_j X_{n+h-j} + \sum_{j=0}^{q} b_j \epsilon_{n+h-j}, \qquad b_0 = 1 \qquad (5.2.1)$$

Then a recurrence relation for the forecasts $f_{n,h}$ is obtained by replacing each element in (5.2.1) by its "forecast" at time n, as follows:

(a)   replace the unknown values X_{n+k} by their forecasts $f_{n,k}$ for $k > 0$;
(b)   "forecasts" of X_{n+k}, $k \leq 0$, are simply the known values x_{n+k};
(c)   since ϵ_t is white noise, the optimal forecast of ϵ_{n+k}, $k > 0$, is simply zero;
(d)   "forecasts" of ϵ_{n+k}, $k \leq 0$, are just the known values ϵ_{n+k}.

(ii)   The ARMA(p, q) process $a(B)X_t = b(B)\epsilon_t$ can be written as an infinite moving average $X_t = c(B)\epsilon_t$ where the elements of $c(B) = c_0 + c_1 B + c_2 B^2 + \cdots$ can be obtained by equating coefficients of B^j, $j = 1, 2, \ldots$, in $a(B)c(B) = b(B)$. Then the forecast errors are given by

$$e_{n,h} = X_{n+h} - f_{n,h} = \sum_{j=0}^{h-1} c_j \epsilon_{n+h-j} \qquad (5.2.2)$$

and hence the variances of the forecast errors are given by

$$V(h) = E\{e_{n,h}^2\} = \sigma_\epsilon^2 \sum_{j=0}^{h-1} c_j^2 \qquad (5.2.3)$$

(iii)   An "updating" formula for the forecasts is given by

$$f_{n,h} = f_{n-1,h+1} + c_h(X_n - f_{n-1,1}) \qquad (5.2.4)$$

These results hold for stationary time series. However, as was seen in Chapter 3, it is very often the case in dealing with economic time series that the integrated model is of importance. That is, for a particular process X_t, one may need to difference d times to produce a stationary series $Y_t = (1 - B)^d X_t$. In the case of seasonal time series, it is often the case that a multiplicative difference filter is required to produce stationarity. However, for the present purposes, this involves no new principle, and so for simplicity of exposition, attention will be restricted to the nonseasonal case. A sensible procedure, then, is to derive forecasts of the series X from those of the stationary series Y. Writing $f_{n,h}^x$ for forecasts of X and $f_{n,h}^y$ for forecasts of Y, an obvious formula for generating forecasts of X is then

$$f_{n,h}^y = (1 - B)^d f_{n,h}^x \qquad (5.2.5)$$

where here B operates on the index h, so that, for example, in the case $d = 1$,

$$f_{n,h}^x = f_{n,h-1}^x + f_{n,h}^y$$

Thus, forecasts could be obtained by a two-step procedure, where the stationary series Y is first forecast and then forecasts of X are obtained from (5.2.5). However, a moment's reflection should indicate that this is unnecessary. Write

$$(1 - A_1 B - A_2 B^2 - \cdots - A_P B^P) = a(B)(1 - B)^d$$

Then, corresponding to (5.2.1), one can write

$$X_{n+h} = \sum_{j=1}^{P} A_j X_{n+h-j} + \sum_{j=0}^{q} b_j \epsilon_{n+h-j}, \qquad b_0 = 1 \qquad (5.2.6)$$

and forecasts may be derived from this equation in the same way as in the stationary case.

Now, define $C(B) = 1 + C_1 B + C_2 B^2 + \cdots$ where

$$A(B)C(B) = b(B) \qquad (5.2.7)$$

Then it is clear that, corresponding to (5.2.2) and (5.2.3), the forecast errors in the integrated case are given by $e_{n,h} = \sum_{j=0}^{h-1} C_j \epsilon_{n+h-j}$, and hence the error variance is

$$V(h) = \sigma_\epsilon^2 \sum_{j=0}^{h-1} C_j^2, \qquad C_0 = 1 \qquad (5.2.8)$$

Further, the updating formula (5.2.4) is now given by

$$f_{n,h} = f_{n-1,h+1} + C_h(X_n - f_{n-1,1}) \qquad (5.2.9)$$

All the necessary equipment for the efficient computation of point forecasts from a fitted ARIMA model, or its seasonal variant, is now at hand. Further, since an expression for the variance of forecast error has been derived, it is possible, provided distributional assumptions are made, to derive interval forecasts. In the remainder of this section, practical procedures for the computation of these forecasts are outlined and the methods involved illustrated with a few specific examples.

Initial Calculation of Point Forecasts

Suppose now that one has a set of observations $x_1, x_2, \ldots, x_n$ on a process X, and that an ARIMA model has been fitted. Then forecasts of future values of the series can be obtained from (5.2.6), substituting in that equation forecasts of each individual term. The forecasting formula can then be written as

$$f_{n,h} = \sum_{j=1}^{P} A_j f_{n,h-j} + \sum_{j=0}^{q} b_j \hat{\epsilon}_{n+h-j}, \qquad b_0 = 1 \qquad (5.2.10)$$

where

$$f_{n,k} = x_{n+k}, \qquad k \leqslant 0$$
$$\hat{\epsilon}_{n+k} = 0, \qquad k > 0 \qquad (5.2.11)$$
$$= \text{estimate of } \epsilon_{n+k}, \qquad k \leqslant 0$$

Equations (5.2.11) require some further explanation. The theoretical development of Chapter 4 concerned the forecasting of X_{n+h} given X_{n-j}, $j \geqslant 0$. That is, it was assumed that an infinite past record of the series to be forecast was available, in which case ϵ_{n-j}, $j \geqslant 0$ would also be known. However in the practical situation, where only a finite run of data is available, the ϵ_{n-j} will not be known, but must be estimated.

In practice, we employ as estimates the residuals $\hat{\epsilon}_{n-j}$ from the fitted model. These residuals, which were also employed in Chapter 3 as the basis for checks on model adequacy, are routinely produced by model estimation programs.

Once a forecasting model has been estimated, the procedure for deriving point forecasts is then quite straightforward. Equation (5.2.10) is employed one step at a time for $h = 1, 2, 3, \ldots$, substituting appropriate values from (5.2.11). Hence, for $h = 1$, the forecast $f_{n,1}$ is obtained immediately from (5.2.10). Next, setting $h = 2$ in (5.2.10), the two-steps-ahead forecast $f_{n,2}$ is obtained using $f_{n,1}$, which has already been calculated. Forecasts can then be obtained as far ahead as is required. To illustrate these calculations, some of the examples introduced in Chapter 3 will be further considered.

EXAMPLE 1   In Sections 3.2 and 3.5, a series of 140 quarterly values of the ratio of consumer installment debt to personal income in the U.S. was examined. The fitted model was the ARIMA(1, 1, 0) process, with constant,

$$(1 - 0.74B)(1 - B)X_t = 0.021 + \epsilon_t \qquad (5.2.12)$$

Transforming this equation to the form of (5.2.10) yields the forecast generating formula

$$f_{n,h} = 0.021 + 1.74 f_{n,h-1} - 0.74 f_{n,h-2} + \hat{\epsilon}_{n+h} \qquad (5.2.13)$$

Now, for $h \geqslant 1$, no values of $\hat{\epsilon}_{n+k}$, $k \leqslant 0$, occur in (5.2.13). Thus, the calculation of point forecasts is particularly straightforward, since all that is

Table 5.1 *Some actual and predicted values for ratio of consumer installment debt to personal income*

h:	-1	0	1	2	3	4	5
$f_{n,h}$:	13.217	13.147	13.116	13.114	13.134	13.170	13.217
h:	6	7	8	9	10	11	12
$f_{n,h}$:	13.273	13.335	13.403	13.473	13.547	13.622	13.699

required are the two most recent values of the series. These, together with forecasts made up to twelve steps ahead, are shown in Table 5.1. Substituting $h = 1$ in (5.2.13) yields

$$f_{n,1} = 0.021 + 1.74 f_{n,0} - 0.74 f_{n,-1} + \hat{\epsilon}_{n+1}$$

Hence, from (5.2.11), using the known values $x_n = 13.147$ and $x_{n-1} = 13.217$ given in Table 5.1,

$$f_{n,1} = 0.021 + (1.74)(13.147) - (0.74)(13.217) = 13.1162$$

Again, from (5.2.13), the two-steps-ahead forecast is given by

$$f_{n,2} = 0.021 + (1.74)(13.1162) - (0.74)(13.147) = 13.11441$$

The first 12 forecasts, rounded to three decimal places, are given in Table 5.1.

EXAMPLE 2   As a second example, consider the series of U.S.–U.K. exchange rates. In Chapter 3 the ARIMA(1, 1, 1) model

$$(1 - 0.26B)(1 - B)X_t = (1 + 0.28B)\epsilon_t$$

was fitted to the given data. Hence, in the formulation (5.2.10), we have

$$f_{n,h} = 1.26 f_{n,h-1} - 0.26 f_{n,h-2} + \hat{\epsilon}_{n+h} + 0.28 \hat{\epsilon}_{n+h-1} \qquad (5.2.14)$$

All that is needed to calculate the forecasts are the last two observations, $x_n = 184.7$ and $x_{n-1} = 188.6$, together with the estimate $\hat{\epsilon}_n = -2.75$ obtained from the estimation stage of the model building procedure. Substituting $h = 1$ in (5.2.14) and using (5.2.11) yields

$$f_{n,1} = (1.26)(184.7) - (0.26)(188.6) - (0.28)(2.75) = 182.916$$

Similarly, substituting $h = 2$ in (5.2.14), it follows that

$$f_{n,2} = (1.26)(182.916) - (0.26)(184.7) = 182.4522$$

Forecasts for this series, made up to 12 steps ahead, are given rounded to one decimal place, in Table 5.2.

EXAMPLE 3   There is no difficulty in applying the forecast generating procedure to seasonal time series. To illustrate, consider again the data on construction begun in England and Wales, for which the fitted model was

$$(1 - B)(1 - B^4)X_t = (1 - 0.37B)(1 - 0.68B^4)\epsilon_t$$

Table 5.2   *Some actual and predicted values for U.S.–U.K. exchange rate*

h:	-1	0	1	2	3	4	5
$f_{n,h}$:	188.6	184.7	182.9	182.5	182.3	182.3	182.3
h:	6	7	8	9	10	11	12
$f_{n,h}$:	182.3	182.3	182.3	182.3	182.3	182.3	182.3

Table 5.3   *Quantities required for forecasting construction begun*

t:	$n-4$	$n-3$	$n-2$	$n-1$	n
x_t:	89966	89566	103912	95504	101191
$\hat{\varepsilon}_t$:	7211.12	10089.82	-10785.66	-7323.88	10804.23

Table 5.4   *Forecasts of construction begun series*

h:	1	2	3	4	5	6
$f_{h,h}$:	91747	115966	109824	106322	99596	123814
h:	7	8	9	10	11	12
$f_{n,h}$:	117673	114170	107444	131663	125522	122019

Transposing this to the form (5.2.10), it is seen that the forecast generating formula is given by

$$f_{n,h} = f_{n,h-1} + f_{n,h-4} - f_{n,h-5}$$
$$+ \hat{\varepsilon}_{n+h} - 0.37\hat{\varepsilon}_{n+h-1} - 0.68\hat{\varepsilon}_{n+h-4} + 0.2516\hat{\varepsilon}_{n+h-5} \quad (5.2.15)$$

Table 5.3 shows relevant quantities for the computation of the forecasts. Substituting $h = 1$ in (5.2.15) yields

$$f_{n,1} = 101191 + 89566 - 89966 - (0.37)(10804.23) - (0.68)(10089.82)$$
$$+ (0.2516)(7211.12) = 91746.68$$

The forecast two steps ahead is now obtained by substituting $h = 2$ in (5.2.15), so that

$$f_{n,2} = 91746.68 + 103912 - 89566 + (0.68)(10785.66)$$
$$+ (0.2516)(10089.82)$$
$$= 115965.52$$

Forecasts of this series made up to twelve quarters ahead are shown in Table 5.4.

Calculation of Interval Forecasts

While it is almost certainly the case that more attention is paid to point forecasts than to any others, it is generally worthwhile to calculate wherever possible confidence intervals associated with these forecasts, if only to provide an indication of their likely reliability. Now, the variance of the error of the point forecast is given by (5.2.8), where the C_j are defined in (5.2.7). In fact this is an *underestimate* of the true variance since it assumes that the coefficients of the forecasting model are known, whereas in fact they must be estimated leading to a corresponding decrease in accuracy in the resulting forecasts. However, for moderately long time series, this factor will be of relatively small importance.

In fact, our proposed procedure for estimating forecast error variance is a somewhat crude approximation for two reasons. We do not in fact know the infinite past of the time series, and the parameters of the model must be estimated. The quality of these estimates is examined in some detail by Ansley and Newbold [1981] who provide a modified estimate that tends to be somewhat more reliable, especially for relatively short seasonal time series. The details of this procedure are a little cumbersome and will not be discussed further here. For most general purposes it should prove adequate to substitute the parameter estimates in (5.2.8).

If, in addition, one is prepared to assume that the forecast errors come from a normal distribution, it is possible to derive, in an obvious way, confidence intervals for the forecasts. Thus an approximate 95% interval is given by

$$f_{n,h} \pm 1.96\hat{\sigma}_\epsilon \sqrt{\sum_{j=0}^{h-1} C_j^2} \qquad (5.2.16)$$

where $\hat{\sigma}_\epsilon$ is the estimated standard deviation of ϵ_t, obtained in estimating the coefficients of the fitted model. Similarly, approximate 75% intervals are given by

$$f_{n,h} \pm 1.15\hat{\sigma}_\epsilon \sqrt{\sum_{j=0}^{h-1} C_j^2} \qquad (5.2.17)$$

To illustrate, consider again the three examples just discussed.

EXAMPLE 1   For the series on the ratio of consumer installment debt to personal income the fitted model is (5.2.12). To determine the C_j of (5.2.8), note that (5.2.7) takes the form

$$(1 - 1.74B + 0.74B^2)(1 + C_1B + C_2B^2 + \cdots) = 1$$

Equating coefficients in B yields

$$C_1 - 1.74 = 0, \qquad C_1 = 1.74$$

Equating coefficients in B^2 yields

$$C_2 - 1.74C_1 + 0.74 = 0 \qquad \text{and hence} \quad C_2 = 2.2876$$

Table 5.5 *The C_j weights for ratio of consumer installment debt to personal income model*

j:	1	2	3	4	5	6	7	8	9	10	11
C_j:	1.74	2.29	2.69	2.99	3.21	3.38	3.50	3.59	3.66	3.71	3.74

Equating coefficients in B^3

$$C_3 - 1.74C_2 + 0.74C_1 = 0 \quad \text{and hence} \quad C_4 = 2.6928$$

Further values of the C_j are shown in Table 5.5.

Now, in estimating the model for this series, the estimated standard deviation of the errors was found to be $\hat{\sigma}_\epsilon = 0.115$. Thus, substituting the C_j of Table 5.5 and the forecasts of Table 5.1 into (5.2.16), it follows that for the one-step-ahead forecast a 95% confidence interval is given by

$$13.116 \pm (1.96)(0.115) = 13.116 \pm 0.225$$

and a 75% interval by

$$13.116 \pm (1.15)(0.115) = 13.116 \pm 0.132$$

Similarly, for the two-steps-ahead forecast the intervals are

95% interval: $\quad 13.114 \pm (1.96)(0.115)\sqrt{1 + (1.74)^2} = 13.114 \pm 0.452$

75% interval: $\quad 13.114 \pm (1.15)(0.115)\sqrt{1 + (1.74)^2} = 13.114 \pm 0.265$

Confidence intervals for the first twelve forecasts are given in Table 5.6, where, for purposes of illustration, the C_j weights used here and throughout this section are correct to two decimal places.

Table 5.6 *Confidence intervals for forecasts of ratio of consumer installment debt to personal income*

Quantity forecast	95% Interval	75% Interval
X_{n+1}	12.891–13.341	12.984–13.248
X_{n+2}	12.662–13.566	12.849–13.379
X_{n+3}	12.448–13.820	12.731–13.537
X_{n+4}	12.254–14.086	12.633–13.707
X_{n+5}	12.080–14.354	12.550–13.884
X_{n+6}	11.925–14.621	12.482–14.064
X_{n+7}	11.787–14.883	12.427–14.243
X_{n+8}	11.665–15.141	12.384–14.422
X_{n+9}	11.556–15.390	12.348–14.598
X_{n+10}	11.460–15.634	12.323–14.771
X_{n+11}	11.374–15.870	12.303–14.941
X_{n+12}	11.298–16.100	12.290–15.108

Table 5.7   *The C_j weights for U.S.–U.K. exchange rate model*

j:	1	2	3	4	5	6	7	8	9	10	11
C_j:	1.54	1.68	1.72	1.73	1.73	1.73	1.73	1.73	1.73	1.73	1.73

EXAMPLE 2   The model

$$(1 - 0.26B)(1 - B)X_t = (1 + 0.28B)\epsilon_t$$

fitted to the U.S.–U.K. exchange rate series may be written as

$$(1 - 1.26B + 0.26B^2)X_t = (1 + 0.28B)\epsilon_t$$

Thus from (5.2.7) it follows that the C_j weights may be found by equating coefficients in

$$(1 - 1.26B + 0.26B^2)(1 + C_1B + C_2B^2 + \cdots) = 1 + 0.28B$$

Equating coefficients in B yields

$$C_1 - 1.26 = 0.28, \qquad C_1 = 1.54$$

Equating coefficients in B^2 gives

$$C_2 - 1.26C_1 + 0.26 = 0, \qquad C_2 = 1.6804$$

Further values of the C_j are shown in Table 5.7.

The estimated standard deviation of the errors from the fitted model was found to be $\hat{\sigma}_\epsilon = 4.269$. Substituting the C_j of Table 5.7 and the forecasts of Table 5.2 into (5.2.16) and (5.2.17), interval forecasts can be obtained. Thus, for example, for the forecast of X_{n+5}, a 75% interval is given by

$$182.3 \pm (1.15)(4.269)\sqrt{1 + (1.54)^2 + (1.68)^2 + (1.72)^2 + (1.73)^2}$$

$$= 182.3 \pm 17.1$$

Confidence intervals for X_{n+j}, $j = 1, 2, \ldots, 12$, are given in Table 5.8.

EXAMPLE 3   As a final example, consider the quarterly seasonal series on construction begun in England and Wales, to which in Chapter 3 the model

$$(1 - B)(1 - B^4)X_t = (1 - 0.37B)(1 - 0.68B^4)\epsilon_t$$

was fitted. The C_j weights are then found, as usual, by equating coefficients of powers of B, from

$$(1 - B - B^4 + B^5)(1 + C_1B + C_2B^2 + \cdots)$$

$$= 1 - 0.37B - 0.68B^4 + 0.2516B^5$$

The weights are given in Table 5.9. The estimated standard deviation of the errors from the fitted model was $\hat{\sigma}_\epsilon = 8179$. Interval forecasts are obtained by substituting the C_j of Table 5.9 and the forecasts of Table 5.4 into (5.2.16)

Table 5.8   *Confidence intervals for forecasts of U.S.–U.K. exchange rate*

Quantity forecast	95% Interval	75% Interval
X_{n+1}	174.5–191.3	178.0–187.8
X_{n+2}	167.1–197.9	173.5–191.5
X_{n+3}	161.5–203.1	170.1–194.5
X_{n+4}	157.0–207.6	167.4–197.2
X_{n+5}	153.1–211.5	165.2–199.4
X_{n+6}	149.7–214.9	163.2–201.4
X_{n+7}	146.7–217.9	161.4–203.2
X_{n+8}	143.8–220.8	159.7–204.9
X_{n+9}	141.2–223.4	158.2–206.4
X_{n+10}	138.7–225.9	156.7–207.9
X_{n+11}	136.4–228.2	155.4–209.2
X_{n+12}	134.2–230.4	154.1–210.4

Table 5.9   *The C_j weights for construction begun model*

j:	0	1	2	3	4	5	6	7	8	9	10	11
C_j:	1	0.63	0.63	0.63	0.95	0.83	0.83	0.83	1.15	1.03	1.03	1.03

and (5.2.17). For example, a 95% interval for the forecast of X_{n+5} is given by

$$99596 \pm (1.96)(8179)\sqrt{1 + (0.63)^2 + (0.63)^2 + (0.63)^2 + (0.95)^2}$$
$$= 99596 \pm 16545$$

Confidence intervals for forecasts made up to twelve quarters ahead are shown in Table 5.10.

Table 5.10   *Confidence intervals for forecasts of construction begun in England and Wales*

Quantity forecast	95% Interval	75% Interval
X_{n+1}	75716–107778	82341–101153
X_{n+2}	97018–134914	104848–127084
X_{n+3}	88343–131305	97220–122428
X_{n+4}	82596–130048	92401–120243
X_{n+5}	71398–127794	83051–116141
X_{n+6}	92634–154994	105520–142108
X_{n+7}	83784–151562	97789–137557
X_{n+8}	77748–150592	92800–135540
X_{n+9}	66629–148259	83497–131391
X_{n+10}	87626–175700	105824–157502
X_{n+11}	78488–172556	97925–153119
X_{n+12}	72179–171859	92776–151262

Updating the Forecasts

Once a forecasting equation has been built, it is generally not necessary to refit a model when a new piece of data becomes available. Neither is it necessary to employ the rather lengthy procedures just described to recompute forecasts. A convenient algorithm, based on (5.2.9), is available for the updating of previously computed forecasts. Writing $n + 1$ for n in that expression, produces

$$f_{n+1,h} = f_{n,h+1} + C_h(X_{n+1} - f_{n,1}) \qquad (5.2.18)$$

where $X_{n+1} - f_{n,1} = \epsilon_{n+1}$ is the error made in forecasting X_{n+1} at time n. In words, the forecast of X_{n+1+h} made at time $n + 1$ can be obtained by adding to the forecast of the same quantity, made at time n, a multiple of the error made in forecasting X_{n+1} at time n. Further, the weights C_h required in this expression will already be known since they will have been calculated for the derivation of interval forecasts. The forecast generating mechanism can thus be viewed as an "error learning process." That is to say, forecasts of future values of the series are modified in the light of past forecasting errors. It is not, of course, necessary to recompute estimates of the widths of appropriate confidence intervals since the estimated variance for an h-step ahead forecast does not change when another observation becomes available.

To illustrate, consider once again the series on construction begun in England and Wales. The forecast of X_{n+1} made at time n was $f_{n,1} = 91747$. In fact, the actual value turned out to be $X_{n+1} = 86332$. Thus the point forecast turned out to be an overestimate (although, as can be seen from Table 5.10, the true value lies well within the 75% confidence interval.). The one-step ahead forecast error is

$$X_{n+1} - f_{n,1} = 86332 - 91747 = -5415$$

Thus, using (5.2.18), the forecasts of Table 5.4 can be updated by the formula

$$f_{n+1,h} = f_{n,h+1} - 5415C_h$$

where the C weights are those given in Table 5.9. Thus, for example, the revised forecast of X_{n+6} is

$$f_{n+1,5} = f_{n,6} - 5415C_5 = 123814 - (5415)(0.83) = 119320$$

The updated forecasts for this series are given in Table 5.11.

Table 5.11   *Updated forecasts of construction begun series*

h:	1	2	3	4	5	6
$f_{n+1,h}$:	112555	106413	102911	94452	119320	113179
h:	7	8	9	10	11	
$f_{n+1,h}$:	109676	101217	126086	119945	116502	

Forecast Errors as a Check for Change in Model Structure

If an ARIMA model has been fitted to a moderately long series of data, it is not necessary to go to the trouble of refitting the model each time a new piece of data becomes available. Rather, the originally estimated model can be retained and forecasts updated in the manner just described. However, this procedure would not be appropriate if the model structure were to change. If such a change is suspected, a check can be based on the forecast errors, following a proposal of Bhattacharyya and Andersen [1974] and Box and Tiao [1976].

Let $f_{n,h}$, $h = 1, 2, \ldots, H$ be forecasts of X_{n+h}, $h = 1, 2, \ldots, H$, all made at time n, with errors

$$e_{n,h} = X_{n+h} - f_{n,h}, \qquad h = 1, 2, \ldots, H$$

Then, assuming the model structure has remained unchanged,

$$E[e_{n,h}] = 0, \qquad h = 1, 2, \ldots, H$$

and, corresponding to (4.3.25),

$$E(e_{n,h}e_{n,h+k}) = \sigma_\epsilon^2 \sum_{j=0}^{h-1} C_j C_{j+k}, \qquad k \geqslant 0 \tag{5.2.19}$$

Now, let

$$E[e_{n,i}e_{n,j}] = \sigma_\epsilon^2 v_{ij}, \qquad i = 1, 2, \ldots, H, \quad j = 1, 2, \ldots, H$$

and $\mathbf{V}$ be the $H \times H$ matrix whose (i, j)th element is v_{ij}. Then, assuming normality of the forecast errors and an unchanged model structure, the quantity

$$Q = \sigma_\epsilon^{-2} \mathbf{e}'_H \mathbf{V}^{-1} \mathbf{e}_H \tag{5.2.20}$$

is distributed as χ^2 with H degree of freedom, where

$$\mathbf{e}'_H = (e_{n,1}, e_{n,2}, \ldots, e_{n,H})$$

Box and Tiao show that a computationally simpler, but equivalent, version of (5.2.20) is

$$Q = \sigma_\epsilon^{-2} \sum_{j=0}^{H-1} e_{n+j,1}^2 \tag{5.2.21}$$

where the $e_{n+j,1}$ are the one-step errors made at time $n + j$ ($j = 0, 1, \ldots, H - 1$).

Thus, the hypothesis of no change in model structure can be checked by computing (5.2.21), with the estimated error variance $\hat{\sigma}_\epsilon^2$ in place of the unknown σ_ϵ^2, and comparing with tabulated values of χ^2.

An Overview of the Box–Jenkins Method

We are now in a position to examine the whole framework of what has come to be called "the Box–Jenkins forecasting method." What is involved is first the definition of a class of models that might be thought to be capable of describing adequately the behavior of many practically occurring time series. The class of models considered is denoted as ARIMA, and a seasonal variant of this class can be introduced as appropriate. Next, for any given set of time series data, one attempts to fit a single ARIMA model, using the techniques described in Chapter 3. The model fitting framework is not sufficiently well defined to allow this to be done automatically. Rather it is necessary to employ judgment at various stages of the procedure, one's judgment being based on particular characteristics of the time series under study. The final stage is the computation of forecasts from the fitted model in the manner just described. Of course, as was seen in Chapter 4, if the time series actually were generated by the chosen model, the resulting forecasts would be the optimal linear forecasts of X_{n+h} given the information set X_{n-j}, $j \geq 0$, and, given further the Gaussian assumption, these forecasts would be optimum in the class of all forecasts based on that information set. However, it is not true, for three reasons, that the Box–Jenkins method will inevitably produce optimal forecasts. First, the class of models considered may be not include the true generating process. Second, in individual cases, the actual model chosen from the class may not be the true one. Third, since the coefficients of the chosen model must be estimated from a finite run of data, they will in practice differ with probability one from the unknown true values.

The Box–Jenkins method does, however, postulate a wide class of potential generating models and defines a strategy that, provided the true model lies within this class, should in general give one a very good chance of achieving a reasonable approximation to that model, provided a sufficiently long run of data is available. There are also a number of ways in which the range of possible models can be extended. For example, a deterministic trend component could be removed from the series prior to a Box–Jenkins analysis. Again, one might consider some instantaneous transformation $T(X_t)$ of the series as being generated by a linear ARIMA model, rather than simply the series itself. Further elaborations, to allow for more complex forms of nonlinearity or nonstationarity are also possible, but present rather more practical difficulties. These points will be discussed in more detail in Chapter 10.

In any forecasting exercise, consideration of the cost of generating forecasts is of great importance and should be balanced against the expected gains to be obtained from having fairly accurate forecasts. Of course, the question of costs is a relative one, and while it is true that for very many purposes the Box–Jenkins approach could not be regarded as prohibitively expensive, it is often the case (for example, in routine sales forecasting) that less expensive, albeit less versatile, methods are required. While, on the average, one would not expect these methods to achieve as high a degree of accuracy as does Box–Jenkins, they may well be sufficiently precise for the purpose at hand. In the next three sections fully automatic forecasting procedures of this kind will be discussed.

5.3 Exponential Smoothing Methods

In the industrial context is it often the case that forecasts of future sales of several thousand products are required for inventory control or production planning. Typically these forecasts are needed for the short term (perhaps up to a year or so ahead) on the basis of monthly data. A number of procedures, which can be grouped under the heading "exponential smoothing," have been developed to handle routine forecasting problems of this kind. The primary requirement here is for an approach that produces forecasts of sufficient accuracy, but which at the same time is quick and inexpensive to operate. Ideally the forecasting method should be fully automatic so as to reduce as far as possible the need for skilled manpower in its operation. Exponential smoothing methods fall into this category, and so retain a good deal of popularity in industrial forecasting in spite of their theoretical limitations when compared with the more sophisticated Box–Jenkins procedure. In this section a number of variants of exponential smoothing that are in current use will be described. Although these methods were developed from an essentially pragmatic viewpoint, it is useful in analyzing them to consider in what circumstances they might be optimal, or to ask what particular view is being taken of the world in embracing these procedures. A great danger in employing a fully automatic predictor is that rather poor forecasts might result unless one exercises some control over the quality of forecasts produced. To meet this need a number of automatic monitoring or tracking systems have been developed for use in conjunction with exponential smoothing procedures. These provide a check on the quality of forecasts produced and can be useful in the modification of inadequate forecasts.

In fact, a wide range of forecasting models can be derived as special cases of a technique, long familiar to engineers, known as Kalman filtering (see, e.g., Kalman [1960, 1963]). However, only a few commonly used exponential smoothing procedures will be considered here.

Forecasting Procedures Based on Exponential Smoothing

Suppose that the available data consist of a series of observations $x_1, x_2, \ldots, x_n$ and that it is required to forecast X_{n+h} for some positive integer h, and denote a forecast of this quantity by $f_{n,h}$. The earliest version of exponential smoothing, called "simple exponential smoothing," regards a time series as being made up locally of its level and a residual (unpredictable) element. It is thus required to estimate the current level of the series, that is, the level at time n. This will then be the forecast of all future values of the series since it represents the latest assessment available of the single (constant) predictable element of the time series. How might the level at time t be estimated using information available up to that time? If the available data consisted of a random sample, then the obvious thing to do would be to take a simple average of the observations. However, in the time series context it is reasonable to give most weight to the most recent observation, rather less weight to the preceding observation, and so on. One way to achieve this is to employ a weighted average, with geometrically (exponentially) declining weights, so that the level of the series at time t is estimated by

$$\bar{x}_t = \alpha x_t + \alpha(1-\alpha)x_{t-1} + \alpha(1-\alpha)^2 x_{t-2}$$

$$+ \alpha(1-\alpha)^3 x_{t-3} + \cdots, \qquad 0 < \alpha < 1 \qquad (5.3.1)$$

Substituting $t-1$ for t in this expression and multiplying through by $1-\alpha$ yields

$$(1-\alpha)\bar{x}_{t-1} = \alpha(1-\alpha)x_{t-1} + \alpha(1-\alpha)^2 x_{t-2} + \alpha(1-\alpha)^3 x_{t-3} + \cdots$$

Subtracting this from (5.3.1) then yields

$$\bar{x}_t = \alpha x_t + (1-\alpha)\bar{x}_{t-1}, \qquad 0 < \alpha < 1 \qquad (5.3.2)$$

Equation (5.3.2) represents the basic algorithm for simple exponential smoothing, replacing the original x_t series by a "smoothed" series $\bar{x}_t$. In order to employ the algorithm, it is necessary to make some "starting up" assumption, the simplest being to set $\bar{x}_1$ equal to x_1. Equation (5.3.2) can then be used recursively for $t = 2, 3, \ldots, n$, the transient introduced by the assumed starting value being of little importance in the determination of $\bar{x}_n$ unless n is small. The quantity α is termed the "smoothing constant," and appropriate choices of its value will be discussed later. The forecasts of all future values of the series are given simply by the latest available smooth value, so that

$$f_{n,h} = \bar{x}_n \qquad (5.3.3)$$

The estimation procedure implied by (5.3.2) can be regarded as an updating mechanism, so that at time t the previous estimate of level $\bar{x}_{t-1}$ is updated in light of the new observation x_t. The new estimate of level $\bar{x}_t$ is then a weighted average of x_t and $\bar{x}_{t-1}$.

It was noted earlier that exponential smoothing procedures have their most common application in routine sales forecasting, where forecasts of future sales of a large number of products might be required. In this context, formulations of the type (5.3.2) have a great advantage from a computational point of view, for they do not require the storage of all past values of a time series, for all that is needed is the most recent smoothed value $\bar{x}_{t-1}$ and the current observation x_t. This saving can be extremely important when many series must be handled at the same time.

In practice, this simple version of exponential smoothing is rarely employed. A number of variants, which regard a time series as consisting locally of level, trend, and (possibly) a seasonal factor in addition to the unpredictable residual element, have been developed. Perhaps the most logical extension of the simple exponential smoothing algorithm is the approach devised by Holt [1957] and Winters [1960]. Initially the case of a nonseasonal time series, which is made up locally of the sum of level, linear trend, and residual, will be considered. Denote the estimate of level at time t by $\bar{x}_t$ and of trend by T_t, where

$$\bar{x}_t = Ax_t + (1 - A)(\bar{x}_{t-1} + T_{t-1}), \qquad 0 < A < 1 \qquad (5.3.4)$$

and

$$T_t = C(\bar{x}_t - \bar{x}_{t-1}) + (1 - C)T_{t-1}, \qquad 0 < C < 1 \qquad (5.3.5)$$

The updating formulas (5.3.4) and (5.3.5), as in the case of simple exponential smoothing, modify previous estimates in the light of a new piece of data. Thus the estimate of level at time $t - 1$, $\bar{x}_{t-1}$, in conjunction with the trend estimate T_{t-1}, would suggest a level $\bar{x}_{t-1} + T_{t-1}$ for time t. This estimate is modified in light of the new observation x_t, according to (5.3.4). At time $t - 1$ trend is estimated by T_{t-1}, but given the new observation x_t an estimate of trend as the difference between the two most recent estimates of level is suggested. The trend estimate at time t is then a weighted average, given by (5.3.5), of the previous estimate and the evidence provided by the new piece of data. Again one needs to make some assumption about "starting up" values in order to employ Eqs. (5.3.4) and (5.3.5). Perhaps the simplest approach is to set T_2 equal to $x_2 - x_1$ and $\bar{x}_2$ equal to x_2. The equations can then be used recursively for $t = 3, 4, \ldots, n$ to calculate the estimates $\bar{x}_n$ and T_n. Forecasts of future values of the series are then given by

$$f_{n,h} = \bar{x}_n + hT_n \qquad (5.3.6)$$

Consider now a seasonal time series with period s (so that $s = 4$ for quarterly data and $s = 12$ for monthly data). The most commonly employed variant of the Holt–Winters method regards the seasonal factor F_t as being multiplicative (while trend remains additive) so that this quantity is estimated as

$$F_t = D(x_t/\bar{x}_t) + (1 - D)F_{t-s}, \qquad 0 < D < 1 \qquad (5.3.7)$$

(It is assumed that $x_t > 0$ for all t.) The level $\bar{x}_t$, which can be thought of as a "deseasonalized" level, is estimated now by

$$\bar{x}_t = A(x_t/F_{t-s}) + (1 - A)(\bar{x}_{t-1} + T_{t-1}), \qquad 0 < A < 1 \qquad (5.3.8)$$

The trend component is again estimated using (5.3.5). In order to employ Eqs. (5.3.5), (5.3.7), and (5.3.8) it is again necessary to specify "starting up" values. A very simple way to accomplish this is to take

$$F_j = x_j \bigg/ \left(\frac{1}{s} \sum_{k=1}^{s} x_k\right), \quad j = 1, 2, \ldots, s, \qquad \bar{x}_s = \frac{1}{s} \sum_{k=1}^{s} x_k, \quad \text{and} \quad T_s = 0$$

The three updating equations are then used recursively for $t = s + 1$, $s + 2, \ldots, n$. Since trend is taken to be additive and seasonality multiplicative, forecasts of future values are given by

$$f_{n,h} = (\bar{x}_n + hT_n)F_{n+h-s}, \qquad h = 1, 2, \ldots, s$$
$$= (\bar{x}_n + hT_n)F_{n+h-2s}, \qquad h = s+1, s+2, \ldots, 2s$$
$$\vdots \qquad\qquad\qquad (5.3.9)$$

The Holt–Winters approach can easily be modified to deal with situations in which the seasonal factor is thought to be additive rather than multiplicative. In this case Eqs. (5.3.7) and (5.3.8) are replaced by

$$F_t = D(x_t - \bar{x}_t) + (1 - D)F_{t-s}, \qquad 0 < D < 1 \qquad (5.3.10)$$

and

$$\bar{x}_t = A(x_t - F_{t-s}) + (1 - A)(\bar{x}_{t-1} + T_{t-1}), \qquad 0 < A < 1 \quad (5.3.11)$$

The forecasting equation (5.3.9) is now replaced by

$$f_{n,h} = \bar{x}_n + hT_n + F_{n+h-s}, \qquad h = 1, 2, \ldots, s$$
$$= \bar{x}_n + hT_n + F_{n+h-2s}, \qquad h = s+1, s+2, \ldots, 2s$$
$$\vdots$$

It remains only to discuss the choice of the smoothing constants A, C, and D employed in the Holt–Winters algorithms (and similarly the choice of α in the simple exponential smoothing formula (5.3.2)). Clearly, the lower the values of these constants the more steady will be the final forecasts since the use of low values implies that more weight is given to past observations and consequently any random fluctuations in the present will exert a less strong effect in the determination of the forecast. One possibility is to choose the smoothing constants according to one's assessment of the characteristics of the particular series under consideration. In general, the more random the series the lower the values of the optimal smoothing constants. If the smoothing constants are chosen in this way, considerable savings in storage and computation time can be effected, proving particularly valuable if many series are to be predicted simultaneously. A more objective approach, proposed by Holt and Winters themselves, is to select those values that would have best "forecast" the given observations. However, even here there remains an element of arbitrariness, for one must decide on a criterion of accuracy (cost of error function) for the forecasts and on how many steps ahead one is evaluating forecast accuracy. The most common procedure is to assume a quadratic cost function and to seek the smoothing constants that provide the best one-step ahead forecasts. The procedure is to choose a grid of possible values of A, C, and D, and to calculate the one-step ahead forecasts $f_{t,1}$, $t = m, m+1, \ldots, n-1$, for each set of values of the smoothing constants. That particular set for which the sum of squared errors

$$S = \sum_{t=m+1}^{n} (x_t - f_{t-1,1})^2$$

is smallest is then used to calculate actual forecasts of all future values of the series. The starting point m for this procedure is taken to be an integer ·sufficiently large as to allow the effects of the choice of initial "starting up" values to have died down. While this approach to the choice of smoothing constants adds greatly to the number of calculations required, it is very easily incorporated into a computer program and the forecast generating mechanism remains, of course, fully automatic. It should be added, however, that this approach also greatly increases storage of data requirements, and hence may not always be feasible.

An alternative procedure, known as general exponential smoothing, is due to Brown [1962]. Assume that locally the time series under study is the linear combination of k known deterministic functions of time, plus a residual, which for convenience can be written

$$x_i = \sum_{j=1}^{k} a_j f_j(i - t) + e_i, \qquad i = 1, 2, \ldots, t \qquad (5.3.12)$$

The k functions f_j are generally taken to be polynomials, exponentials, and mixtures of sine and cosine terms. The model (5.3.12) is assumed to hold only locally, so that a natural estimation procedure is to minimize the discounted sum of squared errors

$$S = \sum_{i=1}^{t} \beta^{t-i} \left(x_i - \sum_{j=1}^{k} a_j f_j(i - t) \right)^2, \qquad 0 < \beta < 1 \qquad (5.3.13)$$

Let

$$\mathbf{x} = \begin{bmatrix} x_1 \\ x_2 \\ \vdots \\ x_t \end{bmatrix}, \qquad \mathbf{a} = \begin{bmatrix} a_1 \\ a_2 \\ \vdots \\ a_k \end{bmatrix}$$

$$\mathbf{H} = \begin{bmatrix} f_1(1 - t) & f_2(1 - t) & \cdots & f_k(1 - t) \\ f_1(2 - t) & f_2(2 - t) & \cdots & f_k(2 - t) \\ \vdots & \vdots & & \\ f_1(0) & f_2(0) & \cdots & f_k(0) \end{bmatrix} = \begin{bmatrix} \mathbf{f}'(1 - t) \\ \mathbf{f}'(2 - t) \\ \vdots \\ \mathbf{f}'(0) \end{bmatrix}$$

$$W = \begin{bmatrix} \beta^{(t-1)/2} & & & \\ & \beta^{(t-2)/2} & & \mathbf{0} \\ & & \ddots & \\ \mathbf{0} & & & 1 \end{bmatrix}$$

The quantity to be minimized (5.3.13) is then

$$S = (\mathbf{Wx} - \mathbf{WHa})'(\mathbf{Wx} - \mathbf{WHa})$$

The minimum, obtained by differentiating with respect to a, occurs at the value given by

$$\hat{\mathbf{a}}(t) = (\mathbf{H'W'WH})^{-1}\mathbf{H'W'Wx}$$

where $\hat{\mathbf{a}}(t)$ is now a function of t. This can be written as

$$\hat{\mathbf{a}}(t) = \mathbf{F}^{-1}(t)\mathbf{g}(t) \qquad (5.3.14)$$

where

$$\mathbf{F}(t) = \mathbf{H'W'WH} = \sum_{i=1}^{t} \beta^{t-i}\mathbf{f}(i-t)\mathbf{f}'(i-t) \qquad (5.3.15)$$

and

$$\mathbf{g}(t) = \mathbf{H'W'Wx} = \sum_{i=1}^{t} \beta^{t-i}x_i\mathbf{f}(i-t) \qquad (5.3.16)$$

Now, it follows immediately from (5.3.15) that

$$\mathbf{F}(t) = \mathbf{F}(t-1) + \beta^{t-1}\mathbf{f}(1-t)\mathbf{f}'(1-t) \qquad (5.3.17)$$

Suppose, now, that there exists a nonsingular matrix $\mathbf{L}$ such that

$$\mathbf{f}(t) = \mathbf{L}\mathbf{f}(t-1)$$

for all values of t. This restriction is not too prohibitive since it allows any polynomial, exponential, and sinusoidal functions. From (5.3.16), it now follows that

$$\mathbf{g}(t) = \beta\mathbf{L}^{-1}\mathbf{g}(t-1) + \mathbf{f}(0)x_t \qquad (5.3.18)$$

Further, for functions that do not die out too quickly, it follows from (5.3.15) that, for moderately large t, $\mathbf{F}(t)$ will converge to some steady state matrix $\mathbf{F}$, so that $\mathbf{a}(t)$ can be written as

$$\mathbf{a}(t) = \mathbf{F}^{-1}\mathbf{g}(t)$$

Thus, the forecast of X_{n+h} is given by

$$f_{n,h} = \hat{\mathbf{a}}'(n)\mathbf{f}(h) \qquad \text{or} \qquad f_{n,h} = \mathbf{g}'(n)\mathbf{F}^{-1}\mathbf{f}(h)$$

where $\mathbf{g}(n)$ is calculated recursively from (5.3.18), the steady state matrix $\mathbf{F}$ is obtained by applying (5.3.17) recursively until convergence obtains and $\mathbf{f}(h)$ is a vector of known constants. It remains only to determine a value for the discount parameter β. This can be achieved either by visual inspection of the characteristics of the series under consideration or by optimizing over a grid of possible values, as for the Holt–Winters predictor. Brown suggests choosing β so that β^k lies in the range 0.75–0.95, the actual value used depending on the stability of the series, while Harrison [1965] proposes that a value in the neighborhood of $\beta^k = 0.8$ would frequently be appropriate. As before, savings in the storage of data result if the discount factor is chosen judgmentally.

Two particular problems should be mentioned with regard to general exponential smoothing. First, Reid [1969] notes that the errors from the fitted model are very often serially correlated, suggesting strongly that suboptimal forecasts will be produced. He suggests fitting a first-order autoregressive model (possibly estimated by discounted least-squares) to these residuals. Forecasts produced by the model may then be modified accordingly, and it was noted that substantial improvement in forecast performance very often results from such a procedure. The second difficulty concerns seasonal time series. In the first place it is difficult to know how many harmonics to fit, and a certain amount of experimentation may be required. Perhaps the best strategy would be to add further terms and test for an improvement in fit. Thus, Reid notes that for one of his series he first tried the model

$$X_t = a_1 + a_2 t + a_3 \cos\left(\frac{2\pi t}{12}\right) + a_4 \sin\left(\frac{2\pi t}{12}\right)$$

$$+ a_5 \cos\left(\frac{2\pi t}{6}\right) + a_6 \sin\left(\frac{2\pi t}{6}\right) \tag{5.3.19}$$

but that a better fit was achieved by adding

$$a_7 \cos\left(\frac{2\pi t}{4}\right) + a_8 \sin\left(\frac{2\pi t}{4}\right)$$

However, when large numbers of coefficients are to be fitted, estimation becomes less efficient, and Reid concludes that "it is normally desirable to keep the number of fitting functions as low as possible provided they still adequately describe the time series." A more serious objection, however, arises from the use in the Brown method of only a single smoothing parameter β. In order to estimate models like (5.3.19) with any precision, β should be fairly large so as to allow a fair number of data points to have appreciable weight, otherwise one is estimating with very few degrees of freedom. On the other hand one very often requires an exponential smoothing procedure to adapt very quickly so as to put most weight on the few most recent observations. These two mutually incompatible requirements should make one suspicious on a priori grounds of the performance of Brown's method for seasonal time series. Put rather bluntly, is it reasonable to expect the Brown predictor to do with a single parameter what requires three parameters for Holt–Winters?

Harrison [1965] has proposed modifications of both the Holt–Winters and the Brown predictors for dealing with seasonal time series. A difficulty with the Holt–Winters approach is that, according to (5.3.7), each seasonal factor is updated only once every year. Harrison's procedure, known as "seatrend," smooths the factors $F_t, F_{t-1}, \ldots, F_{t-s+1}$ by Fourier analysis. The Fourier coefficients are estimated by

$$a_k = \frac{1}{2s} \sum_{j=1}^{s} F_{t-s+j} \cos(ku_j)$$

$$b_k = \frac{1}{2s} \sum_{j=1}^{s} F_{t-s+j} \sin(ku_j), \qquad k = 1, 2, \ldots, \frac{s}{2}$$

where $u_j = [2(j-1)\pi/s] - \pi$. The amplitudes $(a_k^2 + b_k^2)^{1/2}$ are then tested for statistical significance, and smoothed seasonal estimates obtained as

$$\bar{F}_{t-s+j} = 1 + \sum_{\text{sig } k} (a_k \cos(ku_j) + b_k \sin(ku_j)), \qquad j = 1, 2, \ldots, s$$

where $\sum_{\text{sig } k}$ denotes summation over those harmonics for which statistically significant amplitudes were found. Forecasts can now be obtained by replacing F_t by $\bar{F}_t$ in (5.3.9). The approach can be made more "streamlined" by replacing F_{t-s} in (5.3.7) by $\bar{F}_{t-s}$ to obtain initial seasonal estimates for new observations. Harrison's second method, known as "doubts," constitutes a double application of Brown's procedure. At the first step the seasonal cycle is removed by applying a moving average, and the smoothed series is then predicted using a simple Brown trend model. Deviations of the observations about the trend are taken, and Brown's general exponential smoothing is applied to fit sine and cosine terms, representing the seasonal and the harmonics, to these deviations. Different smoothing parameters β can be applied at the two stages, thus avoiding the difficulty mentioned earlier.

Approximate confidence limits can be derived for forecasts based on exponential smoothing methods if one is prepared to make distributional assumptions. Typically it is assumed that the forecast errors are either normal or log normal, and hence confidence limits can be derived using the errors from the fitted model in the usual way.

Optimality of Exponential Smoothing

Up to this point, exponential smoothing predictors have been presented as rather ad hoc, though intuitively reasonable, forecast generating mechanisms. Their theoretical justifications will now be examined and, in particular, an attempt will be made to find the stochastic processes for which these predictors are optimal. Since it is the generating stochastic process that is of interest, X_t will be written for x_t in the following derivations.

Consider the Holt–Winters seasonal predictor in its additive form. This can be written as

$$\bar{X}_t = A(X_t - F_{t-s}) + (1 - A)(\bar{X}_{t-1} + T_{t-1})$$
$$T_t = C(\bar{X}_t - \bar{X}_{t-1}) + (1 - C)T_{t-1} \qquad (5.3.20)$$
$$F_t = D(X_t - \bar{X}_t) + (1 - D)F_{t-s}$$

Denote the one-step ahead forecast of X_t by $f_t \equiv f_{t-1,1}$. Then

$$f_t = \overline{X}_{t-1} + T_{t-1} + F_{t-s}$$

and the forecast error is

$$e_t \equiv e_{t-1,1} = X_t - f_t = X_t - (\overline{X}_{t-1} + T_{t-1} + F_{t-s}) \qquad (5.3.21)$$

Now, from (5.3.20),

$$\overline{X}_t - \overline{X}_{t-1} = T_{t-1} + A(X_t - \overline{X}_{t-1} - T_{t-1} - F_{t-s})$$

and so by (5.3.21)

$$\overline{X}_t - \overline{X}_{t-1} = T_{t-1} + Ae_t \qquad (5.3.22)$$

Again, from (5.3.20), for the trend term

$$T_t - T_{t-1} = C(\overline{X}_t - \overline{X}_{t-1}) - CT_{t-1}$$

and hence, from (5.3.22),

$$T_t - T_{t-1} = ACe_t \qquad (5.3.23)$$

For the seasonal factor, it follows from (5.3.20) that

$$F_t - F_{t-s} = D(X_t - \overline{X}_t - F_{t-s})$$

or, by (5.3.22),

$$F_t - F_{t-s} = D(X_t - \overline{X}_{t-1} - T_{t-1} - F_{t-s} - Ae_t)$$

and so, from (5.3.21),

$$F_t - F_{t-s} = (1 - A)De_t \qquad (5.3.24)$$

Now, introducing the back-shift operator B, it follows from (5.3.22) and (5.3.23) that

$$(1 - B)^2 \overline{X}_t = A[1 - (1 - C)B]e_t \qquad (5.3.25)$$

and from (5.3.23) and (5.3.24) that

$$(1 - B)T_t = ACe_t \qquad (5.3.26)$$

and

$$(1 - B^s)F_t = (1 - A)De_t \qquad (5.3.27)$$

Combining (5.3.25), (5.3.26), and (5.3.27) yields

$$(1 - B)^2(1 - B^s)(\overline{X}_{t-1} + T_{t-1} + F_{t-s})$$
$$= \left[AB(1 - B^s)[1 - (1 - C)B] + ACB(1 - B)(1 - B^s) \right.$$
$$\left. + (1 - A)DB^s(1 - B)^2 \right]e_t$$

Then, from (5.3.21),

$$(1 - B)^2(1 - B^s)X_t = \left[(1 - B)^2(1 - B^s) + AB(1 - B^s)[1 - (1 - C)B] \right.$$
$$\left. + ACB(1 - B)(1 - B^s) + (1 - A)DB^s(1 - B)^2 \right]e_t$$

Now, if the forecasts are optimal, the errors e_t will constitute a white noise process ϵ_t. Thus, if the Holt–Winters additive seasonal predictor is to produce optimal forecasts, it follows that the series X_t must be generated by a process of the form

$$(1 - B)^2(1 - B^s)X_t = (1 + b_1B + b_2B^2 + b_sB^s + b_{s+1}B^{s+1} + b_{s+2}B^{s+2})\epsilon_t$$

where the five coefficients b_1, b_2, b_s, b_{s+1}, and b_{s+2} are all functions of the three smoothing constants A, C, and D. Thus, use of this exponential smoothing predictor is optimal for a process generated by a particular member of the class of seasonal models considered by Box and Jenkins.

One can show in the same fashion that the simple exponential smoothing predictor derived from

$$\overline{X}_t = \alpha X_t + (1 - \alpha)\overline{X}_{t-1}, \qquad 0 < \alpha < 1 \qquad (5.3.28)$$

is optimal if and only if X_t is generated by the ARIMA(0, 1, 1) process $(1 - B)X_t = [1 - (1 - \alpha)B]\epsilon_t$, as was originally shown by Muth [1960].

Similarly for the Holt–Winters nonseasonal predictor generated by

$$\overline{X}_t = AX_t + (1 - A)(\overline{X}_{t-1} + T_{t-1}), \qquad T_t = C(\overline{X}_t - \overline{X}_{t-1}) + (1 - C)T_{t-1}$$
$$(5.3.29)$$

it is straightforward to show that optimality of forecasts implies that X_t is generated by an ARIMA(0, 2, 2) process. This was demonstrated by Harrison [1967], who further showed that (5.3.28) and (5.3.29) are special cases of an early predictor introduced by Box and Jenkins [1962], which itself yielded optimal forecasts only if X_t was generated by an ARIMA(0, k, k) process.

Recently, Cogger [1974] has considered the nonseasonal Brown predictor, obtained by estimating a polynomial in time of degree m, showing that optimality of this predictor implies that the underlying process is generated by an ARIMA(0, $m + 1$, $m + 1$) model. In fact, optimality requires a very specific subclass of these models since all the moving average parameters must be functions of the single discount coefficient β of (5.3.13). This point is discussed further in Ledolter and Box [1978].

An alternative justification for the use of exponential smoothing predictions—in terms of their optimality for certain generating models—is considered by Theil and Wage [1964], Nerlove and Wage [1964], and Harrison [1967]. A particularly simple model might regard the actual value at time t, X_t, as the sum of a "true value" X_t^* and a white noise error $\epsilon_{1,t}$. Further, the true value might be updated from one time period to the next according to a random walk. A plausible generating mechanism then might be

$$X_t = X_t^* + \epsilon_{1,t}, \qquad X_t^* = X_{t-1}^* + \epsilon_{2,t}$$

where $\epsilon_{1,t}$ and $\epsilon_{2,t}$ are independent white noise processes. It can be shown that the simple exponential smoothing procedure (5.3.28), with α determined by the ratio of variances of the white noise processes, produces optimal forecasts for this model. An elaboration of this simple model allows for linear growth in the "true values" of the series, so that a trend term T_t^* is added to the updating equation. If, further, the trend term is taken to be a random walk, a plausible model could be

$$X_t = X_t^* + \epsilon_{1,t}, \qquad X_t^* = X_{t-1}^* + T_t^* + \epsilon_{2,t}, \qquad T_t^* = T_{t-1}^* + \epsilon_{3,t}$$

$$(5.3.30)$$

where $\epsilon_{1,t}$, $\epsilon_{2,t}$, and $\epsilon_{3,t}$ are independent white noise processes. It can be shown that the Holt–Winters nonseasonal approach (5.3.29), with A and C determined by the relative variances of the white noise processes, produces optimal forecasts for this model.

Monitoring Forecast Performance

The great virtue of exponential smoothing for routine sales forecasting is, as previously noted, that it allows forecasts of a large number of series to be generated rapidly and inexpensively. However, as has been shown, particular exponential smoothing methods are optimal only for corresponding underlying stochastic processes, which in many cases are simply subsets of the general class of models considered in a Box–Jenkins analysis. Furthermore, if the true generating process is different from that implicitly assumed, the forecasts produced could be very far from optimal. Thus, in spite of its great convenience, exponential smoothing should be treated with a degree of caution. It would be particularly valuable to have a check on forecast performance, which was itself fully automatic, so that forecasts could be produced routinely until an indication is given that a built-in safeguard in the system has been violated. The forecaster may then devote his attention to those few time series that are causing difficulty, while forecasts of the remaining series continue to be generated in the usual routine manner.

An early proposal in this context is due to Harrison and Davies [1964] who suggest the use of cumulative sum (cusum) techniques for the control of routine forecasts. Let f_t be a (one-step ahead) forecast of X_t with error e_t. Then, if the system begins to produce forecasts for time $t = 1$, the cumulative sums of the forecast errors are

$$C_1 = e_1, \qquad C_j = C_{j-1} + e_j, \qquad j = 2, 3, \dots$$

These cumulative sums when plotted on a chart—called a cusum chart—can be expected to indicate any tendency toward bias in the forecasts. Harrison and Davies suggest a backward sequential test procedure, based on the sum of the most recent forecast errors, so that one defines at time t

$$S_1 = e_t = C_t - C_{t-1}$$
$$S_2 = e_t + e_{t-1} = C_t - C_{t-2}$$
$$\vdots$$
$$S_k = e_t + e_{t-1} + \cdots + e_{t-k+1} = C_t - C_{t-k}$$

The values S_i are calculated as each new observation occurs and are tested against corresponding control limits $\pm L_i$. If a limit is broken, lack of control is signaled. However, in short term forecasting applications, Harrison and Davies note that "the cusum scheme does not, in general, provide more than a vague indication of the way in which the forecasting scheme needs to be adjusted . . . ." Harrison and Davies show that, if the magnitude of the limits L_i is a linear function of the number of observations comprising the sum to be tested, considerable simplification in terms of storage of information is achieved. They suggest that if the forecast errors are independent, appropriate limits can be found through a nomogram of Ewan and Kemp [1960]. Alternatively, appropriate values can be derived by simulation.

An alternative proposal, due to Trigg [1964], computes a "tracking signal" as the ratio of an exponentially weighted estimate of mean error and an exponentially weighted estimate of mean absolute error. Denote the "smoothed error" at time t by E_t, where

$$E_t = \gamma e_t + (1 - \gamma)E_{t-1}, \qquad 0 < \gamma < 1 \qquad (5.3.31)$$

and the "mean absolute deviation" by D_t, where $D_t = \gamma|e_t| + (1 - \gamma)D_{t-1}$. Then at time t, tracking signal = E_t/D_t, and $-1 \leqslant$ tracking signal $\leqslant 1$. The distribution of this quantity is extremely difficult to find since the numerator and denominator are correlated with one another. As an approximation, note that it is well known that, for a wide range of distributions, the standard deviation is approximately equal to 1.2 times the mean absolute deviation. Further, if the available sample is moderately large and γ is taken to be quite small, D_t can be taken as a close approximation to the true population mean absolute deviation. Then

$$\sigma_e \approx 1.2 D_t \qquad (5.3.32)$$

where σ_e is the standard deviation of the error series. Now, from (5.3.31), one can write

$$E_t = \sum_{j=0}^{\infty} \gamma(1 - \gamma)^j e_{t-j}$$

and so, on the assumption that the errors are uncorrelated,

$$\text{Var}(E_t) = \sigma_e^2 \gamma^2 \sum_{j=0}^{\infty} (1 - \gamma)^{2j} = \frac{\sigma_e^2 \gamma}{2 - \gamma}$$

Thus, from (5.3.32), the standard error of the tracking signal is approximately equal to $1.2\gamma/\sqrt{(2\gamma - \gamma^2)}$. Two standard error limits are thus given by

$$\pm 2.4\gamma/\sqrt{(2\gamma - \gamma^2)} \qquad (5.3.33)$$

Trigg derives the cumulative distribution of the tracking signal by simulation (assuming a normal distribution for the errors) and it emerges that for γ equal to 0.1—the value recommended by Trigg as being suitable for most general purposes—(5.3.33) provides a good approximation for a 5% level test. However, the validity of the test does rest crucially on the assumption that the forecasting mechanism is producing errors that are not serially correlated—an assumption that is frequently violated by exponential smoothing predictors. This point is demonstrated in a particular case by Batty [1969]. In a later paper, Trigg and Leach [1967] propose that the tracking signal be employed to modify exponential smoothing systems. Consider the simple exponential smoothing system defined by

$$\overline{X}_t = \alpha X_t + (1 - \alpha) \overline{X}_{t-1}$$

They note that the simplest way to modify a system which has "gone out of control" is to increase the value of the smoothing constant α, so as to give more weight to recent observations, and propose to choose this constant so that α = modulus of tracking signal. They also suggest extending this technique to deal with the modification of forecasts generated by other members of Brown's generalized exponential smoothing family of functions.

A more thorough approach to the problem of changing structure in a given time series is due to Harrison and Stevens [1971]. The model (5.3.30) can be modified to take account of a seasonal factor F_t^* by writing

$$X_t = X_t^* F_t^* + \epsilon_{1,t}, \qquad X_t^* = X_{t-1}^* + T_t^* + \epsilon_{2,t}, \qquad T_t^* = T_{t-1}^* + \epsilon_{3,t}$$

where $\epsilon_{1,t}$, $\epsilon_{2,t}$, and $\epsilon_{3,t}$ have respective variances σ_1^2, σ_2^2, and σ_3^2. Harrison and Stevens envisage the system generating the time series as being in one of four possible states, which may be characterized as follows:

(i) The steady state or no change state—that is, level and trend remain constant. In this situation one would have σ_1^2 taking a "normal" value with σ_2^2 and σ_3^2 being zero.

(ii) A step change, where the series changes level at a particular point. For this case σ_1^2 takes a "normal" value, σ_2^2 is large, and σ_3^2 is zero.

(iii) A slope change at some point in the system. This would imply a "normal" value for σ_1^2, a value zero for σ_2^2, and a large value for σ_3^2.

(iv) A transient, or outlier, in the system. In this case, σ_1^2 assumes a "large" value, while σ_2^2 and σ_3^2 are zero.

Given initial global probabilities of the four states, these are modified in light of data via Bayes' theorem and estimates of the expected level and slope corresponding to each state are calculated. (Seasonal factors are generally treated outside the system.) Thus forecasts are calculated, not on the basis of an assumption that the system is in one particular state, but rather through the use of estimates derived relative to all four states. The weights given to each of these estimates depend on the estimated probabilities of the system being in each particular state. Harrison and Stevens discuss the practical implementation of a forecasting system along these lines and give an example in which, for generated data, the system performs very well in the presence of the four states described.

Further discussion of exponential smoothing is provided by Gardner [1985].

5.4 Stepwise Autoregression

The basic exponential smoothing procedures discussed in the previous section generally postulate a single model from which forecasts are to be generated, and thus do not possess the great virtue of the Box–Jenkins approach, whereby the eventual form of the forecast function is dictated, through the processes of identification and diagnostic checking, by the data itself. Of course, there is some room for experimentation within Brown's generalized exponential smoothing framework, but even here there does not exist any clear-cut identification procedure. (In addition, the restriction to a single parameter renders this approach overly parsimonious in many situations.) The identification and diagnostic checking phases of the Box–Jenkins cycle require manual intervention, however, and it would be desirable for some routine forecasting purposes to eliminate such a requirement. A compromise might be achieved through the design of a forecasting procedure which, while remaining fully automatic, contained a mechanism for discriminating among various possible forms of forecast function. That is, one would like a system to contain an identification procedure which was itself fully automatic. One method for achieving this, briefly introduced by Newbold and Granger [1974], is via stepwise autoregression. The objective is to construct autoregressive models to describe the behavior of given time series. However, for economic data, it is preferable, for reasons discussed in Chapters 2 and 3, to work with changes $Y_t = X_t - X_{t-1}$ rather than with levels of the series. Consider, now, the general kth order autoregressive model

$$Y_t = \sum_{j=1}^{k} a_j Y_{t-j} + \epsilon_t \tag{5.4.1}$$

Typically, models of the form (5.4.1) can, as has been seen, easily be fitted to a given set of data. However, unless k is taken to be quite small, it is likely that the resulting model will be overparametrized. One way out of this dilemma is to employ the technique of stepwise regression. This has been studied in great detail by Payne [1973], and the treatment given here depends heavily on Payne's work.

One way to proceed is to first select the value Y_{t-j} which, on the criterion of residual sum of squares, contributes most toward "explaining" Y_t. At the second step, the lagged value that most improves the fit of the regression equation obtained at step one is added, and so on until addition of further variables produces no significant improvement in the fit of the regression. Variables, entered at an earlier stage, which cease to contribute significantly, can be dropped. An alternative, favored by Payne on the basis of his experience with a number of simulation experiments, is to proceed in the reverse direction, having initially fitted the complete model (5.4.1). At the first step, the lagged-value contributing least to overall explanation of Y_t is dropped from the regression. At the second step the lagged value that contributes least in the model so achieved is dropped, and so on until deletion of further terms significantly worsens the fit of the regression equation. Variables, dropped at an earlier stage, can later be added if doing so would produce a significant improvement in the fit of the achieved regression. The procedure is set out schematically in Fig. 5.1. One might also include a constant term in the formulation (5.4.1). The constant could be treated as any other variable within the stepwise framework, or alternatively

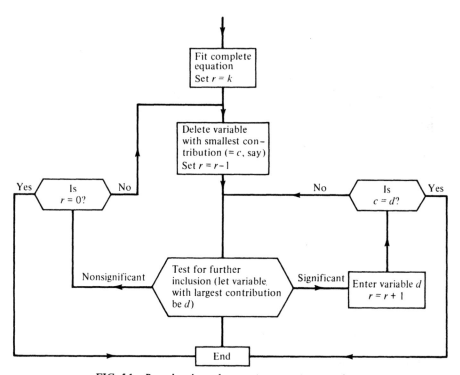

FIG. 5.1   *Payne's scheme for stepwise regression procedure.*

a decision as to its inclusion or exclusion could be made on purely subjective grounds.

Having decided to undertake the fitting of an autoregressive model by stepwise regression methods, three decisions must be taken:

(i)   A value k for the maximum permitted lag in (5.4.1) must be chosen.

(ii)   A significance level for testing for inclusion or exclusion of further variables must be decided upon.

(iii)   An appropriate hypothesis test to determine suitable stopping rules needs to be determined.

Choice of the maximum contemplated lag k is likely to be dictated in part by the nature of the time series under study and by the amount of data available. Our experience indicates that for all nonseasonal series, for quarterly seasonal series and shorter monthly seasonal series, a value $k = 13$ is generally adequate. For longer monthly seasonal time series, a value $k = 25$ is preferable. The question of choosing a suitable significance level for testing variable inclusion or exclusion is by no means a trivial one from a theoretical viewpoint. Looked at in this light, it might be desirable to reflect in one's choice preconceived notions as to how simple a model (in terms of number of parameters) is likely to provide reasonable forecasts. It is possible that one would like the significance level to vary according to how many lagged values have already been included in the model. Nothwithstanding these considerations, however, we have found use of a constant 5% level to be adequate (in terms of forecasting accuracy of the resulting model) for most general purposes.

Testing of hypotheses presents one critical difficulty. Suppose that a stage has been reached where r terms are included in the regression. Clearly if each of the remaining $k - r$ terms was tested for further inclusion at the 5% level, the probability of finding at least one term that apparently significantly improved the fit would be greater than 0.05 even if the true associated coefficient values were also zero. Payne suggests a number of procedures for overcoming this problem, and prefers use of the statistic

$$F' = \frac{m - r}{k - r} \frac{V_r}{V_k} - \frac{m - k}{k - r}$$

where

$$V_j = \frac{\text{residual sum of squares when } j \text{ terms are included in the regression}}{m - j}$$

and m is the effective number of observations for regression, so that if the original sample is $x_1, \ldots, x_n$, one observation is "lost" by differencing and a further k by formulation of the autoregressive model (5.4.1), so that $m = n - k - 1$. Under the null hypothesis that the coefficients on the excluded variables are all zero, the statistic F' is distributed approximately as Fisher's

F with $k - r$ and $m - k$ degrees of freedom. (One is justified asymptotically in employing the usual normal theory regression tests in the context of autoregressive models as a result of Mann and Wald [1943].)

Stepwise autoregression, then, would appear to provide a reasonable alternative to exponential smoothing as a fully automatic forecasting technique. Its great advantage lies in the wide class of models contemplated, together with a built-in identification structure. Calculation of forecasts from the fitted model is straightforward along the lines described in Section 5.2.

5.5 A Fully Automatic Forecasting Procedure Based on the Combination of Forecasts

While either an exponential smoothing predictor or stepwise autoregression might produce optimal or near-optimal forecasts for particular underlying stochastic models, neither procedure can be expected to do so over the whole range of models likely to occur in practice. Given that both procedures may frequently produce suboptimal forecasts, it is worthwhile to attempt to improve the resulting predictions.

Let $F_{1,t}$ be a forecast of X_t based on an exponential smoothing predictor and let $F_{2,t}$ be a forecast of the same quantity derived through stepwise autoregression. Rather than restrict attention to just one of the forecasts, it might be profitable to consider the combined forecast $C_t = k_t F_{1,t} + (1 - k_t)F_{2,t}$ which is simply a weighted average of the two individual forecasts. The subscript on the weight k_t indicates that the appropriate weight for combining may vary through time. Although the computation of the predictor advocated here is quite lengthy, the forecasting procedure remains fully automatic since a single computer program can be written to generate forecasts without manual intervention. Thus calculation of the combined exponential smoothing—stepwise autoregressive predictor is quicker than that of the Box–Jenkins and requires less use of skilled manpower. The idea of combining individual forecasts in the production of an overall forecast was introduced by Bates and Granger [1969]. This concept will be discussed in more detail in Chapter 9, where appropriate choices of combining weights will be considered, and practical experience with the procedure surveyed.

5.6 Comparison of Univariate Forecasting Procedures

Given the availability of so many univariate forecasting techniques, it is natural to attempt to assess their relative worth and to try to come to some conclusion as to which methods are most likely to be successful in particular situations. In our view questions of this kind cannot be usefully answered through abstract consideration of the characteristics of the various procedures, but rather must be attacked through examination of the forecasting methods in action. The only reasonable test would seem to be an evaluation of forecast accuracy when the techniques are applied to "real" data in order to calculate "real" forecasts. This can be achieved by taking a particular time series and dividing it into two parts. A forecasting model is built, using only data in the first part of the series, and this is used to calculate "forecasts" of the known values in the second part, thus allowing forecast accuracy to be assessed. Comparison of forecast performance of the various techniques over a large number of time series should then give an indication of their relative worth, as well as of their various strengths and weaknesses. Of course, since it is impossible to draw a random sample of all time series, or of all economic time series, it will not be possible to make well-defined probabilistic conclusions in the usual hypothesis testing fashion. However, such an exercise is likely to yield valuable insights, although the conclusions drawn must retain an element of subjectivity. It remains only to decide on a standard for assessing forecast accuracy, and here we employ the criterion of mean squared error, although, as noted in Chapter 4, other cost functions may on occasion be appropriate.

Of course, assessment of forecast accuracy is only one side of the coin since strictly speaking this ought to be balanced against the cost of generating the forecasts. The question of cost is indeed very complex, but one on which we have very little to say. A priori, it would be reasonable to expect generation of Box–Jenkins forecasts to be more costly than that of exponential smoothing forecasts. However, the relative costs of the various procedures will depend crucially on the resources of the user and also on his requirements—for example, a computer program that is to be used many times will have a relatively low average cost per job, but might still be prohibitively expensive for a situation where only a few runs are required. Thus, while recognizing the importance of cost considerations, we can think of no general way to evaluate them, and so in the remainder of this section discussion is limited to evaluation of forecast accuracy.

The earliest exercise of any reasonable size attempting to assess the relative merits of univariate predictors on real data was carried out by Wagle *et al.* [1968]. These authors examined the application of four procedures— Holt–Winters, Harrison's seatrend. Brown's multiple smoothing, and a simple linear regression on time—to sales of 20 products. They found Holt–Winters to be best 14 times, seatrend twice, and Brown's approach 4 times. Unfortunately very little detail is given in their report of this study, and in particular it is difficult to assess whether the series under consideration afforded a sufficient variety of characteristics as to make a fair comparison possible.

A much larger study, by Reid [1969], allowed for the first time a comparison of the performance of Box–Jenkins and various exponential smoothing predictors over a large set of real data. Reid assembled a collection of 113 macroeconomic time series and generated forecasts, employing methods he deemed reasonable, to each series. Both the Box–Jenkins and Brown's generalized exponential smoothing predictors were applied to every series in the collection, Holt–Winters was applied to 69 series, and Harrison's seatrend to 47. The Brown predictor modified to take account of the possibility of first-order autoregression in the one-step forecast errors was also evaluated. Reid found for one-step ahead prediction, Box–Jenkins outperformed Brown's method on 88% of occasions, outperformed Holt–Winters 70%, and Harrison 77% of the time. Brown did better than modified Brown 24% of the time, better than Holt–Winters 20%, and better than Harrison 15% of occasions. Modified Brown forecast better than Holt–Winters and Harrison on 28 and 21% of occasions respectively, while Holt–Winters outperformed Harrison on 43% of occasions. Reid noted the large number of labor statistics in his collection tended to bias these results somewhat in favor of the Harrison approach. Reid also noted a tendency for Box–Jenkins to lose some of its advantage over exponential smoothing methods when forecasts over longer lead times are considered. This probably results from the fact that, while the past history of a typical nonseasonal economic time series may well contain valuable information about the next change, it is less likely to do so about subsequent changes. Thus, as one attempts to forecast further ahead, the substantive content in an efficient predictor becomes swamped by the element of uncertainty about distant future changes.

In a further large study, Newbold and Granger [1974] analyzed a collection of 106 time series, 80 of which were monthly and 26 quarterly. The collection included both seasonal and nonseasonal macroeconomic series and micro sales data. The Box–Jenkins, Holt–Winters, and stepwise autoregression methods were applied to every series in the collection. The stepwise autoregression program used in this study employed an arbitrary F ratio of 4.0 to determine whether or not a variable should be added to or dropped from a regression. Subsequently, Payne [1973] has reanalyzed many of the series in this collection, using the superior cutoff criterion described in Section 5.4. He achieved one-step ahead forecasts which, on average, were slightly superior to those obtained in this study. Table 5.12 shows the

Table 5.12 *Comparison of Box–Jenkins (B–J), Holt–Winters (H–W), and stepwise auto-regressive (S–A) forecasts: percentage of series for which first named method outperforms second for various lead times*

Comparisons	Forecast lead times							
	1	2	3	4	5	6	7	8
B–J: H–W	73	64	60	58	58	57	58	58
B–J: S–A	68	70	67	62	62	61	63	63
H–W: S–A	48	50	58	57	55	56	58	59

percentage of occasions one method outperforms another for forecasts made up to eight periods ahead. It is clear from this table that Box–Jenkins performs better than its competition on a sizable majority of series for all lead times. The Box–Jenkins versus Holt–Winters comparison for one-step ahead forecasts is very similar to that obtained by Reid, and here again it is noticed that over longer forecast horizons Box–Jenkins loses some of its relative advantage. The one-step ahead forecast errors are examined in more detail in Table 5.13, which gives an idea of the potential gains in accuracy which can be achieved through using the Box–Jenkins method. It can be seen from this table that Box–Jenkins very often considerably outperforms the two fully automatic procedures, particularly the Holt–Winters method. A feature of this table, which is of some practical relevance, is the wide spread of ranges containing an appreciable number of series in the Holt–Winters versus stepwise autoregression comparison. This suggest that each method contains useful features absent in the other, and consequently that the combined forecast introduced in Section 5.5 may well constitute a worthwhile improvement over the individual procedures. Summary statistics for the information in Table 5.13 are provided by the geometric means of the various ratios of average squared forecast errors. The values obtained for

Table 5.13   *Comparison of average square forecast errors (ASE) of Box–Jenkins, Holt–Winters, and stepwise autoregression in terms of ratios of average squared errors; number of forecasted series (in a total of 106 series) in various ranges*

	Method A Method B	Box–Jenkins Holt–Winters	Box–Jenkins Stepwise	Holt–Winters Stepwise
	0.1–0.2	1	0	0
	0.2–0.3	3	2	0
ASE Method A	0.3–0.4	4	4	2
ASE Method B	0.4–0.5	8	4	4
	0.5–0.6	5	2	4
when A is better	0.6–0.7	10	5	6
	0.7–0.8	13	14	13
	0.8–0.9	19	17	10
	0.9–1.0	14	23	12
Two methods identical		0	2	0
	0.9–1.0	11	14	5
	0.8–0.9	8	13	14
ASE Method B	0.7–0.8	2	3	10
ASE Method A	0.6–0.7	3	1	12
	0.5–0.6	4	0	5
when B is better	0.4–0.5	0	2	2
	0.3–0.4	1	0	3
	0.2–0.3	0	0	4
	0.1–0.2	0	0	0

these geometric means were:

$$\frac{\text{average squared error Box--Jenkins forecasts}}{\text{average squared error Holt--Winters forecasts}} = 0.80$$

$$\frac{\text{average squared error Box--Jenkins forecasts}}{\text{average squared error stepwise autoregressive forecasts}} = 0.86$$

$$\frac{\text{average squared error stepwise autoregressive forecasts}}{\text{average squared error Holt--Winters forecasts}} = 0.93$$

For one-step ahead prediction, the performance of various combined forecasts was also examined by Newbold and Granger. The combined Holt–Winters–stepwise autoregressive forecast was found to outperform Box–Jenkins on 46.25% of the monthly series in the sample. The geometric mean of the ratio of average squared error of the Box–Jenkins forecast to that of the combined forecast was found to be 0.99, using an appropriate procedure for choosing the combining weights. Thus a fully automatic forecast that performs very well indeed can be achieved. It was also found that combination of one or both of the fully automatic procedures with Box–Jenkins produced forecasts which, on the average, were a small improvement over Box–Jenkins taken alone. Detailed discussion of the results on combining is postponed until Chapter 9.

In addition to the forecasting methods that were applied to all the data in the collection, the Brown generalized exponential smoothing and Harrison seatrend procedures were applied to small subsets of the series, in order to obtain some insight into their merits. We noted, as did Reid, that seatrend was generally no better (and indeed, on occasion was much worse) than Holt–Winters, except on those series that had both a very strong seasonal factor and fairly large random (unpredictable) variation. Brown's method did not perform terribly well, particularly on seasonal time series, and we can imagine no circumstances in which we would prefer it to Holt–Winters.

It should be emphasized that the smoothing constants for exponential smoothing were chosen on the basis of goodness of fit over the sample period. It would be reasonable to expect forecast performance to deteriorate further if more arbitrary procedures were employed.

Two further studies are reported in Makridakis and Hibon [1979] and Makridakis *et al.* [1982].

On the basis of the material described here and our general experience in applying univariate forecasting procedures, we now offer tentative guidelines. These should most certainly not be followed religiously but might provide a useful basis for deciding on a forecasting method in any given situation.:

(a) For very short time series (with less than 30 observations), there is little alternative to use of an exponential smoothing predictor, and generally we would prefer Holt–Winters in such circumstances.

(b)   For moderately long series (at least 30 and no more than 40–50 observations), Box–Jenkins is still rather difficult to apply (more so for seasonal than nonseasonal series), but stepwise autoregression becomes feasible, and its use in combination with Holt–Winters seems the most promising approach. For longer series, if for some reason it is impracticable to use Box–Jenkins, then this combined forecast should again prove generally satisfactory.

(c)   For longer time series (at least least 40–50 observations), both its versatility and its success in actual applications would argue for the use of Box–Jenkins in preference to any other single procedure. Very often this will yield forecasts of sufficient accuracy for the purpose at hand, but should it fail to do so, combination with either Holt–Winters or stepwise autoregression or both can be tried. The extra versatility of Box–Jenkins makes it particularly valuable in situations where either a time series has proved difficult to predict by routine methods or one is meeting a particular kind of series for the first time and is uncertain about its characteristics.

(d)   For those series that are strongly seasonal and exhibit large random variations, substitute Harrison's seatrend for Holt–Winters in the above.

(e)   Although we have little experience of the Harrison–Stevens Bayesian predictor, it appears that this approach might well prove useful in the situations for which it was designed—cases where it is suspected that the available data exhibit specific kinds of nonstationarities. Such series might crop up quite frequently in sales forecasting.

The above guidelines should certainly not be followed blindly. If is often the case that, in practice, one has valuable information about the particular series under study. This information should, if at all possible, be injected into the forecast generating mechanism, and may well influence any decision as to what procedure to employ.

CHAPTER SIX

FORECASTING FROM REGRESSION MODELS

Predict, v.   To relate an event that has not occurred, is not occurring and will not occur.
Prophecy, n.   The art and practice of selling one's credibility for future delivery.

AMBROSE BIERCE
"The Enlarged Devil's Dictionary", Doubleday, 1967

6.1 Introduction

Up to this point only methods of forecasting a time series given just its current and past values have been considered. As noted in Chapter 5, such procedures are of considerable practical value. Nevertheless, it will often be the case that forecasts of higher quality can be obtained through the use of a wider information set. One might include in such a set, for example, current and past values of related time series and perhaps also any relevant nonquantifiable information. This latter possibility makes rigorous treatment of the forecasting problem rather difficult. For example, the forecaster may know of the possibility of an impending strike in the coal industry. However, he will generally not know for sure that the strike is to take place and almost certainly will be unsure of its duration. Thus, in addition to assessing the likely impact of the strike on the variable of interest, the forecaster must inject into his forecast an assessment of the probability of the strike taking place at all and also its likely duration. Presumably this kind of subjective judgment could be incorporated into a formal Bayesian treatment of the forecasting problem. However, the methods used in practice are of a more ad hoc nature.

Consideration of a wider information set for forecasting purposes introduces two additional concepts to the previous analysis. First it is necessary to examine and make use of any theory that postulates relationships determining the variable of interest, and second one might attempt to extend the univariate models of Chapter 3 to the multivariate case. In this chapter, traditional econometric approaches to forecasting, whereby economic theory is employed in the construction of equations to be used in prediction, will be discussed. Consideration of multivariate time series methods is postponed until Chapter 7.

6.2 Single Equation Models

Suppose that a variable Y is related to K variables $X_1, X_2, \ldots, X_K$ in such a way that the conditional expectation of Y given the X_j is linear, so that

$$E(Y|X_1, X_2, \ldots, X_K) = \beta_1 X_1 + \beta_2 X_2 + \cdots + \beta_K X_K$$

and let the residual be $\epsilon = Y - E(Y|X_1, X_2, \ldots, X_K)$. Suppose, now, that n equally spaced observations through time are observed on this process. One can write

$$Y_t = \mathbf{x}'_t \boldsymbol{\beta} + \epsilon_t, \qquad t = 1, 2, \ldots, n \tag{6.2.1}$$

where $\mathbf{x}'_t$ constitutes a vector of observations on $X_1, X_2, \ldots, X_K$, made at time t, so that $\mathbf{x}'_t = (x_{1t}, x_{2t}, \ldots, x_{Kt})$ and $\boldsymbol{\beta}$ is a vector of constant coefficients

$$\boldsymbol{\beta}' = (\beta_1, \beta_2, \ldots, \beta_K).$$

The set of equations (6.2.1) may be written more compactly as

$$\mathbf{y} = \mathbf{X}\boldsymbol{\beta} + \boldsymbol{\epsilon} \tag{6.2.2}$$

where $\mathbf{y}' = (Y_1, Y_2, \ldots, Y_n)$, $\boldsymbol{\epsilon}' = (\epsilon_1, \epsilon_2, \ldots, \epsilon_n)$, and

$$\mathbf{X} = \begin{bmatrix} x_{11} & x_{21} & \cdots & \cdots & x_{K1} \\ x_{12} & x_{22} & \cdots & \cdots & x_{K2} \\ \vdots & \vdots & & & \vdots \\ x_{1n} & x_{2n} & \cdots & \cdots & x_{Kn} \end{bmatrix} = \begin{bmatrix} \mathbf{x}'_1 \\ \mathbf{x}'_2 \\ \vdots \\ \mathbf{x}'_n \end{bmatrix}$$

Equation (6.2.2) formulates the (multiple) linear regression model. It should be emphasized that "linearity" refers here to the unknown coefficients $\boldsymbol{\beta}$. There is no reason to preclude consideration of transformed variables from the list of regressors $X_1, X_2, \ldots, X_K$. For example, in explaining change in wage rates it is common to include the reciprocal of unemployment as an explanatory variable. Again, a "dummy variable" taking a value 1 under particular special circumstances (for example, during government imposed wage control periods) and zero otherwise can be included among the X_j. Frequently it is desired to include a constant (intercept) term in the regression equation. This can be achieved by setting $x_{1t} = 1$, $t = 1, 2, \ldots, n$ whereupon the coefficient β_1 denotes the intercept.

In order to analyze the model (6.2.2), it is necessary to make various assumptions, although these may need to be relaxed in specific situations.

The standard assumptions for linear regression are:

(i) $E(\epsilon) = 0$;
(ii) $E(\epsilon\epsilon') = \sigma^2 I$, where I is the identity matrix;
(iii) X is distributed independently of ϵ and, for any realization of the process, $X'X$ is nonsingular with probability 1, i.e., almost certainly.

Now consider the analysis of (6.2.2) for a given set of observations X, it being understood in what follows that expectations are taken conditional on X being fixed. The Gauss–Markov theorem then states that the estimator

$$\hat{\beta} = (X'X)^{-1}X'y \tag{6.2.3}$$

is best linear unbiased for β. That is, in the class of estimators that are linear in y and unbiased for β, $\hat{\beta}$ has smallest variance. It is straightforward to show that $E[(\beta - \hat{\beta})(\beta - \hat{\beta})'] = \sigma^2(X'X)^{-1}$, and that an unbiased estimate of σ^2 is given by

$$s^2 = (y - X\hat{\beta})'(y - X\hat{\beta})/(n - K) \tag{6.2.4}$$

Finally, if ϵ is assumed to be normally distributed, it can be shown that $\hat{\beta}$ is distributed independently of s^2, $\hat{\beta}$ being normal and $(n - K)s^2/\sigma^2$ distributed as χ^2 with $n - K$ degrees of freedom. Hence the quantity

$$\left(\hat{\beta}_j - \beta_j\right)\Big/s\sqrt{a_{jj}} \tag{6.2.5}$$

where a_{jj} is the jth diagonal element of $(X'X)^{-1}$, is distributed at Student's t with $n - K$ degrees of freedom, thus allowing tests of significance of individual regression coefficients to be made.

Suppose now that the regression equation contains a constant term, so that

$$E(Y|X_2, X_3,\ldots, X_K) = \beta_1 + \beta_2 X_2 + \cdots + \beta_K X_K$$

It would be useful to have an indication of how much knowledge of the X_j contributes toward "explaining" Y. One could argue as follows: from (6.2.4) the sum of squared residuals about the regression is $(n - K)s^2$, whereas the variation of Y about its mean in the given sample is $\sum_{i=1}^{n}(Y_i - \bar{Y})^2$. Thus the regression "explains" the amount $\sum_{i=1}^{n}(Y_i - \bar{Y})^2 - (n - K)s^2$ and hence, in proportionate terms, the amount "explained" by the regression is

$$R^2 = 1 - (n - K)s^2\left[\sum_{i=1}^{n}(Y_i - \bar{Y})^2\right]^{-1} \tag{6.2.6}$$

This quantity is called the *coefficient of multiple correlation*. Now, it might be objected that R^2 can overstate the value of a regression fit since the quantity $(n - K)s^2$ can be reduced simply by adding further variables X_j, even if they are not relevant in "explaining" Y. An alternative is to employ a quantity that corrects for degrees of freedom in estimating the residual variance and the variance of Y. Thus one could calculate

$$\bar{R}^2 = 1 - s^2 \left[\sum_{i=1}^{n} (Y_i - \bar{Y})^2 \Big/ (n-1) \right]^{-1} \qquad (6.2.7)$$

This is called the *corrected coefficient of multiple correlation*. It should be noted that, in cases of particularly bad fit, $\bar{R}^2$ can be negative. It is often required to test the hypothesis H_0: $\beta_2 = \beta_3 = \cdots = \beta_K = 0$, that is $X_2, X_3, \ldots, X_K$, taken as a set, contribute nothing (in the linear regression sense) toward explanation of Y. This can be accomplished by noting that, under H_0, the statistic

$$F = \frac{R^2}{1 - R^2} \frac{n - K}{K - 1}$$

is distributed as Fisher's F with $K - 1$ and $n - K$ degrees of freedom. The hypothesis H_0 is rejected for high values of the test statistic.

Suppose that the regression equation (6.2.1) continues to hold for some future time period $n + h$, so that

$$Y_{n+h} = \mathbf{x}'_{n+h}\beta + \epsilon_{n+h} \qquad (6.2.8)$$

If it is required to forecast Y_{n+h} for given $\mathbf{x}_{n+h}$, a natural predictor is obtained by setting ϵ_{n+h} equal to its expected value of zero and substituting $\hat{\beta}$ of (6.2.3) for β in (6.2.8). It will now be proved that this predictor is best linear unbiased. Consider the set of all possible linear predictors $\mathbf{l}'\mathbf{y}$. Then

$$Y_{n+h} - \mathbf{l}'\mathbf{y} = (\mathbf{x}'_{n+h} - \mathbf{l}'\mathbf{X})\beta + \epsilon_{n+h} - \mathbf{l}'\epsilon$$

by (6.2.2) and (6.2.8). Taking expectations (conditional on the fixed x's)

$$E(Y_{n+h} - \mathbf{l}'\mathbf{y}) = (\mathbf{x}'_{n+h} - \mathbf{l}'\mathbf{X})\beta$$

For the forecast to be unbiased, this quantity must be zero for all β, and hence

$$\mathbf{l}'\mathbf{X} = \mathbf{x}'_{n+h} \qquad (6.2.9)$$

The variance of the forecast is

$$E\left[(Y_{n+h} - \mathbf{l}'\mathbf{y})^2\right] = E\left[(\epsilon_{n+h} - \mathbf{l}'\epsilon)^2\right] = \sigma(1 + \mathbf{l}'\mathbf{l}) \qquad (6.2.10)$$

Thus, to obtain the best linear unbiased predictor, it is necessary to choose $\mathbf{l}$ such that $\mathbf{l}'\mathbf{l}$ is minimum subject to the restriction (6.2.9). This can be achieved using Lagrange multipliers. Define the multiplier $\lambda' = (\lambda_1, \lambda_2, \ldots, \lambda_K)$ and the function $F = \mathbf{l}'\mathbf{l} - \lambda'(\mathbf{X}'\mathbf{l} - \mathbf{x}_{n+h})$. Then

$$\partial F/\partial \mathbf{l} = 2\mathbf{l} - \mathbf{X}\lambda, \qquad \partial F/\partial \lambda = \mathbf{X}'\mathbf{l} - \mathbf{x}_{n+h}$$

Setting these partial derivatives equal to zero yields

$$\begin{bmatrix} 2\mathbf{I} & -\mathbf{X} \\ \mathbf{X}' & \mathbf{0} \end{bmatrix} \begin{pmatrix} \mathbf{l} \\ \lambda \end{pmatrix} = \begin{pmatrix} \mathbf{0} \\ \mathbf{x}_{n+h} \end{pmatrix}$$

Solving this set of equations by inverting the partitioned matrix then yields $l' = x'_{n+h}(X'X)^{-1}X'$. Hence the best linear unbiased predictor of Y_{n+h} for given x_{n+h} is given by

$$f_{n,h} = x'_{n+h}\hat{\beta} \qquad (6.2.11)$$

where $\hat{\beta}$ is given by (6.2.3). Further, it follows from (6.2.10) that the variance of this predictor is given by

$$E\left[(Y_{n+h} - f_{n,h})^2\right] = \sigma^2\left(1 + x'_{n+h}(X'X)^{-1}x_{n+h}\right)$$

An unbiased estimate for this variance is obtained by substituting s^2 of (6.2.4) for σ^2.

The forecasting problem solved here is one of *conditional* prediction, that is, the approach yields optimal forecasts of Y_{n+h} for given future values of $X_1, X_2, \ldots, X_K$. In itself this constitutes a worthwhile object since, for example, a policy maker may require estimates of the future values of the variable of interest under various policy options. The problem of *unconditional* prediction—forecasting what Y_{n+h} will actually be—can only be solved if forecasts of $X_{j,\,n+h}$, $j = 1, 2, \ldots, K$, are substituted for x_{n+h} in (6.2.11). Clearly the regression equation (6.2.2) is of no help here; these forecasts must be obtained from some other source—possibly through judgmental considerations or possibly through the application of some univariate or multivariate forecasting method.

The predictor (6.2.11) is, as just shown, optimal given the assumptions made. However, it will often be the case that the assumption concerning the variance–covariance matrix of the errors is untenable. In general, let these errors be written

$$u = y - X\beta \qquad (6.2.12)$$

reserving the symbol ϵ to denote white noise residuals. Suppose, now, that

$$E(u) = 0, \qquad E(uu') = \sigma^2\Omega \qquad (6.2.13)$$

where Ω is some positive definite symmetric matrix. Goldberger [1962] shows, through an approach similar to that employed in deriving (6.2.11), that the best linear unbiased predictor of Y_{n+h} is given by

$$f_{n,h} = x'_{n+h}b + W'\Omega^{-1}e \qquad (6.2.14)$$

where

$$b = (X'\Omega^{-1}X)^{-1}X'\Omega^{-1}y, \qquad e = y - Xb, \qquad W = E(u_{n+h}u) \qquad (6.2.15)$$

Note that b is Aitken's generalized least squares estimator, that is, the best linear unbiased estimate of β in (6.2.12) under the specification (6.2.13). Unfortunately the result (6.2.14) is of little practical value as it stands since it requires knowledge of Ω and W. Typically, in practice, one must specify some plausible form of the covariance structure of the errors and estimate this along with the parameters β of the model. Goldberger also shows that if Ω is wrongly assumed to be the identity matrix I, the loss in prediction efficiency can in certain circumstances be extremely severe.

When dealing with time series data, perhaps the most frequently encountered problem is autocorrelation in the residuals from the regression equation. In the presence of autocorrelated errors the least-squares estimator (6.2.3) remains unbiased since

$$E(\hat{\beta}) = (X'X)^{-1}X'E(y) = (X'X)^{-1}X'E(X\beta + u)$$

from (6.2.12). Hence $E(\hat{\beta}) = \beta$ by (6.2.13). However, the best linear unbiased estimator is given by (6.2.15), which in general will differ from (6.2.3). More seriously, the usual formula for the variance–covariance matrix of the least-squares estimators is incorrect since now $\hat{\beta} - \beta = (X'X)^{-1}X'u$ and hence by (6.2.13)

$$E[(\beta - \hat{\beta})(\beta - \hat{\beta})'] = \sigma^2(X'X)^{-1}X'\Omega X(X'X)^{-1}$$

The usual tests of hypotheses, based for example on (6.2.5) and (6.2.6), are invalid in the presence of serially correlated errors—a point that will be taken up again in Section 6.4—and, as already noted, the forecast (6.2.11) is generally inefficient.

One approach to the problem of autocorrelated errors would be to assume some model from the general autoregressive integrated moving average class of processes $a(B)(1 - B)^d u_t = b(B)\epsilon_t$ introduced in Chapters 1 and 3. In principle, the data could be employed to suggest an appropriate model from this class, which could then be incorporated into the regression equation for estimation and forecasting. However, standard practice in applied economic work appears to be rather less general in terms of the alternative error structures that are contemplated. A white noise error structure is assumed as a null hypothesis, which is generally tested against some simple alternative—almost invariably a first-order autoregressive model—which is then adopted for purposes of estimation and forecasting should the test indicate significant autocorrelation. Occasionally higher order autoregressive processes for the errors are entertained (see, e.g., Wallis [1972]), but this seems to be the exception rather than the rule in current applied work.

The usual assumption, then, is a model of the form $y = X\beta + u$ with

$$u_t = a_1 u_{t-1} + \epsilon_t \tag{6.2.16}$$

The first step in the analysis is to calculate the ordinary least-squares estimate $\hat{\beta}$ of (6.2.3) and to test the null hypothesis that a_1 of (6.2.16) is zero. Denote the residuals from the fitted regression as $\hat{u}_t = Y_t - x_t'\hat{\beta}$, $t = 1, 2, \ldots, n$. The test generally employed is due to Durbin and Watson [1950, 1951], who propose the statistic

$$d = \sum_{t=2}^{n} (\hat{u}_t - \hat{u}_{t-1})^2 \bigg/ \sum_{t=1}^{n} \hat{u}_t^2 \tag{6.2.17}$$

This statistic is available on virtually every standard linear regression program package, and is generally quoted along with R^2 or $\overline{R}^2$ in applied econometric work. Now, writing

$$\sum_{t=1}^{n} \hat{u}_t^2 \approx \sum_{t=2}^{n} \hat{u}_t^2 \approx \sum_{t=2}^{n} \hat{u}_{t-1}^2$$

it follows that

$$d \approx \left(2 \sum_{t=1}^{n} \hat{u}_t^2 - 2 \sum_{t=2}^{n} \hat{u}_t \hat{u}_{t-1} \right) \Big/ \sum_{t=1}^{n} \hat{u}_t^2$$

that is,

$$d \approx 2(1 - \hat{\rho}_1) \tag{6.2.18}$$

where $\hat{\rho}_1$ is the first-order sample autocorrelation of $\hat{u}_t$. Thus, in contrast to the methodology described in Chapter 3, no sample autocorrelations beyond the first are considered in assessing the time series structure of the residuals. Of course, this follows from the fact that only the formulation (6.2.16) is entertained as a possible model. It follows from (6.2.18) that if $\hat{\rho}_1$ is zero, then d is equal to 2. Positive values for $\hat{\rho}_1$ imply $0 < d < 2$ and negative values $2 < d < 4$, the larger is $|\hat{\rho}_1|$ the further from 2 is d. Unfortunately the distribution of the Durbin–Watson statistic d depends on the matrix $\mathbf{X}$. However, Durbin and Watson show that this distribution always lies between that of two other statistics d_L and d_U, which they tabulate for particular values of K and n. The null hypothesis of no autocorrelation is then rejected against the alternative of positive autocorrelation if $d < d_L^*$ and not rejected if $d > d_U^*$, where asterisks indicate tabulated values at appropriate significance levels. If $d_L^* < d < d_U^*$ the test is inconclusive. Tests against the alternative of negative autocorrelation proceed in the same way, except that the appropriate statistic is now $4 - d$. A number of procedures for resolving inconclusive test results are examined by Durbin and Watson [1971] and some alternative tests are described and compared by L'Esperance and Taylor [1975].

Suppose, now, that a model with first order autoregressive errors is assumed. This can be written

$$Y_t - a_1 Y_{t-1} = (\mathbf{x}_t' - a_1 \mathbf{x}_{t-1}')\boldsymbol{\beta} + \epsilon_t \tag{6.2.19}$$

The most direct (though not the most computationally simple) method of estimation is to estimate a_1 and $\boldsymbol{\beta}$ simultaneously through a nonlinear least squares routine, as described in Chapter 3. A number of alternative procedures are discussed in Chapter 13 of Malinvaud [1966]. Given the least-squares estimates $\hat{a}_1$ and $\hat{\boldsymbol{\beta}}$, one can write, approximately, from (6.2.19)

$$Z_t - \hat{a}_1 Z_{t-1} = \epsilon_t \quad \text{where} \quad Z_t = Y_t - \mathbf{x}_t'\hat{\boldsymbol{\beta}}$$

Thus future values of Z, and hence of Y conditional on $\mathbf{X}$, can be forecast using the procedure described in Section 5.2.

As a final point on single equation models, it should be noted that lagged values of the variable Y can be included in the list of explanatory variables $\mathbf{X}$ in the model (6.2.1). Thus, as a simple example, one might have

$$Y_t = \beta_1 + \beta_2 Y_{t-1} + \beta_3 x_t + \epsilon_t \tag{6.2.20}$$

Application of ordinary least squares to models of this type yields an estimate $\hat{\beta}$ which is biased. However, provided the error term is nonautocorrelated, the usual least-squares estimators for β and the variance estimators are consistent—that is, they tend to the true values as the sample size tends to infinity. This is not generally the case if the error term is autocorrelated, however. A more thorough discussion of these results is given in Chapter 6 of Goldberger [1964]. A further difficulty with models of the form (6.2.20) is that the usual Durbin–Watson test is invalid, the test statistic being biased toward 2 (i.e., against rejection of the null hypothesis of no autocorrelation in the errors), as demonstrated by Nerlove and Wallis [1966]. A test for autocorrelated errors, which is valid in large samples, is given by Durbin [1970]. Forecasts of future values of Y are obtained in an obvious fashion from models of the form (6.2.20), along the lines described in Section 5.2.

To summarize, economists are frequently led to fit regression equations of the form (6.2.2), based on some particular theory that suggests an appropriate list of regressors $X_1, X_2, \ldots, X_K$. However, interpretation and analysis of these equations are dependent on the time series structure of the error terms—a point about which economic theory has little or nothing to say.

One approach to the problem of specifying the form of the error, and the dynamic structure, of a regression relationship has been proposed and implemented by Hendry and Mizon [1978] using a procedure known as COMFAC analysis. These authors consider regression equations with lagged dependent and independent variables and autoregressive errors. (No allowance is made for the possibility of a moving average component in the error structure.) To illustrate, consider a regression model with just a single independent variable, where for convenience we omit the intercept term:

$$Y_t = \delta_1 Y_{t-1} + \delta_2 Y_{t-2} + \cdots + \delta_K Y_{t-K} + \beta_0 X_t + \beta_1 X_{t-1}$$
$$+ \cdots + \beta_K X_{t-K} + \epsilon_t$$

where ϵ_t is implicitly assumed to be white noise, a position which could perhaps be achieved by choosing a sufficiently large value for K, the maximum permitted lag.

This regression model can be written as

$$\delta(B) Y_t = \beta(B) X_t + \epsilon_t$$

where

$$\delta(B) = 1 - \delta_1 B - \cdots - \delta_K B^K$$

and

$$\beta(B) = \beta_0 + \beta_1 B + \cdots + \beta_K B^K$$

Suppose now that the polynomials in B, $\delta(B)$ and $\beta(B)$, have a common factor $a(B)$, so that

$$\delta(B) = \delta^*(B)a(B)$$

and

$$\beta(B) = \beta^*(B)a(B)$$

The regression model is then

$$\delta^*(B)Y_t = \beta^*(B)X_t + \frac{1}{a(B)}\epsilon_t$$

This new formulation, with an autoregressive error structure, represents a simplification of the original model, in the sense that it involves fewer unknown parameters.

Hendry and Mizon implement a testing procedure, due to Sargan [1980], in which, beginning with a model involving lagged dependent and independent variables and white noise errors, common factors of this type are sought. This approach is in the same spirit as the model selection procedures of Chapter 3, where the data are allowed to suggest an appropriate model. An interesting distinction is that COMFAC analysis begins with the most elaborate contemplated model and seeks simplifications, whereas the approach of Chapter 3 begins with a simple parsimonious structure, building up to a more elaborate model if the data suggest the advisability of such a course. In the next two chapters we discuss the extension of that approach to the specification of dynamic and error structures for the relationship between time series, allowing for a richer class of models.

6.3 Simultaneous Equation Models

The analysis of the previous section was limited to consideration of the case where a single dependent variable Y is influenced by a set of independent variables $X_1, X_2, \ldots, X_K$, it being assumed that the values taken by these independent variables do not in turn depend on values taken by Y. Such an assumption is frequently untenable in economics. For example, the rate of change of money wages may well depend (among other things) on the rate of change of retail prices. However, it would also be reasonable to hypothesize a dependence of prices on wages, along with other factors. Thus it is often required to analyze in applied economic work a system of simultaneous equations, depicting the various interactions that might be taking place.

An econometric simultaneous equation system is a set of M equations that simultaneously determine the values of M "endogenous" variables $Y_1, Y_2, \ldots, Y_M$ in terms of K "exogenous," or "predetermined," variables.

The endogenous variables can be thought of as the quantities of interest; one might want to explain their behavior or to forecast their future values. The exogenous variables $X_1, X_2, \ldots, X_K$ are quantities that are *not* themselves dependent on the endogenous variables, but that *do* influence the behavior of the endogenous variables. The exogenous variables may not necessarily be of any great interest in themselves, but they help explain the behavior of the endogenous variables, and may help in their prediction. Now, it should be obvious that any system of equations linking economic variables will not hold exactly at all times. Rather, it is necessary to add stochastic error terms, in which case one can think of the system as determining simultaneously the conditional expectations of the endogenous variables given the exogenous. The structures of the individual equations in a system are determined, as in the single equation case, by appeal to economic theory.

Suppose, for the time being, that a linear system is appropriate. Then, with the values $x_1, x_2, \ldots, x_K$ of the exogenous variables determined outside the system, one can write

$$Y_{1,t} = \gamma_{21}Y_{2,t} + \gamma_{31}Y_{3,t} + \cdots + \gamma_{M1}Y_{M,t} + \beta_{11}x_{1,t}$$
$$+ \cdots + \beta_{K1}x_{K,t} + u_{1,t}$$
$$Y_{2,t} = \gamma_{12}Y_{1,t} + \gamma_{32}Y_{3,t} + \cdots + \gamma_{M2}Y_{M,t} + \beta_{12}x_{1,t}$$
$$+ \cdots + \beta_{K2}x_{K,t} + u_{2,t}$$
$$\vdots$$
$$Y_{M,t} = \gamma_{1M}Y_{1,t} + \gamma_{2M}Y_{2,t} + \cdots + \gamma_{M-1M}Y_{M-1,t}$$
$$+ \beta_{1M}x_{1,t} + \cdots + \beta_{KM}x_{K,t} + u_{M,t}$$

for $t = 1, 2, \ldots, n$. In matrix notation this system can be expressed as

$$\mathbf{y}_t'\boldsymbol{\Gamma} = \mathbf{x}_t'\mathbf{B} + \mathbf{u}_t', \qquad t = 1, 2, \ldots, n \qquad (6.3.1)$$

where

$$\mathbf{y}_t' = (Y_{1,t}, Y_{2,t}, \ldots, Y_{M,t}), \qquad \mathbf{u}_t' = (u_{1,t}, u_{2,t}, \ldots, u_{M,t})$$
$$\mathbf{x}_t' = (x_{1,t}, x_{2,t}, \ldots, x_{K,t})$$

$$\boldsymbol{\Gamma} = \begin{bmatrix} 1 & -\gamma_{12} & -\gamma_{13} & \cdots & -\gamma_{1M} \\ -\gamma_{21} & 1 & -\gamma_{23} & \cdots & -\gamma_{2M} \\ -\gamma_{31} & -\gamma_{32} & 1 & \cdots & -\gamma_{3M} \\ \vdots & \vdots & \vdots & \cdots & \vdots \\ -\gamma_{M1} & -\gamma_{M2} & -\gamma_{M3} & \cdots & 1 \end{bmatrix}$$

$$\mathbf{B} = \begin{bmatrix} \beta_{11} & \beta_{12} & \cdots & \beta_{1M} \\ \beta_{21} & \beta_{22} & \cdots & \beta_{2M} \\ \vdots & \vdots & & \vdots \\ \beta_{K1} & \beta_{K2} & \cdots & \beta_{KM} \end{bmatrix}$$

It is generally assumed that Γ is nonsingular and that

$$E(\mathbf{u}_t) = \mathbf{0}, \quad t = 1, 2, \ldots, n, \quad E(\mathbf{u}_t\mathbf{u}_t') = \Sigma(\text{nonsingular}), \quad t = 1, 2, \ldots, n$$

Frequently it is further assumed that the errors u_t are not autocorrelated, so that

$$E(u_{i,t}u_{j,t+k}) = 0 \quad \forall\, i, j \quad \text{and} \quad \forall\, k \neq 0$$

The set of equations (6.3.1) may be written more compactly as

$$\mathbf{Y}\Gamma = \mathbf{X}\mathbf{B} + \mathbf{U} \tag{6.3.2}$$

where

$$\mathbf{Y} = \begin{bmatrix} \mathbf{y}_1' \\ \mathbf{y}_2' \\ \vdots \\ \mathbf{y}_n' \end{bmatrix}, \quad \mathbf{X} = \begin{bmatrix} \mathbf{x}_1' \\ \mathbf{x}_2' \\ \vdots \\ \mathbf{x}_n' \end{bmatrix}, \quad \mathbf{U} = \begin{bmatrix} \mathbf{u}_1' \\ \mathbf{u}_2' \\ \vdots \\ \mathbf{u}_n' \end{bmatrix}$$

Equation (6.3.2) is called the structural form—the structure being imposed by economic theory. Typically, lagged values of the endogenous variables are included in the matrix of regressors $\mathbf{X}$ along with exogenous variables, so that the set $\mathbf{x}_t$ will be referred to as predetermined variables, that is, variables determined outside of the system of simultaneous equations (6.3.1) at time t.

Multiplying through (6.3.2) by the matrix Γ^{-1} yields

$$\mathbf{Y} = \mathbf{X}\mathbf{B}\Gamma^{-1} + \mathbf{U}\Gamma^{-1}$$

or

$$\mathbf{Y} = \mathbf{X}\Pi + \mathbf{V} \quad \text{where} \quad \Pi = \mathbf{B}\Gamma^{-1}, \quad \mathbf{V} = \mathbf{U}\Gamma^{-1} \tag{6.3.3}$$

Equation (6.3.3), which constitutes the solution of the system for the endogenous variables in terms of the predetermined variables and residuals, is called the reduced form. The quantity $\mathbf{X}\Pi$ denotes the conditional expectation of the set of endogenous variables, given the predetermined variables. In general, however, knowledge of this conditional distribution is insufficient to determine $\mathbf{B}$, Γ, and Σ uniquely. To proceed further, prior restrictions must be imposed on the values of these matrices. The simplest approach to this problem of "econometric identification" is to assume, following the specifications of economic theory, that particular elements of $\mathbf{B}$ and Γ are zero.

Thus, a condition for econometric identification of an equation in the system (6.3.2) is that the number of predetermined variables excluded from the equation must be at least as great as one less than the number of endogenous variables included in the equation. This condition is sufficient for identification provided the matrix Π is not ill-conditioned. (For a proof, see Chapter 14 of Judge *et al.* [1985].) A discussion of other types of restrictions and resulting criteria for identification is contained in Fisher [1966].

Application of ordinary least squares to an equation of the system (6.3.2) produces, in general, coefficient estimators that are inconsistent. A number of procedures for obtaining consistent estimators have been proposed and many of these are discussed in standard econometrics textbooks (see, e.g., Judge et al. [1985], Chapter 15); for a synthesis, see Hendry [1976]. These procedures are typically justified on asymptotic grounds, and their behavior in finite samples is extremely difficult to derive. A number of exact results have been obtained for simple specific models (see, e.g., Richardson [1968], Sawa [1969], Mariano and Sawa [1972], Anderson and Sawa [1973, 1979], Mariano [1982], Anderson [1982], and Taylor [1983]).

Suppose, now, that the system of equations has been estimated, yielding estimates $\hat{\mathbf{B}}$ and $\hat{\Gamma}$. Π is then estimated as $\hat{\Pi} = \hat{\mathbf{B}}\hat{\Gamma}^{-1}$. An alternative, of course, would be to estimate Π directly from (6.3.3), but this would ignore the restrictions imposed by economic theory on the structural equations (6.3.2) and hence, as Klein [1960] has argued, would be less efficient, provided the economic specification was correct. Forecasts are most easily calculated through the reduced form (6.3.3), so that if the x's are truly exogenous variables $\mathbf{y}'_{n+h}$ is forecast conditional on the exogenous variables by

$$\mathbf{f}'_{n,h} = \mathbf{x}'_{n+h}\hat{\Pi} \qquad (6.3.4)$$

If lagged values of the endogenous variables are included in the model, then forecasts can be obtained recursively, beginning with $h = 1$, in the usual way, substituting forecasts of endogenous variables for unknown future values in (6.3.4). Econometricians would generally consider such an approach naive, feeling, as will be seen, that judgment ought to be incorporated into the mechanism generating forecasts since no model can hope to take account of all the factors (many of which may be nonquantifiable) affecting the variables to be forecast.

The above discussion of the multivariate forecasting problem is extremely formal and inadequate to describe what actually goes on in an econometric forecasting exercise. To illustrate the practical considerations involved, attention is restricted to macroeconomic forecasting models, noting that essentially similar methodology is employed in microeconomic forecasting—though the models considered are often smaller. (As an example, see Houthakker and Taylor [1966], where an attempt is made to forecast all items of U.S. private consumption six years ahead.)

A good account of the principles involved in constructing a macroeconomic forecasting model (on an annual basis) is given by Suits [1962], who first presents a grossly oversimplified formulation for purposes of illustration. The first step is an appeal to economic theory to postulate various interrelationships in an economy. For example, consumption might depend on disposable income, that is, on gross income less taxes. Investment can be taken as a function of income, but generally with a time lag. In this oversimplified formulation, one might think of taxes as being just a proportion of income. Finally, income is the sum of consumption, investment, and government expenditure. These considerations must then be transposed to algebraic form, and the parameters of the model estimated. Suppose that this simple model, when estimated and ignoring error terms, is of the form

$$Y_{1,t} = 20 + 0.7(Y_{4,t} - Y_{3,t}), \qquad Y_{2,t} = 2 + 0.1Y_{4,t-1}$$

$$Y_{3,t} = 0.2Y_{4,t}, \qquad Y_{4,t} = Y_{1,t} + Y_{2,t} + x_t \qquad (6.3.5)$$

where Y_1 is consumption, Y_2 is investment, Y_3 is taxes, Y_4 is income, and x_t is government expenditure. Solving these equations yields the reduced form

$$\begin{bmatrix} Y_{1,t} \\ Y_{2,t} \\ Y_{3,t} \\ Y_{4,t} \end{bmatrix} = \begin{bmatrix} 1 & 0 & 0.7 & -0.7 \\ 0 & 1 & 0 & 0 \\ 0 & 0 & 1 & -0.2 \\ -1 & -1 & 0 & 1 \end{bmatrix}^{-1} \begin{bmatrix} 20 & 0 & 0 \\ 2 & 0.1 & 0 \\ 0 & 0 & 0 \\ 0 & 0 & 1 \end{bmatrix} \begin{bmatrix} 1 \\ Y_{4,t-1} \\ x_t \end{bmatrix} \qquad (6.3.6)$$

Now, for example, if income in year n is $Y_{4,n} = 100$ and government expenditure in year $n + 1$ is projected to be $x_{n+1} = 20$, then substitution in (6.3.6) yields the forecasts 86.2 for $Y_{1,n+1}$, 12 for $Y_{2,n+1}$, 23.7 for $Y_{3,n+1}$, and 118.2 for $Y_{4,n+1}$ when t is set equal to $n + 1$ in that equation. For year $n + 2$, forecasts are obtained by setting $t = n + 2$ in (6.3.6), inserting a projected value for x_{n+2}, and replacing $Y_{4,n+1}$ on the right-hand side of the equation by its forecasted value of 118.2. In this fashion, forecasts can be made as far into the future as required, given only projections of future government expenditure and a faith in the model continuing to represent adequately the behavior of the system under study. The forecasts so obtained can be viewed in two ways. The forecasts for year $n + 1$ may be thought of as conditional forecasts of the endogenous variables given that the exogenous variable—government expenditure—will actually be $x_{n+1} = 20$. Alternatively, they can be viewed as unconditional forecasts on the assumption that $x_{n+1} = 20$ is a forecast of future government expenditure, which has been obtained in some way from considerations outside of the model. It is a feature of econometric models, insofar as they contain truly exogenous variables, that they are not in themselves sufficient for the production of unconditional forecasts. Estimates of future values of exogenous variables must first be made outside of the model. Of course, it might be argued (see, e.g., Klein [1971a]) that, in many applications, conditional forecasts are of far more value than unconditional. This may well be the case, but what is generally required in such situations are conditional forecasts of endogenous variables given *some* of the exogenous variables (those over which the policy maker can exert some control, for example). In this situation one is still left with the problem of forecasting the remaining exogenous variables.

Moreover, for conditional forecasting of this type the exogenous variables must be truly exogenous. However, many "exogenous" variables in macroeconomic models are instruments of government policy. It would seem to us to be reasonable to assert that government policy is frequently determined in response to prevailing economic conditions, and hence, when building models, should be taken as endogenous, thus requiring the addition of further equations to the system. In that case, as just noted, it would now no longer be possible to use the model to obtain forecasts conditional on the future values of such variables.

Now the set of equations (6.3.5), and the method of generating forecasts just described, constitute a gross oversimplification of macroeconometric forecasting methodology. In particular, four points require further elaboration:

(i)   The vast majority of models in current use have far more equations than does this simple system.

(ii)   In order to depict economic theory faithfully, models frequently are nonlinear in the endogenous variables.

(iii)   A good deal of effort is put into the specification of individual equations to secure inclusion of appropriate variables, and to some extent as regards determination of lag and error structure.

(iv)   Forecasts obtained from models are generally modified judgmentally. In fact, there is often a good deal of adjustment to the model involved in the forecast generating process, which is typically not purely mechanistic.

The simple model (6.3.5) can be expanded in two directions. First, further equations would be required to depict behavior in other sections of the economy—for example, trade, employment, and price level might be explained by the addition of further equations. Moreover, it is generally felt that disaggregation of the quantities explained would allow a more realistic representation and hence lead to more accurate forecasts. Thus, for example, the forecasting model of the U.S. economy presented by Suits [1962] includes four consumption equations, explaining separately demand for automobiles and parts, other durable goods, nondurable goods, and services. The first attempt at large scale macroeconomic model building was due to Tinbergen [1939], further impetus being given by the work of Klein and Goldberger [1955]. Development of the computer allowed the treatment of far more sophisticated models, which began to proliferate in the 1960s. It is now held by an eminent authority in the field (see Klein [1971a]) that a minimum of 50 equations are required to represent adequately the behavior of a national economy. Indeed, many current models are far bigger than this. For several years now, there have been models containing 200 or more equations (see, e.g., Fromm *et al.* [1972]), and recently even larger models have been reported. For example, Eckstein *et al.* [1974] describe a model of 698 equations. However, Klein [1971a, b] would regard these as mere stepping stones along the path of disaggregation, leading eventually to models of a thousand equations for a national economy. In case the mind of a time series analyst, reading of these heroic efforts for the first time, remains insufficiently boggled, it should be added that yet further complexity is envisaged through the·linking of various national models in the production of an international model. Indeed, work along these lines has been in progress for some time (see Ball [1973] and Hickman [1975]).

It has already been seen that faithfulness to economic theories can be a hard taskmaster for the aspiring model builder. Further difficulties follow from the fact that the relationships postulated by theory are often nonlinear in the endogenous variables. The chief implication for forecasting is that it is no longer possible to obtain closed-form solutions like (6.3.6) for the reduced form equations. Instead, the structural form equations are generally solved numerically, using an iterative technique, such as the Gauss–Seidel method (see, for example, Green *et al.* [1972a]).

It is often emphasized by econometric model builders that the construction of appropriate model equations is by no means a simple one–off exercise. For example, attention must be paid to the historical record concerning the sample data to be analyzed. One would hardly expect constant coefficient models to be appropriate if the period of observation includes such exogenous shocks as wars or strikes not specifically accounted for in the model specification. Use of dummy variables over the relevant periods can be of some assistance in such circumstances. It is very often the case that, in addition to postulating a structural form, economic theory specifies the signs of many coefficients in the model. Furthermore, the econometrician will generally have strong feelings as to what magnitudes are or are not "reasonable" for many coefficients. Now, in principle there exists a well-defined framework, using Bayes' theorem, whereby such prior beliefs are modified at the model estimation stage in light of the given data. The final outcome would represent a view of probable coefficient values taking into account both prior belief and the evidence in the data. It must be admitted that, for large models, the computational effort involved in such a procedure would be formidable. Further, its validity rests on the assumption that the model chosen is the correct one. In practice, the procedure followed is far more informal. Standard estimation procedures are employed, and results that do not accord with prior expectations noted. These may well lead to a respecification of the model structure in some way. Thus, as Howrey *et al.* [1974] note, a good deal of experimentation is involved before a satisfactory fitted model is achieved. These authors, rather charmingly, refer to the whole process as the application of "tender loving care," a concept which, while difficult to define rigorously, plays, as will be seen in Chapter 9, an important role in controversies concerning the evaluation of econometric model forecasts. Another area in which experimentation in model building is much used is in the determination of an appropriate time lag structure in specific equations. A number of alternatives may be tried, an appeal to economic theory perhaps being employed to suggest fruitful areas for the search. In our experience, however, although economic theory frequently postulates the existence of time lags in relationships, it is rarely sufficiently specific to be of much help in determining their algebraic nature. A final, and to our minds vital, point concerns the specification of an appropriate time series structure for the errors from the individual equations of econometric models. We have occasionally heard it suggested that, even here, economic theory can be used to suggest an appropriate structure. However, the arguments advanced in favor of such an assertion have always been less than convincing, and accordingly we cannot accept it as realistic. It is very common to see in applied econometric work the tacit assumption that residuals are white noise, even when the reported Durbin–Watson statistic renders such an assumption improbable. Thus, all too often, serial correlation in equation residuals is ignored—at least in the model building stage of the analysis. We could quote many recent examples, but doubtless the reader familiar with applied econometric literature will be well aware of the problem. On occasions, attempts are made to allow for the presence of autocorrelated errors, but the assumption of first-order autoregression is generally substituted for that of white noise in such circumstances (see, e.g., Fair [1970]). Doubtless this will go some way toward alleviating the problems caused by autocorrelated errors. Nevertheless, if some other structure is appropriate, the model remains misspecified, and any conclusions drawn from it will be more or less invalid, depending on the extent of the misspecification. In Chapter 3 a methodology whereby, on the evidence of the data, an appropriate time series model is chosen from a general class was discussed. This technique is only very rarely employed in applied econometric work and, to the best of our knowledge, has never been used in the construction of large macroeconomic forecasting models, although Hendry [1974] does experiment with a number of time series error structures in a small model. Thus it must be assumed, a priori, that the error structure of such models is misspecified. In the next section the consequences that can arise from misspecification of this kind are illustrated.

The progression from completed model to derived forecast (whether conditional or unconditional) is typically not straightforward. Perhaps the most readable discussion of what generally takes place is given by Evans et al. [1972]. These authors distinguish three separate steps that are frequently taken, in addition to mechanical solution of the structural model. First, in order to forecast the endogenous variables, it is necessary, as already noted, to form an assessment of the likely future values of exogenous variables. Almost invariably, the procedures employed here are neither quantifiable nor rigorous. Typically, exogenous variables are forecasted judgmentally, the investigator relying on his knowledge and experience, together with any external indications, or advice from co-workers, which might be available. Second, before the model is solved, adjustments are made to individual equations (or some simple transformation of these equations.) These adjustments are considered as either the setting of a nonzero value for the error from an equation or, equivalently, the adjustment of the constant term in the equation. The adjustments made can be either subjective or mechanistic, or some combination of the two. For example, it might be desired to incorporate into the forecast, information about probable future exogenous developments, such as strikes. The adjustment necessary in such circumstances is generally in the nature of a "best guess" since typically no rigorous quantitative framework is available. It is often the case that residuals from many equations in a model are autocorrelated, and attempts are often made to take account of this in calculating forecasts. Green *et al.* [1972a] suggest fitting, by least squares, to the errors u_t either a first-order autoregressive process $u_t = \rho u_{t-1} + \epsilon_t$ or a second-order process $u_t = \rho_1 u_{t-1} + \rho_2 u_{t-2} + \epsilon_t$. Residuals over the forecast period are set, not equal to zero, but according to one of the formulas

$$u_{n+h} = \hat{\rho}^h u_n, \qquad u_{n+h} = \hat{\rho}^h \left(\frac{u_n + \hat{\rho} u_{n-1}}{2} \right) \qquad (6.3.7)$$

or

$$u_{n+h} = \hat{\rho}_1 u_{n+h-1} + \hat{\rho}_2 u_{n+h-2}, \qquad h = 1, 2, \ldots$$

For reasons that we find neither entirely clear nor convincing, Green *et al.* tend to favor the second form in (6.3.7). It should be added that, even if the assumed form of serial correlation is correct, forecasts obtained through mechanical adjustment procedures such as this can be far from optimal if autocorrelation is not *also* taken into account when the model is estimated. However, at least for forecasting a short distance ahead, the adjustment procedure may well be a good deal better than ignoring autocorrelated errors altogether. In addition to the examples just described, adjustments may also be made to reflect structural change not accounted for in the model and also any data revisions. For the uninitiated, it should be noted that a good deal of macroeconomic data is subject to continual revision, even several years after the event. This problem could be worthy of a separate book, and most certainly is too large to treat here. However, two questions should at least be posed. Suppose one makes the heroic assumption that the final published figure is the "correct" one, and that successive estimates converge to this value. Suppose, now, that in building a model, the latest available data are used. It follows that a severe errors in observation problem may arise—the variance of the errors being higher for recent observations than for distant ones. As far as we know, no attempt has been made to solve the estimation problems posed by such a phenomenon. The second difficulty involves deciding what it is that one should try to forecast. Should it be the first available figure, on the grounds that it is this value to which the policy maker will react? On the other hand, since a model attempts to represent actual behavior in the economy is it not geared toward forecasting the "true value" or the "true" change in the quantity of interest over the forecast period? These questions would seem to merit further study.

At the final stage of the forecasting procedure, the modified model is solved to obtain predictions of the endogenous variables. However, it may well be the case that the forecasts so obtained do not accord with the econometrician's a priori concept of the likely range of future values. In such situations the forecasts may again be modified judgmentally, perhaps through a modification of the forecasts of exogenous variables or of the adjustments to individual structural equations employed in the previous stages. The model must then be re-solved, leading to a further set of forecasts. Not all forecasts derived from econometric models are subject to the high degree of judgmental modification just described. For example, in computing predictions from his model, Fair [1970, 1974] does no more than insert judgmental forecasts of future exogenous variables.

Although, in the presence of severe judgmental modification, it is virtually impossible to specify analytically the forecast generating mechanism, except perhaps in a Bayesian framework (which would probably lead to a prohibitively cumbersome scheme in practice), this should not be taken as an argument against the insertion of judgment into the forecasting procedure. On the contrary, the forecaster ought to employ *all* information available to him at the time the forecast is made, irrespective of whether or not such information lends itself to incorporation in a formal quantitative framework. The quality of the forecasts will then reflect both the quality of the information employed and the efficiency of its use. However, given the prevalence of judgmental adjustments in the derivation of forecasts from econometric models, a difficulty arises when one attempts to evaluate the quality of such work. Should one simply judge the end-product—the forecasts—on their merits? This is certainly worthwhile, but suppose that good forecasts are obtained primarily through the judgmental skill of the investigator. Perhaps he could have done as well, or even better, without the model. Again, it is possible for an adequate model to produce unsatisfactory forecasts if the investigator's judgment is seriously faulty. Thus it would be desirable also to evaluate objectively the worth of the model as a forecasting tool. After all, if reasonable forecasts are obtained without significant aid from the model, one might argue on grounds of efficiency for discarding it or, in the hopes of advancing knowledge or obtaining superior forecasts in the future, for radically modifying it. Discussion of the quality of econometric models and forecasts will be postponed until the methodology of forecast evaluation has been examined in Chapter 9.

Given any econometric model, it is possible in principle, given distributional assumptions, to obtain interval as well as point predictors. In practice, this can be a formidable task when the system contains nonlinearities in the endogenous variables. A good discussion of the problem of interval prediction is given by Klein [1971a], and will not be discussed further here, other than to note that when judgmental adjustment is employed in the forecasting process the usual probability statements relating to confidence intervals are invalidated.

Attempts have been made to improve the forecasting ability of econometric models by including in the structural equations quantities whose presence is justified, not on grounds of economic theory, but rather because changes in them might reasonably be expected to herald changes in the variables of interest. Such quantities are referred to as "anticipations variables." The econometric model relying most heavily on these variables is that of Fair [1970]. Occasionally attempts are made to take an existing model and incorporate into its structure anticipations variables in an effort to determine whether or not forecasting performance can be improved. For example, Adams and Duggal [1974] examine the use of an index of consumer sentiment, investment anticipations based on surveys of businessmen, and housing starts within the framework of the Wharton econometric model. Generally speaking, they conclude that use of these anticipations variables produces some improvement in forecasting accuracy.

6.4 Danger of Spurious Regressions in Econometric Models

The reader may well already have gathered that any skepticism we feel with regard to the worth of econometric models, as generally constructed, as forecasting tools is based not on doubts as to their ability to represent adequately the structure of economic relationships in a functional sense, but rather on their frequently cursory and invariably insufficiently general treatment of the specification of lag and error structure. This should hardly be surprising since, after all, forecasting is preeminently a time-oriented exercise. It is surely only natural, therefore, to expect that inadequate attention to time series concepts would lead to unnecessarily poor forecasts. Of course, misspecification of lag or error structure could occur in a simultaneous equation econometric model in any number of ways. In order to obtain some insight into the potential problems involved, however, it will be convenient to examine again the single equation model. There appears to be no reason to suppose that any difficulties that arise from misspecification here will not also be present in the context of a large simultaneous equation econometric model.

It is by no means uncommon to find in published applied econometric work equations of an apparently high degree of goodness of fit, as measured by the coefficient of multiple correlation R^2 (6.2.6) or the "corrected" coefficient $\bar{R}^2$ (6.2.7), but with extremely low values for the Durbin–Watson d statistic (6.2.17). (The reader who doubts this assertion is referred to the equations of the various models given in Hickman [1972] or Renton [1975].) Perhaps the most severe case of this kind to come our way concerns the "St. Louis Model," reported by Andersen and Carlson [1974]. This model contains only five behavioral equations, and in three of them R^2 is bigger than d. It has already been noted that one of the problems raised by serially correlated errors is that the usual tests of significance are invalid. In this section, the possibility of obtaining a regression equation relating economic time series exhibiting typical behavior, with an apparently high degree of fit, when in fact the independent variables have no explanatory power whatever, is examined.

As a first step, one might ask whether economic variables, taken as a class, exhibit typical time series behavior of any kind. The available evidence, based on both autocorrelation analysis (Reid [1969], Newbold and Granger [1974]) and spectral analysis (Granger [1966]), suggests that some generalization is possible. It appears that, while levels of economic time series are generally nonstationary, stationarity can frequently be achieved by first differencing. Thus, in the terminology of Chapter 3, ARIMA(p, d, q) models with $d = 1$ are frequently appropriate. The simplest model in this class is the random walk $X_t - X_{t-1} = \epsilon_t$ and, indeed, this model has been found to represent well price series in speculative markets, an observation that dates back to Bachelier [1900]. A more general formulation is provided by the first-order moving average process for changes:

$$X_t - X_{t-1} = \epsilon_t + b_1 \epsilon_{t-1} \tag{6.4.1}$$

In our experience, the model (6.4.1)—possibly with the addition of a constant term—provides a very good representation of a wide range of economic time series. We certainly do not advocate the adoption of this model on all occasions, preferring rather to go though the model building procedure described in Chapter 3. However, if some simple specific model is to be assumed on a priori grounds, we feel that the first-order integrated moving average process is a serious candidate for economic time series in general, and would certainly expect it typically to provide a better representation than the first-order autoregressive process $X_t - a_1 X_{t-1} = \epsilon_t$, with a_1 constrained to be less than unity, commonly assumed by earlier writers.

Consider now the regression model

$$Y_t = \mathbf{x}_t' \boldsymbol{\beta} + u_t \tag{6.4.2}$$

where a constant term is included in the regression, so that $x_{1t} = 1$ for all t. Suppose that the null hypothesis

$$H_0: \quad \beta_2 = \beta_3 = \cdots = \beta_K = 0 \tag{6.4.3}$$

is true, so that Y_t does not depend (linearly) on the "explanatory" variables $X_2, X_3, \ldots, X_K$ at all. It is reasonable to ask whether, given the time series properties of the individual series, high values of R^2 are likely to obtain, leading to rejection of the null hypothesis (6.4.3) through the conventional test based on the F statistic, if ordinary linear regression methods are applied to (6.4.2) and the message of the Durbin–Watson statistic is unheeded. This question is approached, largely through simulation, by Granger and Newbold [1974]. First, it should be noted that the usual F statistic

$$F = \frac{R^2}{1 - R^2} \frac{n - K}{K - 1}$$

is only distributed as Fisher's F with $K - 1$ and $n - K$ degrees of freedom under the null hypothesis if the error series u_t is white noise. But, if the null hypothesis is true, then $u_t = Y_t - \beta_1$, in which case the time series structure of u_t is the same as that of Y_t. Thus, if Y_t represents the level of an economic variable, in which case its time series structure will be very far from that of white noise, the conventional test statistic cannot follow its assumed distribution under the null hypothesis, and hence the associated test is invalid. That is to say, high values of R^2 may well occur even if the null hypothesis is true, and one would observe a spurious regression.

The simplest case in which a spurious regression can arise involving IMA(1, 1) series would be the regression of a random walk on an independent random walk. To get some notion of the magnitude of the problems involved, suppose Y_t and X_t are *independent* first-order autoregressive processes $Y_t = aY_{t-1} + \epsilon_t$ and $X_t = a^*X_{t-1} + \eta_t$. Then it is well known that the sample correlation R between X_t and Y_t has variance

$$\text{var}(R) = n^{-1}(1 + aa^*)/(1 - aa^*)$$

(see, e.g., Kendall [1954].) It is instructive to consider the probability distribution of R. Since the whole density must lie in the region $(-1, 1)$, it follows that the distribution cannot have a single mode at zero if its variance is greater than $\frac{1}{3}$, this being the variance of a rectangular (uniform) distribution on $(-1, 1)$. For $n = 20$ and $a = a^*$, $\text{var}(R)$ is greater than $\frac{1}{3}$ if $a > 0.86$, and if $a = 0.9$, $E(R^2) = 0.47$. Thus it is clear that high values of R^2 can arise even from relating independent stationary series.

In order to assess the consequences of relating independent integrated processes, using conventional linear regression methods, Granger and Newbold conducted two simulation experiments. First, the equation $Y_t = \beta_1 + \beta_2 X_t + u_t$ was fitted to generated series of 50 observations, with Y and X independent random walks. The ratio of $\hat{\beta}_2$, in absolute value, to its estimated standard error

$$S = \frac{|\hat{\beta}_2|}{\hat{\text{SE}}(\hat{\beta}_2)}$$

is generally employed to test the null hypothesis $\beta_2 = 0$. In this expression, $\hat{\text{SE}}(\hat{\beta}_2)$ is the estimated standard error of the coefficient estimate obtained from the usual linear regression procedure and is, of course, inappropriate when the error series is not white noise. The frequency distribution of this quantity over 100 simulations is given in Table 6.1. Using the traditional t test at the 5% level, the null hypothesis of no relation would be rejected (wrongly) on about three-fourths of all occasions. Note, further, that for more than one-half of the simulation runs the estimate of β_2 is more than four times its standard error, and is more than six times its standard error on over one-fourth of the runs. Thus an apparently high degree of fit can very often be achieved simply by regressing independent random walks.

Table 6.1   *Regressing two independent random walks*

S:	0–1	1–2	2–3	3–4	4–5	5–6	6–7	7–8
Frequency:	13	10	11	13	18	8	8	5

S:	8–9	9–10	10–11	11–12	12–13	13–14	14–15	15–16
Frequency:	3	3	1	5	0	1	0	1

A second, more comprehensive, simulation involved regressing a series Y on m independent series X_j, $j = 2, 3, \ldots, m + 1$, with m taking values from one to five. The series involved all followed the same time series models, which were taken to be:

   (i)   random walks;
   (ii) white noises—i.e., changes in random walks;
   (iii) IMA(1, 1) processes;
   (iv) MA(1) processes—i.e., first differences of IMA(1, 1).

All the series used in a given run were independent of one another. Typical series were generated as follows. Set W_0 equal to 100 and

$$W_t = W_{t-1} + \eta_t, \qquad t = 1, 2, \ldots, 50$$

where η_t is a white noise process. Set

$$W_t^* = W_t + k\epsilon_t, \qquad t = 1, 2, \ldots, 50, \quad k = 0 \text{ or } 1$$

where ϵ_t is white noise independent of η_t. A value $k = 0$ gives a random walk for W_t^*, and if $k = 1$, W_t^* is IMA(1, 1). The white noise processes used were normally distributed, with zero means and unit variances. Table 6.2 summarizes the results obtained over 100 simulations, the null hypothesis tested being that the set of independent variables contributes nothing toward explanation of variation in the dependent variable. The results in this table ought to occasion a good deal of alarm among the fraternity of applied econometricians prone to report equations with high $\bar{R}^2$'s and dubious values for the Durbin–Watson statistic. Indeed, it is not unreasonable to suggest that a good many economic hypotheses, hitherto regarded as "empirically verified," might warrant reexamination on statistical grounds. The message from the table is very clear. When random walks or integrated moving average processes are involved, the chances of "discovering" a spurious relationship using conventional test procedures are very high indeed, increasing with the number m of independent variables included in the regression. Although the values for $\bar{R}^2$ are not quite as high, on average, when regressions involve IMA(1, 1) processes, the results here are if anything more disquieting than those for random walks since the average values for the associated Durbin–Watson statistics are a good deal higher and might thus be expected to occasion less alarm among the unwary. The main conclusion to be drawn from the results concerning regressions on levels in Table 6.2 is that it will be the rule rather than the exception to find spurious

Table 6.2   *Regressions of a series on m independent "explanatory" series*

	Percent times H_0 rejected[a]	Average Durbin–Watson d	Average $\overline{R}^2$	Percent $\overline{R}^2 > 0.7$
		Random walks		
Levels $m = 1$	76	0.32	0.26	5
$m = 2$	78	0.46	0.34	8
$m = 3$	93	0.55	0.46	25
$m = 4$	95	0.74	0.55	34
$m = 5$	96	0.88	0.59	37
Changes $m = 1$	8	2.00	0.004	0
$m = 2$	4	1.99	0.001	0
$m = 3$	2	1.91	−0.007	0
$m = 4$	10	2.01	0.006	0
$m = 5$	6	1.99	0.012	0
		IMA(1, 1)		
Levels $m = 1$	64	0.73	0.20	3
$m = 2$	81	0.96	0.30	7
$m = 3$	82	1.09	0.37	11
$m = 4$	90	1.14	0.44	9
$m = 5$	90	1.26	0.45	19
Changes $m = 1$	8	2.58	0.003	0
$m = 2$	12	2.57	0.01	0
$m = 3$	7	2.53	0.005	0
$m = 4$	9	2.53	0.025	0
$m = 5$	13	2.54	0.027	0

[a] Overall F test, based on $\overline{R}^2$, at 5% level.

relationships and hence that a high value of R^2 or $\overline{R}^2$ is an indication of nothing at all if the associated value of d is low, except that the model is in some way misspecified. We do not advocate first differencing as a universal panacea for all problems in econometric work. For example, in the IMA(1, 1) case, the null hypothesis is still rejected twice as often as it should be when first differences are employed since the assumed error structure is still not the correct one. The optimal strategy, if at all possible, remains the selection of an appropriate time series specification for the errors from the general autoregressive integrated moving average class. However, in small samples or complex models, this may not be feasible, and in the presence of severe autocorrelation of the errors in such situations, first differencing might be expected to go a long way toward alleviating the problem and is certainly preferable to doing nothing at all. As an example of the effect of such a transformation on the conclusions that might be drawn from a regression analysis, consider some results of Sheppard [1971], who regressed U.K. consumption on autonomous expenditure and midyear money stock for both levels and changes, using annual data over the period 1947–1962. The results are shown in Table 6.3, from which it can be seen that an apparently highly

Table 6.3   *Regression of U.K. consumption*
on autonomous expenditure and midyear
money stock; annual data 1947–1962

	$\overline{R}^2$	d
Levels	0.99	0.59
Changes	− 0.03	2.21

significant relationship (ignoring the message of the d statistic) disappears entirely when first differences are employed.

What can be said then of the many large econometric models containing equations with high values for R^2 associated with suspiciously low values for d? Do they contain relationships that are, in fact, spurious? Such a question could be answered only by reestimating the models with appropriate error structures, but it must be added that the potential for finding such relations inherent in the mode of construction is very high indeed, and this potential is further increased by the experimentation involved in the model building process. One piece of evidence in this context concerns the emphasis placed by model builders on the need to adjust models when estimated coefficients, while significant statistically, have the "wrong" signs. We doubt whether this phenomenon would arise nearly so often if appropriate error structures were employed. It would, of course, be foolish to expect models with spurious equations to forecast successfully. Indeed, if spurious equations are present, we would expect conditional forecasts, the ability to derive which is often claimed as the great strength of econometric models, to be most seriously affected.

The results so far presented in this section serve to highlight a phenomenon that has long been recognized by econometricians, that autocorrelated errors, if ignored, can seriously invalidate the usual tests of significance. Perhaps the best treatment in the econometric literature is given in Chapter 13 of Malinvaud [1966]. Very often, in applied work dealing with single equations, some corrective action is taken when serially correlated errors are detected. However, this is rather more rare in large simultaneous equations model estimation—a notable exception is Fair [1970]. However, as indicated in Section 6.2, the classical approach typically is to test the null hypothesis of white noise residuals against the alternative of first-order autoregression, no other possible formulation being contemplated in the subsequent estimation. We find it very difficult to justify the first-order autoregressive model as being generally appropriate for regression equation error structure. Indeed it would be difficult to make out an a priori case for *any* time series structure as being always the "correct" one. However, some sort of a case can be made for considering the IMA(1, 1) process as at least a reasonable alternative in many situations. It has already been seen that, if the regression equation (6.4.2) involves the levels of economic time series, the integrated moving average formulation for the errors might reasonably be expected to be appropriate under the null hypothesis (6.4.3). Even if the null hypothesis is false, one might argue that the residual u_t is simply the sum of a (possibly very large) number of factors that for one reason or another have been omitted from the list of explanatory variables. If these factors are (or behave like) levels of economic time series, then u_t is the sum of integrated moving average processes of first order, and hence is itself IMA(1, 1), provided the individual processes are independent or have specific simple interrelationships. In fact the argument can be taken further since the sum of independent IMA(1, 1) processes and white noise processes remains IMA(1, 1). It is thus reasonable to conclude that the first-order integrated moving average process deserves consideration as an alternative specification of error structure. (Similar arguments would suggest the possibility of the first-order moving average process when the regression involves first differences.) One is thus led to ask how much is lost, both in testing for autocorrelated errors and in making inference upon correcting for serial correlation, when the alternative of first-order autoregression is assumed and the correct specification is IMA(1, 1). Intuitively the answer would seem to be that this procedure ought to be better than doing nothing at all, but will remain suboptimal since the assumed error structure is still incorrect.

Newbold and Davies [1978] attempt to assess by simulation the potential importance of this type of misspecification. These authors generated independent IMA(1, 1) processes

$$Y_t = Y_{t-1} + \eta_t + b^*\eta_{t-1}, \qquad Y_0 = 100, \quad t = 1, 2, \ldots, 50$$

$$X_{j,t} = X_{j,t-1} + \epsilon_{j,t} + b\epsilon_{j,t-1}, \qquad X_{j,0} = 100, \quad t = 1, 2, \ldots, 50,$$

$$j = 1, 2, \ldots, 4$$

where η_t, $\epsilon_{j,t}$ ($j = 1, \ldots, 4$) were independent normal white noise series, each with variance one. The regressions of Y_t on $X_{1,t}$ and on $X_{j,t}$ ($j = 1, \ldots, 4$) were estimated by ordinary least squares and the significance of the overall regressions tested at the 5% level through the usual t- and F-tests. The Durbin–Watson statistics for these regressions were also computed. The results are summarized in Tables 6.4 and 6.5 for various values of the moving average parameters b and b^*.

It can be seen from these tables that, generally, the spurious regression phenomenon will arise relatively infrequently if the analyst accepts only those regressions where the t- or F-statistics are significant and the Durbin–Watson statistic does not indicate the presence of serially correlated errors. For example, in Table 6.4 there is only cause for concern when $-b^*$ is as high as 0.8. In that case approximately 20% of the fitted regressions yielded significant t-statistics for the slope parameter and insignificant Durbin–Watson statistics. This comes about because the first sample serial correlation coefficient for the IMA(1, 1) error structure of the true model will

Table 6.4   Percentage of times t and d statistics are significant at 5% level in 1,000 replications for regression of an IMA(1,1) series on an independent IMA(1,1) series

| | | b = 0.0 | | b = −0.2 | | b = −0.4 | | b = −0.6 | | b = −0.8 | |
| | | t | | t | | t | | t | | t | |
		Not Significant	Significant	Not Significant	Significant	Not Significant	Significant	Not Significant	Significant	Not Significant	Significant
b* = 0.0	Not Significant	0.0	0.1	0.0	0.0	0.0	0.1	0.0	0.2	0.0	0.0
d	Inconclusive	0.0	0.0	0.0	0.0	0.0	0.1	0.0	0.0	0.0	0.0
	Significant	33.0	66.9	35.6	64.4	37.1	62.7	44.6	55.2	61.0	39.0
	Mean d	0.328		0.355		0.397		0.424		0.362	
b* = −0.2	Not Significant	0.0	0.2	0.0	0.0	0.0	0.0	0.0	0.1	0.0	0.0
d	Inconclusive	0.0	0.0	0.0	0.1	0.0	0.0	0.1	0.0	0.0	0.0
	Significant	33.7	66.1	35.8	64.1	38.6	61.4	45.0	54.8	61.9	38.1
	Mean d	0.449		0.470		0.504		0.521		0.451	
b* = −0.4	Not Significant	0.3	1.6	0.5	1.1	0.5	0.5	0.7	0.5	0.4	0.1
d	Inconclusive	0.1	0.7	0.4	0.7	0.7	1.1	0.5	0.8	0.4	0.2
	Significant	37.2	60.1	36.4	60.9	40.1	57.1	47.0	50.5	64.0	34.9
	Mean d	0.705		0.714		0.721		0.723		0.635	
b* = −0.6	Not Significant	5.1	6.9	6.7	7.7	6.2	7.4	6.7	6.2	5.9	2.4
d	Inconclusive	2.4	2.6	2.0	3.0	1.6	2.4	2.1	2.4	2.7	1.1
	Significant	34.2	48.8	33.9	46.7	38.4	44.0	44.7	37.9	62.7	25.2
	Mean d	1.089		1.104		1.118		1.105		1.016	
b* = −0.8	Not Significant	38.8	21.2	41.9	21.6	37.0	22.2	38.6	19.0	44.2	9.2
d	Inconclusive	6.2	3.3	5.3	2.8	5.6	2.4	6.2	2.3	7.5	1.5
	Significant	19.8	10.7	18.1	10.3	21.0	11.8	23.7	10.2	29.9	7.7
	Mean d	1.664		1.705		1.668		1.650		1.614	

Table 6.5   Percentage of times F and d statistics are significant at 5% level in 500 replications for regression of an IMA(1,1) series on four independent IMA(1,1) series

			b = 0.0 F		b = -0.2 F		b = -0.4 F		b = -0.6 F		b = -0.8 F	
			Not Significant	Significant	Not Significant	Significant	Not Significant	Significant	Not Significant	Significant	Not Significant	Significant
b* = 0.0	d	Not Significant	0.0	0.4	0.0	0.4	0.0	0.4	0.0	0.0	0.0	0.2
		Inconclusive	0.0	1.8	0.0	2.6	0.0	4.0	0.0	3.4	0.0	0.4
		Significant	4.8	93.0	4.0	93.0	5.2	90.4	13.4	83.2	31.0	68.4
		Mean d	0.718		0.771		0.806		0.824		0.702	
b* = -0.2	d	Not Significant	0.0	0.4	0.0	0.4	0.0	1.4	0.2	0.6	0.2	0.0
		Inconclusive	0.0	4.6	0.2	8.2	0.2	6.8	0.2	6.2	0.0	1.8
		Significant	5.6	89.4	7.2	84.0	6.6	85.0	16.2	76.6	36.4	61.6
		Mean d	0.865		0.927		0.933		0.900		0.758	
b* = -0.4	d	Not Significant	0.2	5.8	0.4	6.4	0.8	3.8	0.2	3.0	0.0	0.8
		Inconclusive	0.6	19.8	0.8	21.2	2.2	17.2	2.2	17.6	2.6	6.4
		Significant	8.0	65.6	6.2	65.0	8.8	65.2	15.0	62.0	37.8	52.4
		Mean d	1.142		1.176		1.171		1.138		0.972	
b* = -0.6	d	Not Significant	5.8	28.2	8.6	27.8	4.0	28.0	6.2	17.4	6.2	5.2
		Inconclusive	5.2	27.6	5.6	27.8	6.4	28.4	10.6	23.0	14.8	13.4
		Significant	6.0	27.2	6.8	23.4	6.4	26.8	14.4	28.4	33.0	27.4
		Mean d	1.550		1.561		1.538		1.458		1.286	
b* = -0.8	d	Not Significant	40.6	39.0	38.2	38.2	38.4	37.2	41.4	26.6	40.2	14.4
		Inconclusive	5.2	11.0	9.8	9.4	9.9	10.3	14.8	9.0	23.8	7.0
		Significant	2.0	2.2	1.8	2.6	1.2	3.0	3.6	4.6	9.6	5.0
		Mean d	1.975		1.932		1.938		1.853		WC1.740	

generally be quite small, as is reflected by the relatively high values for the averages of the Durbin–Watson statistics. From Table 6.5 we see that the problem is slightly more serious when there are as many as four independent variables in the regression model. Using this approach, spurious regressions appear quite frequently when $-b^*$ is as high as 0.6.

This, however, is not the end of the story, for, when the possibility of autocorrelated errors is indicated, the regression should be refitted to allow for this factor. Suppose now, as is very common practice, that the analyst assumes a first-order autoregressive process for the error terms and estimates the regression model. Tables 6.6 and 6.7 summarize some results for our generated data, when using the estimation procedure of Cochrane and Orcutt [1949] to "correct" for first-order autoregressive errors. Since the error structure is still misspecified, we would suspect that the spurious regression phenomenon could still occur, and this is confirmed by inspection of these tables.

It can be seen that, for a wide range of values of the two moving average parameters, the appearance of an apparently significant relationship between independent time series will arise disturbingly often. The problem is most serious for higher numbers of independent variables, with large values of $-b^*$ and small or moderate values of $-b$.

The message of these simulation results is that, while taking some corrective action in the face of autocorrelated errors is likely to be better than doing nothing at all, blind adherence to some simple convenient procedure

Table 6.6   *Percentage of times t statistic is significant at 5% level in 1,000 replications for regression of an IMA(1, 1) series on an independent IMA(1, 1) series, "corrected" for first order autoregressive errors*

	$b = 0.0$	$b = -0.2$	$b = -0.4$	$b = -0.6$	$b = -0.8$
$b^* = 0.0$	11.5	8.3	6.5	4.5	4.7
$b^* = -0.2$	15.8	12.3	11.0	7.1	6.6
$b^* = -0.4$	23.6	22.9	15.9	11.0	8.2
$b^* = -0.6$	32.3	30.7	25.5	19.7	9.8
$b^* = -0.8$	28.9	27.3	25.5	22.7	12.0

Table 6.7   *Percentage of times F statistic is significant at 5% level in 500 replications for regression of an IMA(1, 1) series on four independent IMA(1, 1) series, "corrected" for first order autoregressive errors*

	$b = 0.0$	$b = -0.2$	$b = -0.4$	$b = -0.6$	$b = -0.8$
$b^* = 0.0$	24.4	18.6	9.8	6.2	5.0
$b^* = -0.2$	40.0	27.6	20.6	10.0	6.8
$b^* = -0.4$	59.6	54.8	36.0	23.4	10.8
$b^* = -0.6$	66.4	62.2	59.0	37.2	16.8
$b^* = -0.8$	52.6	48.8	59.4	35.8	21.6

could very often lead the analyst astray. Rather than assume *a priori* some specific generating model for the error process, it is preferable to allow for the possibility of a number of alternative models and use the evidence of the data to distinguish among them.

Phillips [1985] has recently obtained some interesting asymptotic results for the sampling distributions of estimators of parameters in a spurious regression. He found that if nondrifting random walks are regressed using a least squares procedure, then, asymptotically, the distribution of R^2 is nondegenerate so that a positive R^2 value can occur, d tends to zero in probability, and the t-statistic when divided by the square root of the sample size tends to a nondegenerate, finite variance distribution but not the t-distribution. He further finds that the estimate of α has variance proportional to the sample size, so that this estimate divided by the square root of the sample size tends to a random variable with finite variance.

CHAPTER SEVEN

MULTIPLE SERIES MODELING AND FORECASTING

Sagittarius (November 22nd–December 22nd)
Precautions should be taken against running into unforeseen occurrences or events.

ASTROLOGER, NEWS CHRONICLE

7.1 Introduction

The first five chapters of this book were concerned with model building and forecasting for a single time series, without use of information provided by other series. In this and the next chapter, a methodology for constructing multiple time series models is developed and illustrated, and the derivation of forecasts from such models considered.

An alternative methodology, whereby forecasts are calculated on the basis of a very wide information set, is the classical econometric approach, discussed in the previous chapter. The procedures employed here differ in two respects. First, the form of the model will be determined by the data alone, economic theory being employed only to suggest what variables might be relevant. Second, just as in the single series case the objective is to find a model that transforms a given series to white noise, the aim here is to build a model that transforms a vector of time series to a white noise vector.

7.2 Theoretical Models for Multiple Time Series

Before examining the practical model building problem, it is necessary to develop some multiple time series theory. Let $\mathbf{X}_t$ be a vector time series, with $\mathbf{X}'_t = (X_{1,t}, X_{2,t}, \ldots, X_{m,t})$, where each individual series is stationary and purely nondeterministic. The set of m series is called jointly covariance stationary if

$$\lambda_\tau^{(i,j)} = \mathrm{cov}(X_{i,t}, X_{j,t-\tau})$$

is independent of t for all i, j, and τ, and $\lambda_0^{(i,i)} < \infty$ for all i. The multivariate generalization of Wold's decomposition theorem then states that X_t can always be represented by

$$X_t = c(B)\eta_t \qquad (7.2.1)$$

where $c(B)$ is an $m \times m$ matrix in the back-shift operator B, with typical element

$$c_{ij}(B) = \sum_{k=0}^{\infty} c_{ij,k} B^k$$

and η_t is a vector white noise process, with $\eta_t' = (\eta_{1,t}, \eta_{2,t}, \ldots, \eta_{m,t})$ having the properties

$$E[\eta_{i,t}] = 0, \quad \text{all } i; \qquad E[\eta_{i,t}\eta_{j,t-\tau}] = 0, \quad \text{all } \tau, \quad i \neq j$$
$$= 0, \quad \tau \neq 0, \quad i = j$$

A proof of this theorem is given in Hannan [1970].

The typical equation in (7.2.1) is

$$X_{i,t} = \sum_k c_{i1,k}\eta_{1,t-k} + \sum_k c_{i2,k}\eta_{2,t-k} + \cdots + \sum_k c_{im,k}\eta_{m,t-k}$$

so that any $X_{i,t}$ is a weighted sum of current and past values of each of m uncorrelated white noise series. The advantage of the matrix notation is obvious.

If the matrix $c(B)$ can in some way be approximated by the product of two matrices, $a^{-1}(B)$ and $b(B)$, each involving only finite-order polynomials in B, one is led to consider the class of linear models

$$a(B)X_t = b(B)\eta_t \qquad (7.2.2)$$

where typical elements of $a(B)$ and $b(B)$ are

$$a_{ij}(B) = \sum_{k=0}^{p_{ij}} a_{ij,k}B^k \quad \text{and} \quad b_{ij}(B) = \sum_{k=0}^{q_{ij}} b_{ij,k}B^k$$

Equation (7.2.2) represents a multivariate mixed autoregressive moving average process, denoted ARMA(p, q) where $p = \{p_{ij}\}$ and $q = \{q_{ij}\}$ are $m \times m$ matrices. If $b(B) = b_0$, a matrix of degree zero in B, then the process is multivariate autoregressive; and if $a(B) = a_0$, the model is multivariate moving average. The process is stationary, in the sense that the model has no explosive solutions, if the roots of $|a(z)| = 0$ all lie outside the unit circle, and is said to be invertible if the roots of $|b(z)| = 0$ lie outside the unit circle. It will be assumed here and throughout this chapter that both conditions hold (possibly after the given series have been suitably differenced). It will also be assumed that $a(z)$ is of full rank for every z in or on the unit circle, so that $a(B)$ can be taken to possess an inverse. A similar assumption is made for $b(z)$.

If a model of the form (7.2.2) is an adequate approximation to reality, with the largest elements of $\mathbf{p}$ and $\mathbf{q}$ of reasonable size, it seems plausible that such models could be identified and estimated, given sufficient data. Practical problems of this kind will be discussed in the next chapter, but for the present it is assumed that data are generated by some multivariate ARMA model, and some consequences of this assumption will be explored.

To begin, a number of alternative representations are considered. It is straightforward to verify that an equivalent representation to (7.2.2) is the transfer function-noise form

$$X_{i,t} = \sum_{j \neq i} \frac{\omega_{ij}^*(B)}{\delta_{ij}^*(B)} X_{j,t} + \frac{\theta_i^*(B)}{\phi_i^*(B)} \eta_{i,t}, \qquad i = 1, 2, \ldots, m \qquad (7.2.3)$$

where all polynomials in B are of finite order.

For example, equations of the form (7.2.3) can be derived from (7.2.2) by considering the inverse of $\mathbf{b}(B)$, $\mathbf{b}^{-1}(B) = |\mathbf{b}(B)|^{-1}\mathbf{b}^*(B)$ where $\mathbf{b}^*(B)$ denotes the adjoint matrix (the transpose of the matrix of cofactors). Hence (7.2.2) can be written

$$\mathbf{b}^*(B)\mathbf{a}(B)\mathbf{X}_t = |\mathbf{b}(B)|\mathbf{\eta}_t$$

from which equations of the type (7.2.3) immediately follow. Models of this form will be fitted to actual data in the next chapter.

Since, in (7.2.2), $\mathbf{a}(B)$ is taken to possess an inverse, the corresponding MA(∞) form is (7.2.1), with $\mathbf{c}(B) = \mathbf{a}^{-1}(B)\mathbf{b}(B)$. As in the single series case, this form is particularly useful in forecasting.

A further form of the model, of some interest, follows by noting that

$$\mathbf{a}^{-1}(B) = \mathbf{a}^*(B)/|\mathbf{a}(B)|$$

where $\mathbf{a}^*(B)$ is the adjoint matrix of $\mathbf{a}(B)$. It follows that (7.2.2) can be written

$$|\mathbf{a}(B)|\mathbf{X}_t = \mathbf{a}^*(B)\mathbf{b}(B)\mathbf{\eta}_t$$

and the ith equation is simply

$$|\mathbf{a}(B)|X_{i,t} = \alpha_i'(B)\mathbf{\eta}_t \qquad (7.2.4)$$

where $\alpha_i'(B)$ is the ith row of $\mathbf{a}^*(B)\mathbf{b}(B)$. Thus each $X_{i,t}$ is now explained in terms of its own past plus an error series in moving average form, although the error series are interrelated from one explanatory equation to another. Now, it appears from (7.2.4) that the autoregressive parts of each of the ARMA single series models, appropriate to the $X_{i,t}$, are identical. In fact this is illusory since $|\mathbf{a}(B)|$ will typically have common factors, or near common factors, with the moving average operator that follows from the right-hand side of (7.2.4). However, this equation does provide a further illustration of why the single series mixed ARMA model might be expected to occur frequently.

In certain circumstances, often assumed by econometricians to arise, the variables X_t may be partitioned into two distinct groups. Consider the model (7.2.2), written as

$$\begin{bmatrix} a^{11}(B) & a^{12}(B) \\ a^{21}(B) & a^{22}(B) \end{bmatrix} \begin{bmatrix} X_t^{(1)} \\ X_t^{(2)} \end{bmatrix} = \begin{bmatrix} b^{11}(B) & b^{12}(B) \\ b^{21}(B) & b^{22}(B) \end{bmatrix} \begin{bmatrix} \eta_t^{(1)} \\ \eta_t^{(2)} \end{bmatrix}$$

where $X_t' = (X_t^{(1)\prime}, X_t^{(2)\prime})$, $\eta_t' = (\eta_t^{(1)\prime}, \eta_t^{(2)\prime})$. If, in this equation, $a^{21}(B)$, $b^{12}(B)$, and $b^{21}(B)$ are all identically zero, the equations decompose into two blocks

$$a^{11}(B)X_t^{(1)} + a^{12}(B)X_t^{(2)} = b^{11}(B)\eta_t^{(1)} \tag{7.2.5}$$

and

$$a^{22}(B)X_t^{(2)} = b^{22}(B)\eta_t^{(2)} \tag{7.2.6}$$

where $X_t^{(1)}$ and $\eta_t^{(1)}$ are vectors of size m_1; $X_t^{(2)}$ and $\eta_t^{(2)}$ are vectors of size m_2; and $m_1 + m_2 = m$. In fact the decomposition arises even if $b^{12}(B) \neq 0$, for then the additional term $b^{12}(B)\eta_t^{(2)}$ in (7.2.5) is equal, by (7.2.6), to

$$\frac{b^{12}(B)(b^{22})^*(B)a^{22}(B)X_t^{(2)}}{|b^{22}(B)|}$$

where $(b^{22})^*(B)$ is the adjoint matrix. Substituting for $b^{12}(B)\eta_t^{(2)}$ in the augmented (7.2.5), multiplying through by $|b^{22}(B)|$ and collecting terms yields an equation in the same form as (7.2.5) above. For such a decomposition to occur, it is necessary that the components of $X_t^{(2)}$ cause those of $X_t^{(1)}$, but not vice versa. The concept of causality is discussed at some length in Section 7.3, and so will not be defined here. The variables $X_t^{(1)}$ are then termed endogenous and $X_t^{(2)}$ exogenous, corresponding to the definitions introduced in Section 6.3. The set of equations (7.2.5) then constitutes the structural equations of the model, while (7.2.6) determines the quantities $X_t^{(2)}$ exclusively in terms of previous values of this vector. The structural form is frequently employed by econometricians, economic theory being employed to suggest some specific values in $a^{11}(B)$ and $a^{12}(B)$ that may well be useful both in identifying model structure and ensuring that the achieved model is estimable, a problem that will be discussed in the following section. The use of structural equations for forecasting purposes was discussed in Section 6.3. However, their primary use is in the analysis of the structure of an economic system.

If $a^{11}(z)$ is of full rank for all $|z| \leq 1$, then (7.2.5) can be transformed to

$$X_t^{(1)} = -(a^{11}(0))^{-1}(a^{11}(B) - a^{11}(0))X_t^{(1)} - (a^{11}(0))^{-1}a^{12}(B)X_t^{(2)}$$
$$+ (a^{11}(0))^{-1}b^{11}(B)\eta_t^{(1)}$$

so that each member of $X_t^{(1)}$ is expressed as a linear sum of past $X_t^{(1)}$ values, current and past $X_t^{(2)}$ values, and a moving average error term. This corresponds to the reduced form of Section 6.3, and is clearly useful for forecasting $X_t^{(1)}$ conditioned on $X_t^{(2)}$ being given.

One further form is obtained by multiplying through (7.2.5) by $(a^{11}(B))^{-1}$, so that each endogenous variable is expressed as the linear combination of current and past values of the exogenous variables and an ARMA error term. The resulting system of transfer function-noise equations is called the final form of the model. The uses of the various forms of the basic model (7.2.2) have been discussed by Zellner and Palm [1974] and Wallis [1977]. Although theoretically equivalent, some forms are easier to estimate, some convenient for the introduction of prior information, and some for forecasting. Various situations may call for one form rather than another, as will be seen in later sections.

One final point concerning structural forms should be added. Econometricians will typically analyze a system of equations like (7.2.5), ignoring (7.2.6). However, it follows from the derivation, and is otherwise obvious since in general m equations are required to determine m variables, that such a system is incomplete, requiring addition of the mechanism by which the exogenous variables are generated. This is the reason that econometric models can typically be used directly to calculate only conditional rather than unconditional forecasts. In the computation of unconditional forecasts, the usual econometric approach is to first forecast the exogenous variables judgmentally, rather than through a system of equations like (7.2.6).

7.3 Causality and Feedback

Research workers often find it necessary to discuss the causation of an event or sequence of events, and when analyzing a vector of time series it is useful to ask if one group of series is generated separately from another group. To give operational meaning to these ideas, acceptable definitions need to be derived and in particular a testable definition of causality obtained. A possible way of doing this is discussed in this section. Specific methods of testing the definition presented here will be discussed in Section 8.5.

Two assumptions are made, which are found to be generally acceptable:

(i) The future cannot cause the past. Strict causality can only occur with the past causing the present or future.

(ii) A cause contains unique information about an effect that is not available elsewhere.

Given these rules, a possible definition of causality is as follows: Let $F(A|B)$ denote the conditional distribution function of A given B, let Ω_t represent all the information in the universe at time t, and ask whether the series Y_t cause the series X_t. Then if

$$F(X_{t+k}|\Omega_t) = F(X_{t+k}|\Omega_t - Y_t) \qquad (7.3.1)$$

for all $k > 0$, where $\Omega_t - Y_t$ is all the information in the universe apart from the series Y_t, then Y_t does not cause X_t. If (7.3.1) does not hold, then Y_t does cause X_t. It is seen that the series Y_t has information helping to characterize future X's that is unique. Not everyone would agree that causation is the correct term to use for this situation, but we shall continue to do so as it is both simple and clearly defined. It should also be noted that Ω_t will include X_t, so that Y_t contains information about some X_{t+k}, and this information is not to be found in past X's.

Feedback will occur if Y causes X and also X causes Y. These need not both occur, as some simple examples can show. The definition given above does not allow for instantaneous causality (IC). Unfortunately, data limitations often make something akin to IC appear likely. If the true delay between cause and effect is one day but if the stochastic processes are only observed monthly, IC will seem to occur. A definition of apparent IC between Y_t and X_t would be

$$P(X_{t+1}|\Omega_{t+1} - X_{t+1}) \neq P(X_{t+1}|\Omega_{t+1} - X_{t+1} - Y_{t+1})$$

Whether all IC can be explained in terms of data inadequacies is unclear, although various possibilities are discussed in Granger [1985a]. However, it is clear that it is not possible, in general, to differentiate between instantaneous causation in either direction and instantaneous feedback. Thus, the idea of instantaneous causality is of little or no practical value. One might be able to make conditional interpretations if one adds extra information or structure to the situation, such as "I know X_t cannot cause Y_t."

The definition as it stands is too general to be testable. It is possible to reach a testable definition only by imposing considerable simplification and particularization to this definition. It must be recognized that, in so doing, the definition will become less intuitively acceptable and more prone to error. Suppose that an information set J_n is available at time n, including X_{n-j} and $\mathbf{Z}_{n-j}$, $j \geq 0$, where $\mathbf{Z}$ is some vector of other series but excluding Y_{n-j}, $j \geq 0$. Furthermore, define the expanded information set J_n': J_n plus Y_{n-j}, $j \geq 0$. Denote by $F(X_{n+k}|J_n)$ the conditional distribution of X_{n+k} given J_n, so that this distribution has mean $E[X_{n+k}|J_n]$. The following definitions particularize those given previously.

DEFINITION 1 Y_n does not cause X_{n+k} with respect to J_n', if $F(X_{n+k}|J_n)$ $= F(X_{n+k}|J_n')$, all $k > 0$ so that the extra information in J_n' does not affect the conditional distribution. A necessary condition is that

$$E[X_{n+k}|J_n] = E[X_{n+k}|J_n'] \tag{7.3.2}$$

in which case one says that Y_n does not cause X_n in mean with respect to the information set J_n'.

DEFINITION 2   If

$$F(X_{n+k}|J_n') \neq F(X_{n+k}|J_n) \qquad (7.3.3)$$

then Y_n is said to be a *prima facie* cause of X_{n+k} with respect to the information set J_n'. Presumably one is considering such conditional distributions because Y_n is considered to be a possible cause of future X's. The inequality in (7.3.3) means that Y_n has at least satisfied this test, but it still remains *prima facie* because it is always possible that, if a different information set were used, then Y_n would fail the new test. Only if J_n' were the universal set could the words "*prima facie*" be dropped. If the equality in (7.3.2) were an inequality, then Y_n would be a *prima facie* cause of X_{n+k} in mean with respect to the information set J_n'." It is usual to call this a Granger cause or a Wiener–Granger cause in the literature and to consider the definition with just $k = 1$. In this case Y_n helps in providing an improved least squares forecast for X_{n+1} than if Y_n is not used. A number of apparently different, derivative definitions have been suggested but have usually been proved to be equivalent (see Chamberlain [1982]).

There are a number of consequences of the definitions.

(i)   Backward filters of the form $\sum_{j \geq 0} a_j B^j$, $a_0 \neq 0$ can be applied to X_t, Y_t without any changes in the causal interpretations.

(ii)   If X_t is a deterministic series, so that it can be forecast perfectly from its own past, then there is no possibility of the definition finding that any other series is a cause. In the extreme case, if $X_t = a + bt$, a straight line trend, then it is impossible to test for a causation by any other series, such as another trend.

(iii)   If Y causes X then X may or may not cause Y.

(iv)   If Y causes X and X causes W, then Y may or may not cause W.

Problems with the test can arise from measurement errors (see Newbold [1978]) or from temporal aggregation, where a one-way cause can be made to look like feedback or where a cause can appear to be an instantaneous cause. An extended discussion of the advantages and problems with these definitions can be found in Granger [1980] and Newbold [1982]. A discussion of the relationship between these definitions and some of the definitions of causation used by philosophers can be found in Spohn [1983].

Although tests based on these definition have been widely used in economics and other fields, not everyone believes them to be correct. It has been suggested, for example, that causation can only be accepted if the empirical evidence is associated with a complete and convincing theory explaining how the cause produces the effect. If this viewpoint is taken then "smoking causes cancer" would not be accepted. In Granger [1980] a different viewpoint, a rather casual Bayesian one, is proposed. Suppose that one has a prior belief about the correctness of some theory and that this belief can be expressed in terms of a probability. Thus, when thinking about the proposition that drinking milk causes some internal disorder, we might have a belief probability of 0.3 before undertaking any investigation. If data are gathered and a proper testing procedure undertaken, then the results may make one increase the probability to 0.6. If one does not like the definition used or has doubts about the quality of the data, the correctness of the empirical methods, or the honesty of the investigator, one may not wish to alter the probability of belief. In any case, it is most unlikely that even if the tests are satisfactory, the probability will go to 1.0, which would correspond to total belief in the proposed causality. The application of a definition to data may, nevertheless, produce a significant change in a belief and thus in personal behavior and economic decisions—and this is the major object of most research.

Because a stationary series can be considered to be the sum of many uncorrelated components, these components are related to different frequencies, as discussed in Chapter Two. It is natural to ask if the causal relationships can differ across frequency. Some theoretical procedures were suggested by Granger [1969b] and a rather different but practical procedure has been discussed by Geweke [1982].

The relationships between these approaches and their relevance when applied to actual data has yet to be determined.

A concept related to, and yet different from, causality that is important in classical econometrics, is that of exogeneity. The original idea behind this concept is that one variable, say Z_t, may be generated in one system and then have its value entered as a causal variable in another system. For example, monthly rainfall is generated by the local meteorological system and then enters the agricultural economy as a causal variable. If there is always a distinct lag between the generation of the exogenous variable and its appearance in the second system, then the causality testing mechanism would be appropriate to test for exogeneity. However, the presence of instantaneous or contemporaneous relationships destroys this possibility, and other attempts to provide useful definitions based on the original idea have not been successful. It is frequently the case that a classical econometric model is constructed with some group of variables assumed to be exogenous; in this case the quality of the model achieved will depend on the correctness of the assumption.

A rather different approach is taken by Engle, Hendry, and Richard [1983] who carefully define a number of different types of exogeneity and discuss their interrelationships. For example, let $\mathbf{X}_t$ be a vector of series $\mathbf{X}'_t = (Y_t, \mathbf{Z}_t)'$ where $\mathbf{Z}_t$ is possibly exogenous. Define the residual vector

$$\mathbf{u}_t = \mathbf{X}_t - E[\mathbf{X}_t|\mathbf{X}_{t-j}, \, j > 0]$$

Here, $\mathbf{u}_t$ is assumed to be white noise, which it will be if $\mathbf{X}_t$ is either stationary or integrated of a finite order. Then $\mathbf{Z}_t$ is said to be predetermined if it is independent of $\mathbf{u}_{t+i}$, for all $i \geqslant 0$ and to be strictly exogenous if $\mathbf{Z}_t$ is independent of $\mathbf{u}_{t+i}$ for all i. This latter concept reflects the classical idea of exogeneity. The remaining definitions of exogeneity by Engle, Hendry, and Richard are primarily concerned with estimation. Consider the data matrix $\mathbf{X}_t^*$ consisting of the stacked vectors $\mathbf{X}_1, \ldots, \mathbf{X}_t$ and focus attention on the conditional density functions $D(\mathbf{X}_t | \mathbf{X}_{t-1}^*, \theta)$, where θ is a finite dimensional vector of parameters. Note that one has Granger noncausality of $\mathbf{Z}_t$ by Y_{t-j}, $j > 0$ if

$$D(\mathbf{Z}_t | \mathbf{X}_{t-1}^*, \theta) = D(\mathbf{Z}_t | \mathbf{Z}_{t-1}^*, j > 0, \theta)$$

Suppose that θ can be divided into two components of parameters, $\theta = (\theta_1, \theta_2)$, where θ_1 are the parameters of interest for which estimates are required from the sample and θ_2 are nuisance parameters that are not being estimated. Then $\mathbf{Z}_t$ is said to be weakly exogenous for θ_1 if

$$D(\mathbf{X}_t | \mathbf{X}_{t-1}^*, \theta) = D(\mathbf{Y}_t | \mathbf{Z}_t, \mathbf{X}_{t-1}^*, \theta_1) D(\mathbf{Z}_t | \mathbf{X}_{t-1}^*, \theta_2)$$

provided there are no cross restrictions linking θ_1 and θ_2 such as a linear constraint between a component of θ_1 and a component of θ_2. If $\mathbf{Z}_t$ is weakly exogenous for θ_1, it follows that one need not set up a likelihood function for all $\mathbf{X}_t$ but only for the subset $\mathbf{Y}_t$, conditioned on current $\mathbf{Z}_t$ and lagged $\mathbf{X}_t$. The relationship between $\mathbf{Z}_t$ and $\mathbf{X}_{t-1}$ need not be specified when estimating θ_1 without any loss of information or efficiency.

If $\mathbf{Z}_t$ is both weakly exogenous and Y_{t+j}, $j > 0$ does not cause $\mathbf{Z}_t$, then $\mathbf{Z}_t$ is said to be strongly exogenous with respect to θ_1. In this case the likelihood can be factored as

$$D(\mathbf{X}_t, \theta) = D(\mathbf{Y}_t | \mathbf{Z}_t, \theta_1) D(\mathbf{Z}_t, \theta_2)$$

In all these expressions, conditioning on initial values has been ignored.

If $\mathbf{Z}_t$ is weakly exogenous with respect to θ_1, then, for inference about θ_1, $\mathbf{Z}_t$ may be treated as if it were determined outside the conditional model under study, making the analysis simpler and more robust. If $\mathbf{Z}_t$ is strongly exogenous for θ_1, then $\mathbf{Z}_t$ may be treated as fixed for estimation, and forecasting of $\mathbf{Y}_t$ can be made conditional on fixed future $\mathbf{Z}$'s. The definitions can be extended to the situation where parameter values change, such as when a new policy regime is introduced, and tests using Lagrange multipliers have been discussed for weak exogeneity by Engle [1985].

7.4 Co-Integrated Series and Error-Correction Models

There are some special situations in which the models considered in the previous two sections are not the correct specification. There can exist special linear constraints between variables, capable of economic interpretation, that lead to invertibility problems with the Wold representation. Recall that a variable X_t is said to be integrated of order d, denoted $X_t \sim I(d)$, if $(1 - B)^d X_t = Z_t$, where

$$a_p(B) Z_t = b_q(B) \epsilon_t$$

where $a_p(1) \neq 0$, $b_q(1) \neq 0$, and ϵ_t is white noise. Thus, the d-differenced X_t is a finite variance ARMA process. If X_t and Y_t are a pair of $I(d)$ series, then it will be generally true that a linear combination, such as

$$Z_t = X_t - A Y_t$$

will also be $I(d)$. However, it can happen that there exists a constant A such that $Z_t \sim I(d - b)$, $b > 0$. When this happens, the pair of variables X_t and Y_t will be said to be *co-integrated* and denoted $(X_t, Y_t) \sim CI(d, b)$. For ease of exposition, we concentrate on the case of greatest practical importance, with $d = b = 1$, so that X_t, Y_t both need to be differenced once, but there exists an A such that $Z_t = X_t - A Y_t$ is stationary, i.e., $Z_t \sim I(0)$. This is a rather special condition, because it means that both series individually have extremely important long-run components but that in forming Z_t these long-run components cancel out and vanish. A simple analogy is if two series each have seasonal components but they cancel out in Z_t so that Z_t is nonseasonal.

Consider a more general situation, in which a vector $\mathbf{X}_t = \{ X_{jt}, j = 1, \ldots, N \}$ of series has each component $I(1)$ but there exists a vector of weights $\boldsymbol{\alpha}$ such that

$$Z_t = \boldsymbol{\alpha}' \mathbf{X}_t \sim I(0) \tag{7.4.1}$$

Here, $\boldsymbol{\alpha}$ will be called the co-integrating vector, if it exists. Because each component is $I(1)$, there will necessarily be a multivariate Wold representation of the form

$$(1 - B)(\mathbf{X}_t - \mathbf{m}) = \mathbf{C}(B)\epsilon_t \tag{7.4.2}$$

For simplicity, it will be assumed that $\mathbf{m} = \mathbf{0}$ in the rest of this section. When the vector $\boldsymbol{\alpha}'$ is applied to this group of equations, it follows that

$$(1 - B)Z_t = \boldsymbol{\alpha}'\mathbf{C}(B)\epsilon_t$$

By considering the spectrum of each side of this equation, it follows that for Z_t to be $I(0)$ it is necessary that

$$\boldsymbol{\alpha}'\mathbf{C}(1) = \mathbf{0} \tag{7.4.3}$$

where $\mathbf{0}$ is a $1 \times N$ vector of zeros. It then follows that for $\mathbf{X}_t$ to be co-integrated it is necessary that $\mathbf{C}(1)$ be singular. A consequence of this is that $\mathbf{C}(B)$ cannot simply be inverted to give an autoregressive form of (7.4.2). However, by careful consideration of the properties of the adjoint matrix of $\mathbf{C}(B)$ it is shown in Granger [1984] and Granger and Engle [1985] that (7.4.2) can be transformed into

$$(1 - B)\mathbf{X}_t = \mathbf{A}^*(B)(1 - B)\mathbf{X}_t - \boldsymbol{\rho}Z_{t-1} + \mathbf{D}(B)\epsilon_t \tag{7.4.4}$$

where $\mathbf{A}^*(0) = \mathbf{0}$, $\boldsymbol{\rho}$ is a vector of constants, $Z_t = \boldsymbol{\alpha}'\mathbf{X}_t$ as before and $\det(\mathbf{C}(B)) = (1 - B)D(B)$. Thus (7.4.4) gives that changes in the jth component of $\mathbf{X}_t$ are explained in terms of lagged changes of all components plus a constant ρ_j times the lagged Z_t plus a moving average operator (the same for all j) on the jth component of $\boldsymbol{\epsilon}_t$. It should be noted that all components of (7.4.4) are $I(0)$ and so the equation can exist. If $\mathbf{X}_t$ are not co-integrated, then Z_t will be $I(1)$ and the two sides could not be equal, since an infinite variance component cannot explain one of finite variance.

Equation (7.4.4) has an interesting and important interpretation in terms of equilibrium relationships. If a dynamic process is in equilibrium, then changes in the variable will be zero and there will be no innovations $\boldsymbol{\epsilon}_t$. If this occurs then necessarily $Z_{t-1} = 0$ so that the components of $\mathbf{X}_t$ obey a linear constraint $\boldsymbol{\alpha}'\mathbf{X}_t = 0$. In fact, many economic theories are expressed in terms of equilibria of just this sort. Now Z_t can be interpreted as the equilibrium error, that is, the extent to which the economy is out of equilibrium. If the economy prefers to be at or near the equilibrium, then the variables involved should be influenced by the extent to which the economy is out of equilibrium, and this occurs in (7.4.4) through the terms ρZ_{t-1}. Because of this, equations such as (7.4.4) have been called error correction models and have been discussed by Sargan [1964], Davidson, Hendry, Srba, and Yeo [1978], Hendry and von Ungern-Sternberg [1981], Currie [1981], Salmon [1982], Granger and Weiss [1983], and others. It should be noted that if $\mathbf{X}_t$ is not co-integrated, the usual vector ARMA model can be as (7.4.4), with differences being explained by other differences and with $\rho \equiv \mathbf{0}$. Such a model cannot produce equilibrium results of the kinds suggested by economic theory. If the series are co-integrated, it suggests a further possible explanatory variable to explain changes.

The theory presented here can be generalized to any values of d and b and several linear constraints for a large enough vector $\mathbf{X}_t$. Details may be found in Granger [1984]. Methods of testing for co-integratedness will be discussed in Chapter 8.

One important implication of co-integration is that if a vector of series is modeled from the error-correction equation (7.4.4), the vector of h-step forecasts will, for h large, obey the linear restriction

$$\boldsymbol{\alpha}'\mathbf{f}_{n,h} = 0$$

This result was proved by Yoo [1986]. Thus, the forecasts of levels of co-integrated economic variables will "hang together" in a way likely to be viewed as sensible by an economist, whereas forecasts produced in some other way, such as by a group of individual, univariate Box–Jenkins models, may well not do so.

7.5 Properties of Optimal Multiseries Forecasts

Suppose that $\mathbf{X}_t' = (X_{1,t}, X_{2,t}, \ldots, X_{m,t})$ is a vector time series generated by the model

$$\mathbf{a}(B)\mathbf{X}_t = \mathbf{b}(B)\boldsymbol{\eta}_t \tag{7.5.1}$$

where $\boldsymbol{\eta}_t$ is a zero-mean white noise vector, so that

$$E[\boldsymbol{\eta}_t] = 0 \quad \text{and} \quad E[\boldsymbol{\eta}_t \boldsymbol{\eta}_s'] = 0, \qquad t \neq s$$
$$= \Sigma, \qquad t = s$$

The completely general situation will be considered, so that the matrices $\mathbf{a}_0$, $\mathbf{b}_0$, and Σ are not constrained. The only conditions assumed to hold are that the roots of the equations $|\mathbf{a}(z)| = 0$, $|\mathbf{b}(z)| = 0$ all lie in the region $|z| > 1$. These conditions ensure stationarity and invertibility, respectively.

Throughout this section, the assumption will be made that the model (7.5.1) is known exactly. Given this assumption, the optimal h-steps ahead forecast of $\mathbf{X}_t$ will be derived and its properties examined, thus generalizing the results of Section 4.3. A comparison of the two sections will show that the multiseries results are virtually identical to those for single series, apart from the use of vectors and matrices.

Denote the MA(∞) model, equivalent to (7.5.1), by

$$\mathbf{X}_t = \mathbf{c}(B)\boldsymbol{\eta}_t \qquad (7.5.2)$$

where

$$\mathbf{a}(B)\mathbf{c}(B) = \mathbf{b}(B) \qquad (7.5.3)$$

Taking

$$\mathbf{a}(B) = \sum_{j=0}^{p} \mathbf{a}_j B^j, \qquad \mathbf{b}(B) = \sum_{j=0}^{q} \mathbf{b}_j B^j, \qquad \mathbf{c}(B) = \sum_{j=0}^{\infty} \mathbf{c}_j B^j$$

then, by equating coefficients of B^j in (7.5.3), one obtains the relationships

$$\sum_{k=0}^{j} \mathbf{a}_k \mathbf{c}_{j-k} = \mathbf{b}_j, \qquad j = 0, 1, 2, \ldots \qquad (7.5.4)$$

Now, let $\mathbf{f}_{n,h}$ be a vector of forecasts of $\mathbf{X}_{n+h}$ made at time n, so that the ith component of $\mathbf{f}_{n,h}$ is the h-step linear forecast of $X_{i,n+h}$. This forecast will be based on the information set

$$I_n = \{\mathbf{X}_{n-j}; \; j \geq 0\}$$

and is thus of the form

$$\mathbf{f}_{n,h} = \sum_{j=0}^{\infty} \boldsymbol{\lambda}_{j,h} \mathbf{X}_{n-j} \qquad (7.5.5)$$

where $\boldsymbol{\lambda}_{j,h}$ is an $m \times m$ matrix. Thus one can write

$$\mathbf{f}_{n,h} = \boldsymbol{\lambda}_h(B)\mathbf{X}_n$$

Substituting from (7.5.2), this becomes

$$\mathbf{f}_{n,h} = \boldsymbol{\phi}_h(B)\boldsymbol{\eta}_n \qquad (7.5.6)$$

where

$$\boldsymbol{\phi}_h(B) = \boldsymbol{\lambda}_h(B)\mathbf{c}(B) \qquad (7.5.7)$$

To find the optimal forecast, it is necessary to determine the matrix $\lambda_h(B)$, or equivalently $\phi_h(B)$. It is also necessary, of course, to have a criterion of optimality. To derive such a criterion, the following definition is first required. If V_1 and V_2 are two real positive definite $m \times m$ matrices, then V_1 will be said to be smaller than V_2, provided that, for every nonzero $m \times 1$ vector d,

$$d'V_1d < d'V_2d$$

Such a relationship will be denoted $V_1 < V_2$. If $\{V(s)\}$ represents a set of positive definite $m \times m$ matrices, a particular one, V_0, will be called the smallest if $V_0 < V_j$ for every $V_j \neq V_0$ contained in $\{V(s)\}$.

Denote the h-step error series by

$$e_{n,h} = X_{n+h} - f_{n,h} \tag{7.5.8}$$

and let this vector have covariance matrix

$$V(h) = E[e_{n,h}e'_{n,h}] \tag{7.5.9}$$

since $E[e_{n,h}] = 0$. Then a forecast vector $f_{n,h}$ will be said to be (linearly) optimal if the corresponding $V(h)$ is the smallest of all the possible error covariance matrices. The optimality criterion, stated in this form, is both more convenient and more general than the more frequently used ones of minimizing the determinant or trace of $V(h)$.

Substituting for X_{n+h} and $f_{n,h}$ from (7.5.2) and (7.5.6) into (7.5.8) gives

$$e_{n,h} = [c(B) - B^h\phi_h(B)]\eta_{n+h} = \sum_{j=0}^{h-1} c_j\eta_{n+h-j} + \sum_{j=0}^{\infty} (c_{j+h} - \phi_{h,j})\eta_{n-j} \tag{7.5.10}$$

so that, from (7.5.9),

$$V(h) = \sum_{j=0}^{h-1} c_j\Sigma c'_j + \sum_{j=0}^{\infty} (c_{j+h} - \phi_{h,j})\Sigma(c_{j+h} - \phi_{h,j})'$$

As $\phi_h(B)$ varies, this set of positive definite matrices clearly has smallest value

$$V(h) = \sum_{j=0}^{h-1} c_j\Sigma c'_j \tag{7.5.11}$$

and this is achieved by taking

$$\phi_{h,j} = c_{j+h} \tag{7.5.12}$$

Thus, the optimal forecasts are given by

$$f_{n,h} = \sum_{j=0}^{\infty} c_{j+h}\eta_{n-j} \tag{7.5.13}$$

with corresponding errors

$$\mathbf{e}_{n,h} = \sum_{j=0}^{h-1} \mathbf{c}_j \boldsymbol{\eta}_{n+h-j} \tag{7.5.14}$$

In particular, the one-step errors are $\mathbf{e}_{n,1} = \mathbf{c}_0 \boldsymbol{\eta}_{n+1}$ and so comprise a white noise vector. It is also clear, from (7.5.11), that $V(h_1) \geqslant V(h_2)$ for $h_1 > h_2$, so that, as is to be expected, the further ahead one forecasts, the less well one does, on average.

Rearranging (7.5.13) gives

$$\mathbf{f}_{n,h} = \mathbf{c}_h \boldsymbol{\eta}_n + \sum_{j=0}^{\infty} \mathbf{c}_{j+h+1} \boldsymbol{\eta}_{n-1-j}$$

so that

$$\mathbf{f}_{n,h} = \mathbf{f}_{n-1,h+1} + \mathbf{c}_h \mathbf{c}_0^{-1}(\mathbf{X}_n - \mathbf{f}_{n-1,1}) \tag{7.5.15}$$

which is the generalization of the updating formula (4.3.24).

Now consider

$$\sum_{j=0}^{p} \mathbf{a}_j \mathbf{f}_{n,h-j} = \sum_{i=0}^{\infty} \sum_{j=0}^{p} \mathbf{a}_j \mathbf{c}_{i+h-j} \boldsymbol{\eta}_{n-i} = \sum_{i=0}^{\infty} \mathbf{b}_{i+h} \boldsymbol{\eta}_{n-i} \tag{7.5.16}$$

from (7.5.4), taking $\mathbf{b}_i \equiv 0$ for all $i > q$. This generalizes the single series equation (4.4.15) and is used in exactly the same way to form the sequence of optimal forecasts, as h increases with n fixed. Thus, for example, it is easily shown that the optimal one-step forecast for the generalized AR(p) process, with $\mathbf{b}(B) = \mathbf{b}_0$, is given by

$$\mathbf{f}_{n,1} = -\mathbf{a}_0^{-1} \sum_{j=1}^{p} \mathbf{a}_j \mathbf{X}_{n-j+1} \tag{7.5.17}$$

Similarly, the optimal h-step forecast of the AR(1) process $\mathbf{a}_0 \mathbf{X}_t + \mathbf{a}_1 \mathbf{X}_{t-1} = \boldsymbol{\eta}_t$ is given by

$$\mathbf{f}_{n,h} = (-\mathbf{a}_0^{-1}\mathbf{a}_1)^h \mathbf{X}_n \tag{7.5.18}$$

The frequency domain approach to the forecasting problem can also be generalized to the multiseries case, but will not be considered here, as it provides few, if any, extra results of practical importance. Details are given in Hannan [1970, Chapter 3].

Throughout this section the completely unrealistic assumption that the generating model is known exactly has been made. In Chapter 8 some practical multivariate time series model building techniques are described. To produce forecasts, the models thus derived are taken to be true models, and the methods of this section can then be employed.

7.6 Forecasting Aggregates

The quantities being forecast in macroeconomics, as well as elsewhere, are often aggregates. For example, national GNP is the sum of GNP generated by different regions or by different sectors of the economy. One way to forecast an aggregate is to form forecasts of components and then merely sum them. An alternative is to try to forecast the aggregate directly from the total information set, but it is usually cheaper to forecast the aggregate just from previous values of the aggregate. As a general rule, the more information one uses, the better will be the forecast obtained. Necessary and sufficient conditions for this rule not to apply for aggregates have been given by Kohn [1982].

Denote the components by the vector $\mathbf{X}_t$ and the aggregate by Y_t, where

$$Y_t = \mathbf{d}'\mathbf{X}_t$$

and $\mathbf{d}$ is the vector of weights used in the aggregate. If $\mathbf{X}_t$ and thus Y_t are stationary, with Wold representations

$$\mathbf{X}_t = \sum_{j=1}^{\infty} \mathbf{C}_j \mathbf{e}_{t-j} + \mathbf{e}_t \tag{7.6.1}$$

$$Y_t = \sum_{j=1}^{\infty} c_j \epsilon_{t-j} + \epsilon_t \tag{7.6.2}$$

respectively, then denote the two optimum linear forecasts of Y_{n+1} by $f_{n,1}(I_1), f_{n,1}(I_2)$, where $I_1 : \mathbf{X}_{n-k}, k \geq 0$; $I_2 : Y_{n-k}, k \geq 0$ are the full information set and the aggregate information set, respectively. Kohn proves that the necessary and sufficient condition for $f_{n,1}(I_1) = f_{n,2}(I_2)$ is that

$$\mathbf{d}'\mathbf{C}_j = k_j \mathbf{d}', \qquad j \geq 1 \tag{7.6.3}$$

where the k_j constitute a sequence of constants, which from the proof of the theorem are found to be $k_j \equiv c_j$. In the case where $\mathbf{d}$ is just a vector of ones, $\mathbf{d} = \mathbf{1}$, so that the aggregate is just the unweighted sum of its components, the condition says that the sum of each column of $\mathbf{C}_j$ is equal to the same constant, and this holds true for each j. This is seen to be a rather severe condition, which is unlikely to hold in practice.

If one starts with a vector AR representation for $\mathbf{X}_t$, of the form

$$\mathbf{X}_t + \sum_{j=1}^{P} \mathbf{A}_j \mathbf{X}_{t-j} = \mathbf{e}_t$$

the necessary and sufficient condition for the two forecasts to be identical is

$$\mathbf{d}'\mathbf{A}_j = \alpha_j \mathbf{d}' \tag{7.6.4}$$

where the α_j are some sequences of constants. If this condition holds, then Y_t obeys the AR(P) model

$$Y_t + \sum_{j=1}^{P} \alpha_j Y_{t-j} = \epsilon_t$$

Kohn also proves that if (7.6.3) holds, then

$$f_{n,h'}(I_1) = f_{n,h'}(I_2)$$

so that all multistep linear forecasts are identical.

The necessary part of (7.6.3) follows from noting that the optimum forecast of $\mathbf{X}_{n+1}$ given I_1 is

$$\mathbf{f}_{n,1} = \sum_{j=1}^{\infty} \mathbf{C}_j \mathbf{e}_{n-j+1}$$

from (7.6.1) and assuming invertibility, so that the best forecast of Y_{n+1} given I_1 is

$$f_{n,1}(I_1) = \mathbf{d}'\mathbf{f}_{n,1} = \sum_{j=1}^{\infty} \mathbf{d}'\mathbf{C}_j \mathbf{e}_{n-j+1}$$

and thus

$$Y_{n+1} - f_{n,1}(I_1) = \mathbf{d}'\mathbf{e}_{n+1}$$

Similarly

$$Y_{n+1} - f_{n,1}(I_2) = \epsilon_{n+1}$$

If the forecasts are identical, it follows that

$$\mathbf{d}'\mathbf{e}_{t+1} = \epsilon_{t+1}$$

Substituting into (7.6.2) gives

$$Y_t = \mathbf{d}'\mathbf{e}_t + \sum_{j=1}^{\infty} c_j \mathbf{d}'\mathbf{e}_{t-j} \tag{7.6.5}$$

and also directly from (7.6.1)

$$Y_t = \mathbf{d}'\mathbf{X}_t = \mathbf{d}'\mathbf{e}_t + \mathbf{d}'\mathbf{C}_j \mathbf{e}_{t-j} \tag{7.6.6}$$

Thus, by comparing (7.6.5) and (7.6.6), the condition (7.6.3) follows directly.

There is an intermediate forecasting situation between the two that have just been considered. If each component of $\mathbf{X}_t$, with X_{it} a typical variable, is forecast just from its own past, giving a forecast of $X_{i,n+1}$ denoted by $f_{n,1}(I_i)$, $I_i : X_{i,t-k}$, $k \geqslant 0$, then a forecast of Y_{n+1} can be formed as

$$\bar{f}_{n,1} = \sum_i d_i f_{n,1}(I_i)$$

where the d_i are the components of $\mathbf{d}$. It is no longer clear whether $\bar{f}_{n,1}$ will be inferior or superior to $f_{n,1}(I_2)$, although it will clearly generally be inferior to $f_{n,1}(I_1)$.

A case not considered by Kohn where little is lost in forecasting an aggregate variable from just its own past is where the microseries contain a common factor. To illustrate this situation, consider the vector of microseries

X_{jt}, $j = 1, \ldots, N$ that have components Y_{jt} and Z_t of the form

$$X_{jt} = Y_{jt} + c_j Z_t$$

where all the Y_{jt} are stationary series independent of each other and of the common factor Z_t, all series having zero mean. If all that is observed are the aggregate series

$$X_t = \sum X_{jt}, \qquad Y_t = \sum Y_{jt}$$

then

$$X_t = Y_t + NCZ_t$$

where $C = (1/N)\sum_j c_j$ is the average c_j value.
With the assumptions given

$$\text{var}(X_t) = \text{var}(Y_t) + N^2 C^2 \, \text{var}(Z_t)$$

but, as all Y_{jt} are independent, $\text{var}(Y_t) = O(N)$ and the second term in this expression will dominate if N is very large and $C \neq 0$. Thus, X_t will be well approximated by NCZ_t, and forecasts of X_t from its own past will be almost equivalent to forecasts made from the complete information set $[Y_{jt}, \ j = 1, \ldots, N, \ Z_t]$. This will not be true, of course, for forecasts of each individual X_{jt}. The relevance of common factors in time series modeling and forecasting has been considered in more detail by Granger [1985b].

Lütkepohl [1985] has considered the effects on forecasting of both temporally and contemporaneously aggregated multivariate series, using theory and simulation and assuming both full information about the generating mechanism and estimated models. He considers six different forecasts based on a variety of information sets involving varying amounts of aggregation. The completely disaggregated set is found to be always superior in theory but not necessarily in practice, since correct model specification is vital in many situations.

7.7 Rational Expectations

Expectations by consumers or industrialists arise frequently in economic theories and models, but since these quantities are rarely observed in practice, they are often difficult to handle in the modeling process. A method used frequently in early work involved the assumption that expectations are made by simple extrapolation techniques, such as the adaptive models discussed in Chapter 5. If the cost of making a forecast has to be kept low, which might arise from a cost–benefit study of the potential benefits of using a more sophisticated forecasting method, then such expectations may well be realistic. However, if relevant information is plentiful and cheap and one has a sound understanding of the generating mechanism of the economy, then it could not be considered logical—or rational—to use forecasts that are suboptimal. This was pointed out by Muth [1961], and subsequently there has been a considerable literature generated studying the implications of this idea. A model that contains rational expectations has to obey specific constraints, so that the expectations formed within the model are in fact rational. Details may be found in Wallis [1980], and many of the most important articles in the field, including those by Muth and Wallis quoted here, can be found in a collection of papers edited by Lucas and Sargent [1981]. A useful critical survey of the results achieved is given by Begg [1982].

To illustrate some aspects of the effect of rational expectations, consider the classical static model

$$\mathbf{C}\mathbf{y}_t + \mathbf{A}\mathbf{y}_t^* + \mathbf{\Gamma}\mathbf{x}_t = \mathbf{u}_t \tag{7.7.1}$$

where $\mathbf{y}_t$ is a vector of endogenous variables, $\mathbf{y}_t^*$ an expectation of $\mathbf{y}_t$ made at time $t-1$ and based on the information set Ω_{t-1}, $\mathbf{x}_t$ a vector of exogenous variables, and $\mathbf{u}_t$ an unobserved white noise input series. The usual reduced form of the model is

$$\mathbf{y}_t = \mathbf{\Pi}_1\mathbf{y}_t^* + \mathbf{\Pi}_2\mathbf{x}_t + \mathbf{v}_t \tag{7.7.2}$$

where

$$\mathbf{\Pi}_1 = -\mathbf{C}^{-1}\mathbf{A}, \qquad \mathbf{\Pi}_2 = -\mathbf{C}^{-1}\mathbf{\Gamma}, \qquad \mathbf{v}_t = \mathbf{C}^{-1}\mathbf{u}_t$$

By assuming a least squares cost function, when forming forecasts, one has

$$\mathbf{y}_t^* = E[\mathbf{y}_t|\Omega_{t-1}]$$

Therefore, taking the conditional expectation in (7.7.2), assuming $E[\mathbf{v}_t|\Omega_{t-1}] = 0$, and denoting $E[\mathbf{x}_t|\Omega_{t-1}] = \mathbf{x}_t^*$ gives

$$\mathbf{y}_t^* = (\mathbf{I} - \mathbf{\Pi}_1)^{-1}\mathbf{\Pi}_2\mathbf{x}_t^* \tag{7.7.3}$$

This produces the observable reduced form, from (7.7.2),

$$\mathbf{y}_t = \mathbf{P}_1\mathbf{x}_t^* + \mathbf{P}_2\mathbf{x}_t + \mathbf{V}_t \tag{7.7.4}$$

where

$$\mathbf{P}_1 = \mathbf{\Pi}_1(\mathbf{I} - \mathbf{\Pi}_1)^{-1}\mathbf{\Pi}_2, \qquad \mathbf{P}_2 = \mathbf{\Pi}_2$$

In practice, one could form $\mathbf{x}_t^*$ by fitting a multivariate ARIMA model to the vector of exogenous variables $\mathbf{x}_t$, giving $\mathbf{x}_t^* = \psi(B)\mathbf{x}_t$, $\psi(0) = 0$. Because the terms in $\mathbf{P}_1$ and $\mathbf{P}_2$ are related, there are particular econometric identification and estimation problems associated with the observed reduced form. There has been an extensive discussion of the policy implications of the resulting model for $\mathbf{y}_t$ in terms of present and lagged $\mathbf{x}_t$'s, some of which may be policy variables. If the economy forecasts optimally the values the policy variables take, the effects of these policies will be anticipated and become much less effective. On the other hand, if the method by which policy, and hence the values of the parameters in $\psi(B)$, are determined change with a new regime, then the traditional structural matrices in (7.7.1) are found to vary with ψ and so lose the classical interpretation. These results become less clear if there are constraints placed on the economy that prevent rapid adaptation to new policies, such as long-term contracts between agents or components of the economy not knowing all of Ω_{t-1} or the parameters in Π_1 and Π_2 with certainty, which will generally be true. In practice, a very real problem is knowing what is contained in the information set Ω for actual economic agents and whether all of Ω is observable. The implications for the effects on rational expectations of inserting these realistic problems plus questions on the effects of learning are still under investigation in the literature.

University Administrator, debating budget cuts: "I wonder if we could get away with combining parapsychology and economic forecasting"

TIMES (OF LONDON) HIGHER
EDUCATION SUPPLEMENT

8.1 Introduction

In Chapter 7 we considered the possibility of building models relating two or more time series and outlined the properties of some possible models. In this chapter we will discuss various procedures for fitting such models to economic time series data. As will be seen, the difficulty of this problem and the kinds of approaches that appear to offer the best prospects for success depend both on the number of time series analyzed and the nature of the causal relationships. We will begin here with the simplest possible case, discussing more complex problems in the later sections of this chapter.

8.2 Building Bivariate Models: Unidirectional Causality

The simplest possible situation in multivariate time series analysis is that in which one has a pair of zero-mean stationary series Y_{1t} and Y_{2t}, which may have been derived through the application of differencing or other appropriate transformations from given series X_{1t} and X_{2t}, where Y_{2t} causes Y_{1t}, but Y_{1t} does not cause Y_{2t}. By assuming a linear relationship, we can write the dependence of Y_{1t} on Y_{2t} as

$$Y_{1t} = V_0 Y_{2t} + V_1 Y_{2,t-1} + V_2 Y_{2,t-2} + V_3 Y_{2,t-3} + \cdots + e_t$$
$$= V(B) Y_{2t} + e_t \qquad (8.2.1)$$

In (8.2.1)

$$V(B) = V_0 + V_1 B + V_2 B^2 + V_3 B^3 + \cdots$$

where the V_j are unknown fixed parameters, and e_t is a stochastic error term uncorrelated with $Y_{2,t-j}$ ($j = \ldots, -1, 0, 1, \ldots$).

There is no particular reason to believe that this error term will necessarily be white noise, and in general we allow it to follow the ARMA(p, q) model

$$\phi(B)e_t = \theta(B)\eta_t \qquad (8.2.2)$$

where

$$\phi(B) = 1 - \phi_1 B - \cdots - \phi_p B^p$$
$$\theta(B) = 1 + \theta_1 B + \cdots + \theta_q B^q$$

and η_t is white noise.

As it stands, model (8.2.1) is not, in general, in a suitable form for practical model building, since a large number of parameters V_j may be needed to achieve an adequate representation of the relationship between the two time series. A more parsimonious structure can often be achieved by approximating the infinite-order polynomial $V(B)$ by the ratio of two finite-order polynomials, setting

$$V(B) = \frac{\omega_0 + \omega_1 B + \cdots + \omega_r B^r}{1 - \delta_1 B - \cdots - \delta_s B^s} = \frac{\omega(B)}{\delta(B)} \qquad (8.2.3)$$

where the roots of the polynomial equation in z, $\delta(z) = 0$, are assumed to lie outside the unit circle, thus implying eventual decay towards zero of the V_j, with increasing j.

Substitution of (8.2.2) and (8.2.3) into (8.2.1) then yields

$$Y_{1t} = \frac{\omega(B)}{\delta(B)} Y_{2t} + \frac{\theta(B)}{\phi(B)} \eta_t \qquad (8.2.4)$$

This is the *transfer function–noise model*, for which a model building strategy was developed and implemented by Box and Jenkins [1970]. To complete the specification of the model, we need to specify a generating process for the input series Y_{2t}. This will be taken to be of ARMA form and written as

$$a_2(B)Y_{2t} = b_2(B)\epsilon_{2t} \qquad (8.2.5)$$

with

$$\text{corr}(\epsilon_{2t}, \eta_s) = 0 \qquad \text{for all} \quad t, s$$

We now proceed to discuss a practical strategy for fitting to data transfer function–noise models, given observations (Y_{1t}, Y_{2t}; $t = 1, \ldots, n$). We will illustrate by considering series of 102 monthly observations on unemployment in manufacturing (X_{1t}) and production in manufacturing (X_{2t}) in the U.S. Both series require a single differencing to induce stationarity, so that the Y_{it} are first differences, with 101 pairs of observations available.

In outline, the approach followed is along the same lines as for the single series case of Chapter 3, so that model building involves a three-stage iterative cycle of model selection, parameter estimation, and diagnostic checking. Perhaps not surprisingly, it is the problem of initially selecting what might be an appropriate model that causes the most practical difficulties.

At the model selection stage it is necessary, based on statistics computed from the data, to choose orders for the four polynomials in the back-shift operator in (8.2.4). We begin with the transfer function part of the model

$$V(B) = \omega(B)/\delta(B)$$

employing the technique of prewhitening the input series, as proposed by Box and Jenkins. To see the rationale behind this approach, suppose for now that the model generating Y_{2t} is known and write, from (8.2.5),

$$\epsilon_{2t} = b_2^{-1}(B)a_2(B)Y_{2t}$$

Also, define

$$Z_t = b_2^{-1}(B)a_2(B)Y_{1t}$$

Then, from (8.2.1), it follows that we can write

$$Z_t = V_0\epsilon_{2t} + V_1\epsilon_{2,t-1} + V_2\epsilon_{2,t-2} + V_3\epsilon_{2,t-3} + \cdots + u_t \qquad (8.2.6)$$

where the error term u_t is

$$u_t = b_2^{-1}(B)a_2(B)e_t$$

Now, multiplying through (8.2.6) by $\epsilon_{2,t-j}$ ($j = 0, 1, 2, \ldots$) and taking expectations yields

$$\mathrm{corr}(Z_t, \epsilon_{2,t-j}) = V_j\left[\frac{\mathrm{var}(\epsilon_{2t})}{\mathrm{var}(Z_t)}\right]^{1/2} \qquad (j = 0, 1, 2, \ldots)$$

We have therefore shown that the transfer function weights V_j are proportional to the correlations between Z_t and $\epsilon_{2,t-j}$. Hence, given these correlations, their pattern should help in identifying appropriate orders for the polynomial operators in the transfer function. For example, suppose that

$$V(B) = \frac{\omega(B)}{\delta(B)} = \frac{\omega_0 + \omega_1 B}{1 - \delta B}$$

Then

$$(1 - \delta B)(V_0 + V_1 B + V_2 B^2 + V_3 B^3 + \cdots) = \omega_0 + \omega_1 B$$

from which it follows that

$$V_0 = \omega_0; \quad V_1 = \delta\omega_0 + \omega_1; \quad V_j = \delta V_{j-1} \qquad (j = 2, 3, \ldots)$$

Thus, since $|\delta| < 1$, there is a simple geometric decay in the V_j from $j = 2$ onwards.

Of course, in practice, the model (8.2.5) generating the input series will not be known. However, given the data, the methods of Chapter 3 can be used to fit an appropriate model. If we denote by

$$\hat{\epsilon}_{2t} = \hat{b}_2^{-1}(B)\hat{a}_2(B)Y_{2t}$$

the residuals from this fitted ARMA process, we can construct the series

$$\hat{Z}_t = \hat{b}_2^{-1}(B)\hat{a}_2(B)Y_{1t}$$

and base identification of the transfer function structure on the sample cross-correlations between $\hat{Z}_t$ and $\hat{\epsilon}_{2,t-j}$.

For the differenced data on production in manufacturing in the U.S., we obtained an adequate fit from the first-order autoregressive model

$$Y_{2,t} - 0.64Y_{2,t-1} = \epsilon_{2t}$$
$$[0.08]$$

where, here and throughout, measurements are expressed in terms of discrepancies from the series means. Accordingly, with

$$\hat{\epsilon}_{2t} = Y_{2t} - 0.64Y_{2,t-1}$$

and

$$\hat{Z}_t = Y_{1t} - 0.64Y_{1,t-1}$$

we show, in Table 8.1, the sample cross-correlations between $\hat{Z}_t$ and $\hat{\epsilon}_{2,t-j}$.

As a guide to assessing their magnitude, the sample cross correlations of Table 8.1 can be compared with asymptotic standard errors of $n^{-1/2} \simeq 0.10$, which would be appropriate on the hypothesis of independence of the two series. We see that there are large values for $j = 0, 1$, while all the others are relatively small, suggesting that the transfer function part of the model can be represented as

$$V(B) = \omega_0 + \omega_1 B$$

The low values for the cross correlations at negative lags in Table 8.1 suggest that causality does indeed run in only one direction, from production to unemployment.

At first sight, the input prewhitening approach to transfer function identification may appear unnecessarily cumbersome, and the reader might wonder why we do not simply compute cross-correlations from the original series. The difficulties involved in interpreting the cross correlogram of raw data were described and illustrated in a particular extreme case by Box and

Table 8.1 *Cross correlations between $\hat{Z}_t$ and $\hat{\epsilon}_{2,t-j}$ for unemployment and production data*

j:	0	1	2	3	4	5	6
$\hat{\rho}_j$:	-0.25	-0.40	-0.07	-0.03	-0.02	-0.12	0.04
j:		7	8	9	10	11	12
$\hat{\rho}_j$:		0.05	-0.13	-0.08	-0.08	-0.03	0.05
j:		-1	-2	-3	-4	-5	-6
$\hat{\rho}_j$:		-0.01	-0.04	0.03	-0.17	0.13	0.04
j:		-7	-8	-9	-10	-11	-12
$\hat{\rho}_j$:		0.13	-0.10	0.04	-0.03	0.02	0.00

Newbold [1971], who considered the consequences of cross correlating two independent random walk series $(1 - B)X_{j,t} = \epsilon_{j,t}$, $j = 1, 2$. It was noted that the resulting sample cross correlograms tended to contain quite large values, which is simply a manifestation of the spurious regression problem discussed in Section 6.4, and also to be very smooth. An example, based on 100 pairs of observations, is shown in Fig. 8.1a. For comparison, the cross correlogram between the differenced (white noise) series is shown in Fig. 8.1b. Box and Newbold showed that the smoothness resulted from the fact that the sample cross covariances

$$\hat{\lambda}_k = \hat{\text{cov}}(X_{1t}, X_{2, t-k})$$

behave approximately as an ARIMA(0, 2, 0) time series, i.e.,

$$\hat{\lambda}_k \simeq 2\hat{\lambda}_{k-1} - \hat{\lambda}_{k-2} + u_k$$

where u_k is white noise. Thus, not only does one have to contend with the spurious regression phenomenon of the size of the sample cross correlations, but also the shape of the cross correlogram is impossible to interpret sensibly.

Having identified the transfer function part of the model, it remains to decide on an appropriate ARMA structure for the noise component. This can be accomplished by estimating the parameters of the model

$$Y_{1t} = \frac{\omega(B)}{\delta(B)} Y_{2t} + e_t$$

as if e_t were white noise. The properties of the residuals $\hat{e}_t$ are then used to suggest a model for the unobservable process e_t. For the unemployment and production data, we found

$$Y_{1t} = (-0.089 - 0.125B)Y_{2t} + e_t$$
$$[0.021] \quad [0.021]$$

The first residual autocorrelation, -0.249, was quite large compared with an asymptotic standard error of 0.100, while the remaining residual autocorrelations were generally rather small. This suggests a first-order moving average error structure. The transfer function noise model finally chosen then was of the form

$$Y_{1t} = (\omega_0 + \omega_1 B)Y_{2t} + (1 - \theta B)\eta_t \tag{8.2.7}$$

The most straightforward asymptotically efficient estimation procedure for the parameters of (8.2.4) is through least squares. Multiplying through (8.2.4) by $\delta(B)\phi(B)$ produces

$$\phi(B)\delta(B)Y_{1t} = \phi(B)\omega(B)Y_{2t} + \delta(B)\theta(B)\eta_t$$

which can be written in the form

$$\eta_t = Y_{1t} - \Phi_1 Y_{1, t-1} - \cdots - \Phi_H Y_{1, t-H} - \Omega_0 Y_{2t}$$
$$- \Omega_1 Y_{2, t-1} - \cdots - \Omega_J Y_{2, t-J} - \Theta_1 \eta_{t-1} - \cdots - \Theta_I \eta_{t-I} \tag{8.2.8}$$

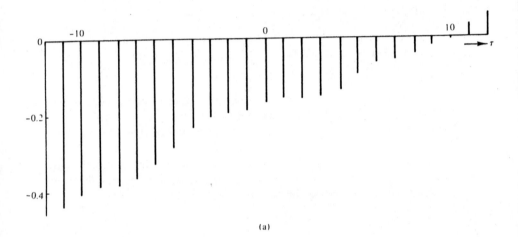

(a)

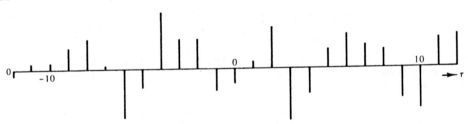

(b)

FIG. 8.1 (a) *Sample cross correlations for series of length 100 generated from independent random walks.* (b) *Sample cross correlations of first differences of data used in* (a).

where H, J, and I are known integers and the Φ's, Ω's, and Θ's are known functions of the ϕ's, θ's, ω's, and δ's. The parameters of (8.2.4) are estimated by calculating, using (8.2.8), η_t, $t = \max(H + 1, J + 1), \ldots, n$, as a function of the data and the coefficients and setting the "starting up" values η_t, $t = \max(H, J), \ldots, \max(H, J) - I + 1$ equal to zero. The transient introduced by this approximation will typically be of negligible importance for moderately long series. The coefficients of (8.2.4) are then estimated by minimizing the sum of squares of the calculated η_t using a nonlinear regression algorithm.

For the data on unemployment and production, we obtained in this way the fitted model

$$Y_{1t} = (-0.094 - 0.123B)Y_{2t} + (1 - 0.302B)\eta_t$$
$$[0.020] \quad [0.020] \qquad\qquad [0.101]$$

An alternative approach to estimation is through full maximum likelihood using, for example, the approach of Newbold [1973b] to the derivation of the likelihood function.

Having fitted a transfer function–noise model, its adequacy can be checked along lines similar to those discussed in Chapter 3 for the single series case. In particular, Lagrange multiplier tests against alternatives involving additional parameters in either the transfer function or noise part of the model have been discussed by Poskitt and Tremayne [1981a, b] and Newbold [1983]. Let us denote the originally specified model as TFARMA[$(r, s), (p, q)$]. As for the single series case of Section 3.6, Lagrange multiplier tests of model adequacy are based on the partial derivatives of the log likelihood function with respect to the parameters. The log likelihood function is, to a close approximation in large samples,

$$\log L = \text{const} - \frac{n}{2}\log \sigma_\eta^2 - \frac{\sum_{t=1}^{n} \eta_t^2}{2\sigma_\eta^2}$$

Then, on differentiation,

$$\frac{\partial \log L}{\partial \phi_i} = \frac{\sum_{t=1}^{n} v_{t-i}\eta_t}{\sigma_\eta^2}$$

where

$$v_t - \phi_1 v_{t-1} - \cdots - \phi_p v_{t-p} = \eta_t$$

$$\frac{\partial \log L}{\partial \theta_i} = \frac{\sum_{t=1}^{n} u_{t-i}\eta_t}{\sigma_\eta^2}$$

where

$$u_t + \theta_1 u_{t-1} + \cdots + \theta_q u_{t-q} = \eta_t$$

$$\frac{\partial \log L}{\partial \omega_i} = \frac{\displaystyle\sum_{t=1}^{n} w_{t-i} \eta_t}{\sigma_\eta^2}$$

where

$$\theta(B)\delta(B)w_t = \phi(B)Y_{2t}$$

and

$$\frac{\partial \log L}{\partial \delta_i} = \frac{-\displaystyle\sum_{t=1}^{n} z_{t-i} \eta_t}{\sigma_\eta^2}$$

where

$$\theta(B)\delta(B)z_t = \theta(B)\eta_t - \phi(B)Y_{1t}$$

Appropriate tests then follow by replacing unknown parameters by their estimates under the null hypothesis that the model is correctly specified and the error terms η_t by the residuals $\hat{\eta}_t$ from the fitted model. Thus, the transfer function part of the specification is tested against the TFARMA$[(r + m, s), (p, q)]$ alternative of m extra parameters through estimating by least squares the regression

$$\hat{\eta}_t = \alpha_0 \hat{w}_t + \cdots + \alpha_{r+m} \hat{w}_{t-r-m} + \beta_1 \hat{z}_{t-1} + \cdots + \beta_s \hat{z}_{t-s} + e_t$$

where e_t is an error term. Under the null hypothesis that the model is correctly specified, the statistic

$$T = n\left[1 - \left(\sum \hat{e}_t^2 / \sum \hat{\eta}_t^2\right)\right] \tag{8.2.9}$$

has an asymptotic χ^2 distribution with m degrees of freedom. The null hypothesis is rejected for large values of this test statistic. The same test follows against the TFARMA$[(r, s + m), (p, q)]$ alternative.

To test the noise specification against the alternative of either TFARMA$[(r, s), (p + m, q)]$ or TFARMA$[(r, s), (p, q + m)]$, fit by least squares the regression

$$\hat{\eta}_t = \alpha_1 \hat{v}_{t-1} + \cdots + \alpha_{p+m} \hat{v}_{t-p-m} + \beta_1 \hat{u}_{t-1} + \cdots + \beta_q \hat{u}_{t-q} + e_t$$

and, exactly as before, base the test on a statistic of the form (8.2.9).

In fitting a transfer function–noise model to data, it has been implicitly assumed that causality is unidirectional, from Y_2 to Y_1. This hypothesis can be tested against the alternative that there is feedback in the system by considering the possibility of the more elaborate model

$$Y_{1t} = \sum_{j=1}^{m} \Pi_{-j} Y_{2, t+j} + \frac{\omega(B)}{\delta(B)} Y_{2t} + \frac{\theta(B)}{\phi(B)} \eta_t$$

The null hypothesis of no feedback from Y_1 to Y_2 then implies that the coefficients Π_{-j} ($j = 1, \ldots, m$) are all zero. Differentiating the log likelihood function with respect to these extra parameters, under the null hypothesis, we obtain

$$\frac{\partial \log L}{\partial \Pi_{-i}} = \frac{\sum_{t=1}^{n} g_{t+i}\eta_t}{\sigma_\eta^2}$$

where

$$g_t + \theta_1 g_{t-1} + \cdots + \theta_q g_{t-q} = Y_{2t} - \phi_1 Y_{2, t-1} - \cdots - \phi_p Y_{2, t-p}$$

The null hypothesis can be tested through a least squares fit of

$$\hat{\eta}_t = \alpha_0 \hat{w}_t + \cdots + \alpha_r \hat{w}_{t-r} + \hat{\beta}_1 \hat{z}_{t-1} + \cdots + \beta_s \hat{z}_{t-s}$$
$$+ \gamma_1 \hat{g}_{t+1} + \cdots + \gamma_m \hat{g}_{t+m} + e_t$$

The test statistic is again of the form (8.2.9).

In Section 3.6 we saw how the residual autocorrelations from a fitted ARMA model could be employed to check model adequacy. Analogous findings hold for transfer function–noise models, as shown by Pierce [1972]. First, let $\hat{\eta}_t$ denote the residuals from the fitted model (8.2.4), and define the residual autocorrelations

$$\hat{r}_\tau = \sum_{t=\tau+1}^{n} \hat{\eta}_t \hat{\eta}_{t-\tau} \Big/ \sum_{t=1}^{n} \hat{\eta}_t^2$$

Comparison of these quantities with bounds $\pm 2n^{-1/2}$ provides a rough assessment of the suitability of the assumed noise structure, though, in fact, as in the single series case, the true asymptotic standard error of $\hat{r}_\tau$ can be a good deal smaller than $n^{-1/2}$ for small τ. For moderately large M, a portmanteau test of the adequacy of the noise specification can be based on the statistic

$$Q = n(n + 2) \sum_{\tau=1}^{M} (n - \tau)^{-1} r_\tau^2$$

which, under the hypothesis that the model is correctly specified, has an asymptotic χ^2 distribution with $M = p - q$ degrees of freedom. This test, then, is of precisely the same form as that following from (3.6.5).

The appropriateness of the transfer function specification can be similarly checked by examining the cross-correlations between the $\hat{\eta}_t$ and the residual series $\hat{\epsilon}_{2t}$ obtained when the model (8.2.5) is fitted to the input series. Let

$$\hat{r}_\tau^* = \sum_{t=\tau+1}^{n} \hat{\eta}_t \hat{\epsilon}_{2, t-\tau} \Big/ \left[\sum_{t=1}^{n} \hat{\eta}_t^2 \sum_{t=1}^{n} \hat{\epsilon}_{2, t}^2 \right]^{1/2}$$

Again, a crude comparison of the size of these residual cross-correlations can be made with bounds $\pm 2n^{-1/2}$, while a portmanteau test of the transfer function specification is based on

$$Q^* = n \sum_{\tau=0}^{M} \hat{r}_{\tau}^{*2}$$

For moderately large M, this statistic has, under the null hypothesis that the transfer function specification is correct, an asymptotic χ^2 distribution with $M + 1 - r - s$ degrees of freedom.

In fact, when the checks discussed here were applied to the model fitted to our unemployment and production data, no substantial grounds were found for questioning the adequacy of the initially chosen TFARMA[(1, 0), (0, 1)] model. Accordingly, it seems appropriate to proceed with this model for forecasting purposes.

Our discussion in this section has been restricted to the case of a single input series. There is, however, no great difficulty in principle in extending these methods to the case of several inputs, provided that all of the relationships involved exhibit causality in at most one direction. An illustration is provided by Snorrason, Newbold, and Maxwell [1984].

8.3 Building Vector ARMA Models

In this section, we outline a procedure for fitting to data vector autoregressive–moving average models of the form

$$\mathbf{X}_t - \mathbf{a}_1 \mathbf{X}_{t-1} - \cdots - \mathbf{a}_p \mathbf{X}_{t-p} = \boldsymbol{\eta}_t + \mathbf{b}_1 \boldsymbol{\eta}_{t-1} + \cdots + \mathbf{b}_q \boldsymbol{\eta}_{t-q} \quad (8.3.1)$$

which we write more compactly, using the back shift operator notation, as

$$\mathbf{a}(B)\mathbf{X}_t = \mathbf{b}(B)\boldsymbol{\eta}_t$$

In (8.3.1), $\mathbf{X}_t' = (X_{1t}, X_{2t}, \ldots, X_{mt})$ and $\boldsymbol{\eta}_t$ is zero-mean vector white noise, so that

$$E(\boldsymbol{\eta}_t) = \mathbf{0} \quad \text{and} \quad E(\boldsymbol{\eta}_t, \boldsymbol{\eta}_s') = \mathbf{0} \quad t \neq s$$
$$= \boldsymbol{\Sigma} \quad t = s$$

Generalizing the corresponding conditions for the single series case, this representation is stationary provided the roots of $|\mathbf{a}(z)| = 0$ all lie outside the unit circle and invertible if the roots of $|\mathbf{b}(z)| = 0$ lie outside the unit circle. In addition, as shown by Hannan [1969], further restrictions are required to ensure uniqueness of representation of this model. Specifically, it is required that $\mathbf{a}(z)$ and $\mathbf{b}(z)$ have no common left factors and that the matrix $[\mathbf{a}_p : \mathbf{b}_q]$ be of full rank. The necessity for this last condition can be seen through a simple example. Consider the MA(1) model

$$X_{1t} = \eta_{1t} + \theta \eta_{2, t-1}$$
$$X_{2t} = \eta_{2t}$$

Clearly, this could equally well be written as an AR(1) model

$$X_{1t} - \theta X_{2, t-1} = \eta_{1t}$$

$$X_{2t} = \eta_{2t}$$

Since, for purposes of exposition, we have assumed a zero-mean process, the matrices of autocovariances and cross-covariances for the process (8.3.1) can be written as

$$\Lambda_\tau = E(\mathbf{X}_t \mathbf{X}'_{t-\tau})$$

Then, given stationarity, (8.3.1) can be expressed in the form

$$\mathbf{X}_t = \boldsymbol{\eta}_t + \mathbf{c}_1 \boldsymbol{\eta}_{t-1} + \mathbf{c}_2 \boldsymbol{\eta}_{t-2} + \cdots$$

Multiplying through this expression by $\boldsymbol{\eta}'_{t+j}$ ($j > 0$) and taking expectations then yields immediately

$$E(\mathbf{X}_t \boldsymbol{\eta}'_{t+j}) = \mathbf{0} \qquad (j > 0) \qquad (8.3.2)$$

Then, on multiplying through (8.3.1) by $\mathbf{X}'_{t-\tau}$, taking expectations, and employing (8.3.2), we find

$$\Lambda_\tau - \mathbf{a}_1 \Lambda_{\tau-1} - \cdots - \mathbf{a}_p \Lambda_{\tau-p} = \mathbf{0} \qquad (\tau = q+1, q+2, \dots) \quad (8.3.3)$$

and, in particular, for a pure moving average process of order q (so that $p = 0$)

$$\Lambda_\tau = \mathbf{0} \qquad (\tau = q+1, q+2, \dots)$$

which extends the corresponding result for the single series case.

Our aim here, given data $\mathbf{x}_t$ ($t = 1, 2, \dots, n$), is to consider the extension of the model building methodology of Chapter 3. Thus, we discuss in turn model selection, parameter estimation, and diagnostic checking, as in Newbold and Hotopp [1986].

Model Selection

The reader will probably not be surprised at this point to learn that it is the selection stage of the model building cycle that gives rise to the most practical difficulty. Indeed, even in the case of just a pair of related time series, model selection is in practice far more difficult when there is feedback than is the case for the unidirectional causal models of the previous section. Here we will introduce an approach that we have found to work well for a small number of related time series, postponing until the next section a discussion of the case of many related series.

As in the single series case, it is convenient to first consider separately the possibilities of pure moving average or pure autoregressive models before discussing the problem of identifying more general ARMA(p, q) generating processes. For a pure moving average process of order q, we know that the autocovariance matrices Λ_τ are all zero for $\tau > q$. We can estimate these autocovariance matrices by

$$\mathbf{C}_\tau = \sum_{t=\tau+1}^{n} \mathbf{X}_t \mathbf{X}'_{t-\tau}/n$$

It is, however, easier to interpret correlations than covariances. The corresponding sample autocorrelation matrices $\mathbf{R}_\tau$ have (i, j) elements

$$r_{\tau; i, j} = c_{\tau; i, j} / [c_{0; i, i} c_{0; j, j}]^{1/2}$$

where $c_{\tau; i, j}$ is the (i, j) element of $\mathbf{C}_\tau$. For a pure moving average process of order q, the elements of the matrices $\mathbf{R}_\tau$ should not differ significantly from zero for $\tau > q$. In checking for moving average behavior of order q, the sample autocorrelations and cross-correlations can be compared with their asymptotic standard errors, given by Bartlett [1946] as

$$\mathrm{SE}[r_{\tau; i, j}] = n^{-1/2} \left[1 + 2 \sum_{h=1}^{q} \rho_{h; i, i} \rho_{h; j, j} \right]^{1/2}$$

In practice, the population autocorrelations $\rho_{h; i, i}$ in this expression must be replaced by the corresponding sample estimates $r_{h; i, i}$. As a crude approximation, sample autocorrelations and cross-correlations can be compared with bounds of $\pm 2n^{-1/2}$.

As in the single series case, partial autocorrelations can be useful in detecting pure autoregressive models. Consider the regression of $\mathbf{X}_t$ on $\mathbf{X}_{t-j}$ $(j = 1, \ldots, k)$

$$\mathbf{X}_t = \mathbf{a}_{k1}\mathbf{X}_{t-1} + \cdots + \mathbf{a}_{kk}\mathbf{X}_{t-k} + \mathbf{e}_{k, t} \tag{8.3.4}$$

with error term $\mathbf{e}_{k, t}$ having covariance matrix $\mathbf{\Sigma}_k$, and the regression of $\mathbf{X}_t$ on $\mathbf{X}_{t+j}$ $(j = 1, \ldots, k)$

$$\mathbf{X}_t = \mathbf{a}^*_{k1}\mathbf{X}_{t+1} + \cdots + \mathbf{a}^*_{kk}\mathbf{X}_{t+k} + \mathbf{e}^*_{k, t} \tag{8.3.5}$$

where the error term $\mathbf{e}^*_{k, t}$ has covariance matrix $\mathbf{\Sigma}^*_k$. Denote by $\mathbf{A}_k$ and $\mathbf{A}^*_k$ the symmetric square roots of the matrices $\mathbf{\Sigma}_k$ and $\mathbf{\Sigma}^*_k$. Then Quenouille [1957] defines the multiple partial autocorrelation matrix of order $k + 1$ to be

$$\mathbf{P}_{k+1} = \mathbf{A}_k^{-1} E(\mathbf{e}_{k, t} \mathbf{e}^{*\prime}_{k, t-k-1}) \mathbf{A}_k^{*-1}$$

Therefore, if $\mathbf{X}_t$ is generated by an autoregression of order k, then $\mathbf{e}_{k, t}$ and $\mathbf{e}^*_{k, t-k-1}$ will be uncorrelated, so that $\mathbf{P}_{k+1}$ is zero.

Ledolter [1978] and Ansley and Newbold [1979b] extend the algorithm of Durbin [1960] to the efficient computation in the multivariate case of sample partial autocorrelations $\hat{\mathbf{P}}_{k+1}$, given the sample autocovariance matrices. Hannan [1970] has shown that, if the true generating process is autoregressive of order k, the members of the sample partial autocorrelation matrices $\hat{\mathbf{P}}_{k+j}$ $(j \geqslant 1)$ have independent asymptotic normal distributions, with zero means and standard deviations $n^{-1/2}$. It therefore follows, in this case, that the statistics

$$s_{k+j} = n \operatorname{Tr} \hat{\mathbf{P}}_{k+j} \hat{\mathbf{P}}_{k+j}$$

have asymptotic χ^2 distributions with m^2 degrees of freedom. Examination of these statistics, which can also be expressed as

$$s_{k+j} = n \operatorname{Tr} \hat{\mathbf{a}}_{k+j, k+j} \hat{\mathbf{a}}^*_{k+j, k+j}$$

where the $\hat{\mathbf{a}}$'s are estimates of the corresponding parameter matrices in (8.3.4) and (8.3.5), should prove useful in detecting pure autoregressive models.

In the single series case, one possible approach to model selection is through visual inspection of the sample statistics in search of a pattern analogous to that of (8.3.3). However, in the multivariate case this will be of little direct help in identifying mixed models, since it is hardly possible through visual inspection to detect such difference equation patterns *in matrices* of autocovariances. We have, however, found an extension of the Hannan–Rissanen procedure, discussed in Section 3.2, to be valuable here. First, estimates of the innovations $\boldsymbol{\eta}_t$ of (8.3.1) are obtained through the approximation of this process by an autoregression of order k. To find an appropriate order, the model (8.3.4) is estimated for all positive integer values of k up to some maximum, which we generally take as 10. In fact, this involves no additional computations, as the resulting error covariance matrices $\hat{\boldsymbol{\Sigma}}_k$ will already have been found in the algorithm employed to calculate the sample partial autocorrelations. The order of the approximating autoregression is chosen, using the AIC criterion, as that value k for which

$$\log|\hat{\boldsymbol{\Sigma}}_k| + 2km^2/n$$

is smallest.

Now, letting k^* denote this chosen order, and $\hat{\mathbf{a}}_i$ $(i = 1, \ldots, k)$ the corresponding estimates of the parameter matrices, the innovations generating the ARMA model are estimated by

$$\hat{\boldsymbol{\eta}}_t = \mathbf{X}_t - \hat{\mathbf{a}}_1 \mathbf{X}_{t-1} - \cdots - \hat{\mathbf{a}}_{k^*} \mathbf{X}_{t-k^*}$$

The second stage of the procedure is to regress, for various values of p and q, $\mathbf{X}_t$ on $\mathbf{X}_{t-i}$ $(i = 1, \ldots, p)$ and $\hat{\boldsymbol{\eta}}_{t-j}$ $(j = 1, \ldots, q)$. Thus we estimate, by least squares, models of the form

$$\mathbf{X}_t = \mathbf{a}_1 \mathbf{X}_{t-1} + \cdots + \mathbf{a}_p \mathbf{X}_{t-p} + \mathbf{b}_1 \hat{\boldsymbol{\eta}}_{t-1} + \cdots + \mathbf{b}_q \hat{\boldsymbol{\eta}}_{t-q} + \boldsymbol{\eta}_t$$

Let $\hat{\boldsymbol{\Sigma}}_{p,q}$ denote the estimated error covariances. Then the order (p, q) of the ARMA model is chosen as that for which

$$\log|\hat{\boldsymbol{\Sigma}}_{p,q}| + (p + q)m^2 \log n/n \tag{8.3.6}$$

is smallest.

Now, in using the statistics (8.3.6), we see this procedure as suggesting one or possibly more models that might usefully be carried forward for further analysis. We do not treat it as an order estimation criterion designed to give once and for all a single model for subsequent efficient estimation. Accordingly, we feel that it is important, once a chosen model has been estimated, to check its adequacy.

The procedures for model selection outlined here, examination of sample autocorrelations and partial autocorrelations and application of the Hannan–Rissanen procedure, have, in our experience, been extremely useful in suggesting good starting points for the analysis of a small number of related time series. They are not, however, the only aids to model selection that have been proposed in the literature: other possibilities are suggested by Jenkins and Alavi [1981], Tiao and Box [1981], Cooper and Wood [1982], Tiao and Tsay [1983], and Tsay and Tiao [1984].

Parameter Estimation

The parameters of the model (8.3.1) can be estimated by computing the likelihood function conditional on assumed starting values for the innovations. Thus, if we set $\boldsymbol{\eta}_{p+1-j} = \mathbf{0}$ ($j = 1, \ldots, q$), the remaining innovations can be computed recursively, as functions of the parameter matrices, from

$$\boldsymbol{\eta}_t = \mathbf{X}_t - \mathbf{a}_1 \mathbf{X}_{t-1} - \cdots - \mathbf{a}_p \mathbf{X}_{t-p} - \mathbf{b}_1 \boldsymbol{\eta}_{t-1} - \cdots - \mathbf{b}_q \boldsymbol{\eta}_{t-q}$$
$$(t = p + 1, \ldots, n)$$

as proposed by Wilson [1973]. The conditional likelihood function is then

$$L = \text{const} |\boldsymbol{\Sigma}|^{-n/2} \exp\left[-\tfrac{1}{2} \text{Tr} \, \boldsymbol{\Sigma}^{-1} \mathbf{S}(\mathbf{a}, \mathbf{b}) \right]$$

where

$$\mathbf{S}(\mathbf{a}, \mathbf{b}) = \sum_t \boldsymbol{\eta}_t \boldsymbol{\eta}_t'$$

Approximate maximum likelihood estimates may then be obtained numerically, for example, by minimization of $|\mathbf{S}(\mathbf{a}, \mathbf{b})|$. This procedure is asymptotically efficient and should usually be quite satisfactory in practice. However, it is less adequate for smaller sample sizes, particularly when the moving average operator of the model is close to being noninvertible. In such circumstances it is preferable to proceed through maximization of the exact likelihood function. Procedures for deriving the exact likelihood for vector ARMA models have been given by Nicholls and Hall [1979] and Hillmer and Tiao [1979]. More recently, interest has centered on the use of the Kalman filter as a computationally efficient means of deriving the likelihood function for this and other time series models. (See, for example, Akaike [1974], Gardner, Harvey, and Phillips [1980], and Ansley and Kohn [1983], who show how to incorporate the possibility of missing or aggregated data.)

Diagnostic Checking

Having fitted to data an ARMA(p, q) model of the form (8.3.1), a natural check on adequacy would be to test this specification against an alternative, such as $\text{ARMA}(p, q + k)$, involving k additional parameter matrices. Lagrange multiplier tests for the vector ARMA model are discussed by Hosking [1981a] and Poskitt and Tremayne [1982].

Writing the log likelihood function as, approximately,

$$\log L = \text{const} - \frac{n}{2}\log|\Sigma| - \frac{1}{2}\sum_t \eta_t'\Sigma^{-1}\eta_t$$

it follows that

$$\frac{\partial \log L}{\partial a_{l,i,j}} = \sum_t \eta_t'\Sigma^{-1}V_{i,j,t-l}$$

where $a_{l,i,j}$ is the (i, j) element of $\mathbf{a}_l$ and

$$\mathbf{V}_{i,j,t} + \mathbf{b}_1\mathbf{V}_{i,j,t-1} + \cdots + \mathbf{b}_q\mathbf{V}_{i,j,t-q} = \mathbf{E}_{ij}\mathbf{X}_t \qquad (8.3.7)$$

where $\mathbf{E}_{ij}$ is the $m \times m$ matrix whose (i, j) element is one, with all other elements zero. Similarly

$$\frac{\partial \log L}{\partial b_{l,i,j}} = \sum_t \eta_t'\Sigma^{-1}U_{i,j,t-l}$$

where $b_{l,i,j}$ is the (i, j) element of $\mathbf{b}_l$ and

$$\mathbf{U}_{i,j,t} + \mathbf{b}_1\mathbf{U}_{i,j,t-1} + \cdots + \mathbf{b}_q\mathbf{U}_{i,j,t-q} = \mathbf{E}_{ij}\eta_t \qquad (8.3.8)$$

To compute the Lagrange multiplier test statistic, the unknown parameters in (8.3.7) and (8.3.8) are replaced by their estimates from the fit of (8.3.1) and the innovations η_t by the residuals from that fit.

Poskitt and Tremayne then show that the Lagrange multiplier test statistic for checking against the $\text{ARMA}(p, q + k)$ alternative follows from the regression of $\hat{\eta}' = (\hat{\eta}_n', \hat{\eta}_{n-1}', \dots)$ on

$$\hat{\mathbf{Z}} = \begin{bmatrix} \hat{\mathbf{V}}_{n-1} & \cdots & \hat{\mathbf{V}}_{n-p} & \hat{\mathbf{U}}_{n-1} & \cdots & \hat{\mathbf{U}}_{n-q-k} \\ \hat{\mathbf{V}}_{n-2} & \cdots & \hat{\mathbf{V}}_{n-p-1} & \hat{\mathbf{U}}_{n-2} & \cdots & \hat{\mathbf{U}}_{n-q-k-1} \\ \vdots & & \vdots & \vdots & & \vdots \end{bmatrix}$$

Under the null hypothesis that the $\text{ARMA}(p, q)$ specification is correct, the error covariance matrix for this regression is consistently estimated by $\mathbf{I} \otimes \hat{\Sigma}$, where $\hat{\Sigma}$ is the error covariance matrix from the fit of (8.3.1). The Lagrange multiplier test statistic is then

$$\text{LM} = \hat{\eta}'(\mathbf{I} \otimes \hat{\Sigma}^{-1})\hat{\mathbf{Z}}[\hat{\mathbf{Z}}'(\mathbf{I} \otimes \hat{\Sigma}^{-1})\hat{\mathbf{Z}}]^{-1}\hat{\mathbf{Z}}'(\mathbf{I} \otimes \hat{\Sigma}^{-1})\hat{\eta} \qquad (8.3.9)$$

Under the null hypothesis that the assumed model specification is correct, this statistic has an asymptotic χ^2 distribution with km^2 degrees of freedom. Poskitt and Tremayne also show that, asymptotically, the same test results if the alternative hypothesis is an $\text{ARMA}(p + k, q)$ specification.

Further insight into the structure of this test can be obtained by writing the derivative of the log likelihood function with respect to the moving average parameters as

$$\frac{\partial \log L}{\partial b_{l,i,j}} = \sum_t \boldsymbol{\eta}_t' \boldsymbol{\Sigma}^{-1} \mathbf{b}^{-1}(B) \mathbf{E}_{ij} \boldsymbol{\eta}_{t-l}$$

$$= \operatorname{Tr} \mathbf{b}^{-1}(B) \mathbf{E}_{ij} \sum_t \boldsymbol{\eta}_{t-l} \boldsymbol{\eta}_t' \boldsymbol{\Sigma}^{-1}$$

Then, writing the residual autocovariance matrices from the fitted model (8.3.1) as

$$\hat{\mathbf{C}}_\tau = \sum_{t=\tau+1}^n \hat{\boldsymbol{\eta}}_t \hat{\boldsymbol{\eta}}_{t-\tau}'/n \qquad (8.3.10)$$

it follows that the Lagrange multiplier test is essentially based on the first k of these matrices.

As in Section 3.6 for the single series case, it is also possible to derive a portmanteau test against more general alternatives This test, which Hosking [1981a] and Poskitt and Tremayne [1982] show can also be derived as a Lagrange multiplier test, is based on the first K residual autocovariance matrices (8.3.10), where K must be moderately large. More direct derivations of this test are provided by Hosking [1980b] and Li and McLeod [1981], while Hosking [1981b] demonstrates the equivalence of the different specifications. The test statistic is

$$P = n^2 \sum_{\tau=1}^K (n - \tau)^{-1} \operatorname{Tr}(\hat{\mathbf{C}}_\tau' \hat{\mathbf{C}}_0^{-1} \hat{\mathbf{C}}_\tau \hat{\mathbf{C}}_0^{-1}) \qquad (8.3.11)$$

Under the null hypothesis that the model is correctly specified, the statistic (8.3.11) has, for moderately large K, an asymptotic χ^2 distribution with $m^2(K - p - q)$ degrees of freedom.

Although the test (8.3.9) is, as we have already indicated, essentially based on the residual autocovariances, we nevertheless find it useful to examine the residual autocorrelations from a fitted model. These statistics can be useful in identifying the source of any inadequacy detected in the model. Therefore, we compute the matrices $\hat{\mathbf{R}}_\tau$ whose (i, j) elements are

$$\hat{r}_{\tau,i,j} = \hat{c}_{\tau,i,j}/[\hat{c}_{0,i,i}\hat{c}_{0,j,j}]^{1/2}$$

A very crude check follows from comparing these quantities with limits $\pm 2n^{-1/2}$.

In addition to the checks and formal tests just described, we have often found useful a further informal check on model adequacy. The rationale behind this procedure is based on the presumption that finding a well specified model will typically be a good deal easier in the single series case than in the case of multivariate model building. Now, as we saw in Section 7.2, any multivariate ARMA model implies specific models for the generating processes of the individual series. Indeed, it follows from equation (7.2.4) that, if $\mathbf{X}_t$ is generated by the vector ARMA(p, q) model (8.3.1), its individual elements are generated by univariate ARMA[$mp, (m - 1)p + q$] processes of the form

$$|\mathbf{a}(B)| X_{it} = b_i(B)\epsilon_{it} \qquad (8.3.12)$$

where ϵ_{it} is white noise and the $(m - 1)p + q$ moving average coefficients in $b_i(B)$ can be found as functions of the autoregressive and moving average coefficient matrices and the innovation error covariance matrix of (8.3.1). Hence, having estimated a vector ARMA model, we can determine with a little algebraic manipulation the models implied for the individual series. Next, without reference to the multivariate analysis, we can, using the methods of Chapter 3, fit models to the individual series. The models achieved are then compared with those implied by the multivariate model. This comparison is informal, but, given greater certainty about our ability to proceed successfully with model building in the single series case, could lead to the detection of inadequacies in the multivariate model. The procedure discussed in this paragraph has been used by Wallis [1977] and Chan and Wallis [1978] as the basis of an approach to multivariate time series model selection. In our own empirical work, the burden imposed on (8.3.12) is less heavy. Its purpose is only to provide a supplementary informal check on model adequacy.

We proceed now to illustrate the methodology of this section through some examples. These, and others reported in Hotopp [1985], lead us to believe that the approach outlined here will often prove successful in practice in building vector ARMA models relating two or three time series.

EXAMPLE 1 *Employment and Wages.* Our first example is of 135 quarterly seasonally adjusted observations on rates of change of employment in manufacturing (X_1) and hourly wages in manufacturing (X_2) in the United States. The sample autocorrelation matrices contained high values even at quite large lags, so that a pure moving average model is not indicated. The partial autocorrelation statistics are shown in Table 8.2, and should be compared with tabulated values of the χ^2 distribution with four degrees of freedom. It appears that, if a pure autoregressive model is to be fitted, the order should be at least two, while the values of these statistics at lags three and four are also moderately large.

The criterion (8.3.6) selected an ARMA(1, 1) model, and it was decided to proceed with this specification. Thus, we fit by maximum likelihood the

Table 8.2 *Partial autocorrelation statistics for employment and wages data*

k:	1	2	3	4	5	6	7	8	9	10
s_k:	121.99	13.94	6.21	8.61	2.24	2.62	2.97	2.64	7.43	0.53

model

$$X_t - aX_{t-1} = \alpha + \eta_t + b\eta_{t-1}$$

where the constant vector α is included since both series appeared to have nonzero means. The parameter estimates obtained (with estimated standard errors in brackets) were

$$\hat{\alpha} = \begin{bmatrix} 0.0087 & [0.0038] \\ 0.0014 & [0.0008] \end{bmatrix}; \quad \hat{a} = \begin{bmatrix} 0.43 & [0.12] & -0.53 & [0.25] \\ 0.077 & [0.032] & 0.88 & [0.05] \end{bmatrix};$$

$$\hat{b} = \begin{bmatrix} 0.28 & [0.12] & 0.35 & [0.31] \\ -0.069 & [0.051] & -0.34 & [0.10] \end{bmatrix}$$

As a first step in checking the adequacy of this fitted model, Table 8.3 shows the residual autocorrelation matrices of order up to ten. A crude check follows from comparison of these figures with limits $\pm 2n^{-1/2} \simeq \pm 0.17$. By this standard, very nearly all of the 40 residual autocorrelations and cross-correlations shown in the table are satisfactorily small. However, there is a very large correlation between $\hat{\eta}_{1t}$ and $\hat{\eta}_{1,t-5}$, and also between $\hat{\eta}_{2t}$ and $\hat{\eta}_{2,t-9}$. Now, in principle we could add extra terms to the model to get rid of the awkward residual autocorrelations. Certainly, this would yield a better fitting model, but in general in such circumstances we do not favor this course. It is our experience that models purpose-built to flatten residual autocorrelations at moderately high lags often produce disappointing forecast performance. A possible explanation of these large residual autocorrelations is that they are artifacts induced by the seasonal adjustment process.

The Lagrange multiplier statistics (8.3.9) were computed to test the assumed model against alternatives involving one and two additional parameter matrices, yielding 2.53 and 7.23, which are not unduly large compared with tabulated values of the χ^2 distribution with four and eight degrees of freedom.

The portmanteau statistic (8.3.11) was computed for $K = 10$, 15, and 20, yielding, respectively, 47.3, 62.1, and 77.2. When compared with tabulated values of the χ^2 distribution with 32, 52, and 72 degrees of freedom, the second and third of these are insignificant at the usual levels, but the first is

Table 8.3   *Residual autocorrelation matrices for ARMA(1,1) model fitted to employment-wages data*

k:	1		2		3		4		5	
$\hat{R}_k$:	.00	−.01	.01	.01	.02	.06	−.06	−.07	−.28	−.08
	.02	.03	.01	−.04	−.06	.02	.00	.03	−.04	−.07

k:	6		7		8		9		10	
$\hat{R}_k$:	.01	.04	−.05	−.03	−.05	.06	.02	.12	.10	.04
	−.02	.11	.08	.02	.13	−.04	.02	.25	.14	.10

just significant at the 5% level. This is a reflection of the large residual autocorrelations already noted at lags 5 and 9, and, as we have already indicated, we are disinclined to specify an exotic modification of the model in response to these values.

As a final check, we computed the univariate models implied by the fitted bivariate model: these are

$$(1 - 1.308B + 0.417B^2) X_{1t} = (1 - 0.599B - 0.212B^2) \epsilon_{1t} \quad (8.3.13)$$

and

$$(1 - 1.308B + 0.417B^2) X_{2t} = (1 - 0.728B + 0.195B^2) \epsilon_{2t} \quad (8.3.14)$$

On the other hand, applying directly the univariate model building procedures of Chapter 3, we obtained

$$(1 - 0.736B + 0.216B^2) X_{1t} = \epsilon_{1t} \quad (8.3.15)$$

and

$$(1 - B) X_{2t} = (1 - 0.380B) \epsilon_{2t} \quad (8.3.16)$$

The best way to compare these models is to express them as autoregressions. Thus, from (8.3.13) and (8.3.14) we find

$$(1 - 0.709B + 0.204B^2 - 0.028B^3 + 0.026B^4 + 0.010B^5 + \cdots) X_{1t} = \epsilon_{1t} \quad (8.3.17)$$

and

$$(1 - 0.580B - 0.200B^2 - 0.053B^3 + 0.015B^4 + 0.017B^5 + \cdots) X_{2t} = \epsilon_{2t} \quad (8.3.18)$$

Notice that (8.3.17) is very similar to (8.3.15). Also, from (8.3.16), we have

$$(1 - 0.620B - 0.236B^2 - 0.090B^3 - 0.034B^4 - 0.013B^5 + \cdots) X_{2t} = \epsilon_{2t}$$

which again is similar to (8.3.18). Thus, this check fails to provide any evidence of misspecification. It should be added, however, that the fifth sample autocorrelation of the series X_1 was quite large, a factor ignored in specifying (8.3.15) for reasons already discussed. We might conclude then that this check has also pointed to a possible source of model inadequacy already noted from Table 8.3 and the portmanteau test. While our own preference is to retain the ARMA(1, 1) model, these checks will have provided for less conservative analysts consistent indications of a possible problem with that model, a clear indication as to where the difficulty lies, and thus a possible means of correcting it.

EXAMPLE 2 *Sales and Advertising.* The second example is of a frequently analyzed data set containing 54 annual observations on sales (X_1) and advertising expenditures (X_2) of Lydia E. Pinkham: the data are given in

Table 8.4 *Partial autocorrelation statistics for sales and advertising data*

k:	1	2	3	4	5	6	7	8	9	10
s_k:	65.96	7.00	13.87	5.11	3.38	1.55	2.84	3.02	1.21	1.57

Erickson [1981]. The sample autocorrelation matrices did not suggest a pure moving average model as a likely generating mechanism for these data. Table 8.4 shows the first ten partial autocorrelation statistics. Comparing these with tabulated values of the χ^2 distribution with four degrees of freedom suggests a third-order autoregressive model as a possibility. However, according to the criterion (8.3.6), an ARMA(2, 1) model is preferred, with ARMA(3, 0) a close second choice. We decided to fit both these models.

The residual covariance matrices for the two fitted models were

$$\text{ARMA}(2,1): \hat{\Sigma} = \begin{bmatrix} 35382 & 15649 \\ 15649 & 23564 \end{bmatrix}; \quad \text{ARMA}(3,0): \hat{\Sigma} = \begin{bmatrix} 36414 & 14671 \\ 14671 & 23426 \end{bmatrix}$$

Since the two models involve the same number of parameters and the residual covariance matrix determinant is smaller for the ARMA(2, 1) model, that model is preferred.

For the process

$$\mathbf{X}_t - \mathbf{a}_1\mathbf{X}_{t-1} - \mathbf{a}_2\mathbf{X}_{t-2} = \boldsymbol{\alpha} + \boldsymbol{\eta}_t + \mathbf{b}\boldsymbol{\eta}_{t-1}$$

the maximum likelihood parameter estimates obtained were

$$\hat{\boldsymbol{\alpha}} = \begin{bmatrix} 237 & [94] \\ 174 & [129] \end{bmatrix}; \quad \hat{\mathbf{a}}_1 = \begin{bmatrix} 1.37 \; [0.27] & -0.29 \; [0.21] \\ -0.42 \; [0.37] & 0.69 \; [0.38] \end{bmatrix}$$

$$\hat{\mathbf{a}}_2 = \begin{bmatrix} -0.26 \; [0.28] & -0.16 \; [0.18] \\ 0.75 \; [0.39] & -0.53 \; [0.31] \end{bmatrix}; \quad \hat{\mathbf{b}} = \begin{bmatrix} -0.06 \; [0.31] & 0.20 \; [0.23] \\ 1.05 \; [0.40] & -0.27 \; [0.42] \end{bmatrix}$$

The residual autocorrelation matrices from the fitted ARMA(2, 1) model are displayed in Table 8.5. When these are compared with bounds $\pm 2n^{-1/2} \simeq \pm 0.27$, only one of the 40 statistics, and that at lag 8, seems unduly large. We find in these residual autocorrelations and cross correlations, then, no strong grounds to question the adequacy of the ARMA(2, 1) specification.

Table 8.5 *Partial autocorrelation matrices for ARMA(2, 1) model fitted to sales and advertising data*

k:	1		2		3		4		5	
$\hat{\mathbf{R}}_k$:	.01	.00	−.05	−.04	−.04	−.02	.02	.04	.09	.22
	.05	.02	.01	.01	−.00	−.07	.14	.20	−.08	.06

k:	6		7		8		9		10	
$\hat{\mathbf{R}}_k$:	−.09	−.26	.07	.07	−.05	−.10	−.10	.03	.18	.22
	−.01	−.13	.20	.18	.30	.15	.06	.16	.03	−.04

The Lagrange multiplier test statistics (8.3.9) for testing against the addition of one and two extra parameter matrices were 2.95 and 10.20, which are not significant at the usual levels when compared with tabulated values for the χ^2 distribution with 4 and 8 degrees of freedom. The portmanteau statistics (8.3.11) for values of $K = 10, 15$, and 20 were 19.6, 30.8, and 35.2. Comparison of these with tabulated values of the χ^2 distribution with 28, 48, and 68 degrees of freedom certainly fails to raise any cause for concern about the adequacy of the ARMA(2, 1) specification.

Finally, the single series models implied by the bivariate ARMA(2, 1) model are ARMA(4, 3). By expressing these as infinite-order autoregressions, we found, when the constant term is ignored,

$$(1 - 1.236B + 0.456B^2 - 0.064B^3 - 0.027B^4 + 0.050B^5$$
$$+ 0.036B^6 + \cdots)X_{1t} = \epsilon_{1t} \quad (8.3.19)$$

and

$$(1 - 0.900B + 0.399B^2 - 0.297B^3 - 0.008B^4 - 0.021B^5$$
$$+ 0.025B^6 + \cdots)X_{2t} = \epsilon_{2t} \quad (8.3.20)$$

An independent modeling of the sales data, using the procedures of Chapter 3, yielded

$$(1 - 1.180B + 0.358B^2)X_{1t} = \epsilon_{1t}$$

which is satisfactorily similar to (8.3.19). The partial autocorrelations of the advertising data are displayed in Table 8.6. Since the first three of these are quite large, a third-order autoregression is a possible generating model for this series. Fitting this model we obtain

$$(1 - 0.999B + 0.458B^2 - 0.323B^3)X_{2t} = \epsilon_{2t}$$

which is quite close to the form (8.3.20) implied by our fitted vector ARMA(2, 1) model. However, this analysis ignores the large partial autocorrelation at lag 5, a course we might be tempted to follow in the interests of parsimony. The fitted AR(5) model for the advertising series is

$$(1 - 1.000B + 0.328B^2 - 0.135B^3 - 0.382B^4 + 0.385B^5)X_{2t} = \epsilon_{2t}$$

Notice from (8.3.20) that our fitted bivariate model does not predict this higher-order autoregressive structure. Thus, the bivariate model appears to have faithfully represented the first three partial autocorrelations of the advertising series but not the fifth. Some analysts may prefer in these

Table 8.6 *Partial autocorrelations for advertising data*

k:	1	2	3	4	5	6	7	8	9	10
$\hat{a}_{kk}$:	.81	$-.17$	.29	.00	$-.38$	$-.04$	.03	$-.10$	$-.01$	$-.17$

circumstances to fit a higher-order vector model, an obvious choice being AR(5). Though this is a possibility, our own preference, particularly since the series are quite short, is to retain the original ARMA(2, 1) model.

EXAMPLE 3 *Prices, Man-hours Worked, and Output.* Our final example is of series of 145 quarterly seasonally adjusted observations on rates of change of prices (X_1), man-hours worked (X_2), and output (X_3) in the United States. The sample autocorrelation matrices did not suggest a low-order moving average process as a likely generating mechanism. Table 8.7 shows the first ten partial autocorrelation statistics. Comparing these with tabulated values of the χ^2 distribution with nine degrees of freedom, a third-order autoregression is suggested. Although the AIC criterion also selects AR(3) as the best autoregressive model, a first-order autoregression is narrowly preferred by the criterion (8.3.6). However, when the AR(1) model was fitted, it was rejected against the alternative of two additional parameter matrices by the Lagrange multiplier test based on (8.3.9). We therefore proceeded to fit an AR(3) model.

For the model

$$X_t - a_1 X_{t-1} - a_2 X_{t-2} - a_3 X_{t-3} = \alpha + \eta_t$$

we obtained the maximum likelihood estimates

$$\hat{\alpha} = \begin{bmatrix} 0.005 & [0.0011] \\ 0.0015 & [0.0018] \\ 0.0087 & [0.0017] \end{bmatrix};$$

$$\hat{a}_1 = \begin{bmatrix} 0.42 \ [0.08] & 0.07 \ [0.06] & 0.08 \ [0.06] \\ -0.14 \ [0.13] & -0.17 \ [0.09] & 0.41 \ [0.09] \\ -0.13 \ [0.12] & 0.21 \ [0.09] & 0.25 \ [0.09] \end{bmatrix};$$

$$\hat{a}_2 = \begin{bmatrix} 0.03 \ [0.08] & 0.13 \ [0.06] & 0.08 \ [0.06] \\ 0.08 \ [0.14] & -0.20 \ [0.10] & 0.07 \ [0.10] \\ -0.19 \ [0.13] & 0.04 \ [0.09] & 0.06 \ [0.10] \end{bmatrix};$$

$$\hat{a}_3 = \begin{bmatrix} 0.39 \ [0.07] & 0.11 \ [0.06] & -0.02 \ [0.06] \\ -0.08 \ [0.12] & 0.10 \ [0.09] & -0.17 \ [0.09] \\ -0.09 \ [0.12] & -0.05 \ [0.09] & -0.12 \ [0.09] \end{bmatrix}$$

For testing this model against alternatives involving one and two extra parameter matrices, the Lagrange multiplier test statistics (8.3.9) were 13.86

Table 8.7 *Partial autocorrelation statistics for prices, man-hours and output data*

k:	1	2	3	4	5	6	7	8	9	10
s_k:	112.97	13.50	29.89	14.38	8.78	4.73	11.55	6.62	9.17	19.95

and 20.18. Comparing these with tabulated values of the χ^2 distribution with 9 and 18 degrees of freedom fails to provide any strong indication of model inadequacy. For the portmanteau statistics (8.3.11), with $K = 10$, 15, and 20, we obtained 80.5, 132.6, and 177.7; compared with tabulated values of the χ^2 distribution with 63, 108, and 153 degrees of freedom, none of these is significant at the 5% level. Also, the individual elements of the residual autocorrelation matrices were satisfactorily small, and the single series models implied by the vector AR(3) model were quite similar to those achieved by an independent analysis of the data sets. Accordingly, we regard the original model as likely to be satisfactory for forecasting purposes.

8.4 Building Forecasting Models for Several Related Time Series

In our experience, the procedures discussed in the previous section generally work satisfactorily in practice for the analysis of a small number of related time series. However, as the number of series considered increases we come face to face with what Jenkins and Alavi [1981] call "the curse of higher dimensionality." The problem is that, for a fully parametrized ARMA model, the number of coefficients increases at the rate of the square of the number of time series. Thus, even if we had any confidence in our ability to identify an ARMA(p, q) model relating say seven or eight time series, the full parametrization would involve a huge number of unknown parameters. Not only is model estimation extremely expensive in this case, it is also rather foolhardy, since though such a nonparsimonious structure may fit an observed data set well, it is likely to prove very disappointing when extrapolated forward for forecasting purposes. A number of possibilities for fighting "the curse" have been proposed in the literature, generally based, for both conceptual and computational ease, on vector autoregressive models. In this section we will briefly discuss three of these approaches.

Multivariate Autoregressive Index Models

The AR(p) generating model for $X'_t = (X_{1t}, X_{2t}, \ldots, X_{mt})$,

$$X_t = a_1 X_{t-1} + \cdots + a_p X_{t-p} + \eta_t$$

has a total of $m^2 p$ parameters. Suppose, however, that there exists an $r \times m$ matrix d_0, and p $m \times r$ matrices c_i ($i = 1, \ldots, p$) such that

$$a_i = c_i d_0 \qquad (i = 1, \ldots, m)$$

so that the autoregressive model can be written as

$$X_t = c_1 d_0 X_{t-1} + \cdots + c_p d_0 X_{t-p} + \eta_t \qquad (8.4.1)$$

Then, model (8.4.1) contains a total of $mr(p + 1)$ parameters. However, it is not, as it stands, identified since, if P is any nonsingular matrix, then $(c_i P)(P^{-1} d_0) = c_i d_0$. To achieve identification a normalization condition can be imposed; for example, we can write

$$\mathbf{d}_0 = (\mathbf{I}_r : \mathbf{d}_2)$$

where $\mathbf{I}_r$ is the $r \times r$ identity matrix and $\mathbf{d}_2$ is an $r \times (m - r)$ matrix of free parameters. Thus, when such a condition is imposed, model (8.4.1) contains a total of $mrp + r(m - r)$ parameters, a number which can be much less than the number of parameters in the unrestricted AR(p) model if r is much less than m.

Autoregressive index models of the form (8.4.1) have been considered by Reinsel [1983]. In this formulation, each X_{it} depends linearly, not on past values of all X_{jt}, but on past values of r linear combinations, or indices, of the X_{jt}. Reinsel discusses, for given p and r, the estimation of the parameters of model (8.4.1) and suggests that the choice of appropriate values for p and r be based on an order estimation criterion. Similar models are also discussed by Sims [1981].

Reduced Rank Autoregressive Models
A similar structure is considered by Velu, Reinsel, and Wichern [1986]. These authors discuss the fitting of the model

$$\mathbf{X}_t = \mathbf{c}_0\mathbf{d}_1\mathbf{X}_{t-1} + \cdots + \mathbf{c}_0\mathbf{d}_p\mathbf{X}_{t-p} + \mathbf{\eta}_t \tag{8.4.2}$$

where $\mathbf{c}_0$ is $m \times r$, $\mathbf{d}_i$ ($i = 1,\ldots, p$) are $r \times m$, and again a normalization condition on $\mathbf{c}_0$ is required. The model (8.4.2), which is closely related to the canonical analysis proposed by Box and Tiao [1977], has the same potential as (8.4.1) for yielding a reduction in the number of parameters compared with the unrestricted AR(p) model. Velu, Reinsel, and Wichern discuss the estimation of the parameters of the structure (8.4.2). Again, the choice of r and p can be based on an order estimation criterion.

One possible approach to multivariate time series model building for several related variables is to fit both autoregressive index and reduced rank autoregressive models—there seems to be no strong *a priori* reason for favoring one over the other—and then comparing, through the corresponding order estimation statistics, the best model of each type achieved.

Autoregressive Models with Realistic Prior Distributions
The two approaches just discussed attack the curse of higher dimensionality by searching for more parsimoniously parameterized structures than an unconstrained vector autoregressive model. An alternative approach when faced with a heavily parameterized model is to shrink the usual maximum likelihood estimates towards prior means. In the context of regression models, the potential for improved sampling properties of estimators and forecasts resulting from such an approach are well known. (See, for example, Stein [1974].)

Essentially this idea is applied by Doan, Litterman, and Sims [1984] to the development of vector autoregressive forecasting models for a moderately large number of possibly related time series. These authors use a Bayesian approach to shrink the usual least squares estimates to a prior mean, for which each equation in the system is a random walk, possibly with drift; that is, the prior mean is represented by

$$X_{it} = \alpha_i + X_{i,t-1} + \eta_{it}$$

This approach, whose details we will not discuss here, seems to offer interesting possibilities, though the full specification of the prior distribution is rather tricky, involving a good deal of experimentation, together with examination of the resulting in-sample "forecasts." A full evaluation of its merits must await the development of a longer track record in the publication of post-sample economic forecasts.

8.5 Testing for Causality

In this section we consider the problem of testing for causal direction, restricting attention to the case where the available information set consists of current and past observations on the series $\mathbf{X}'_t = (\mathbf{X}'_{1t} : \mathbf{X}'_{2t})$, and we wish to test the null hypothesis that $\mathbf{X}_2$ does not cause $\mathbf{X}_1$. For ease of exposition in what follows, $\mathbf{X}_{1t}$ and $\mathbf{X}_{2t}$ will be taken to be scalars so that we concentrate on the bivariate case. We can then concentrate on testing for predictive gains one step ahead.

The most commonly used tests of causality are not based on efficiently parameterized models fitted to the available data. Instead, the tests are typically carried out in the framework of a heavily parameterized structure. For example, what has come to be called the "Granger test," because it is implicit in Granger [1969b], is based on the idea that the process generating (X_{1t}, X_{2t}) can be expressed as an infinite-order autoregression. To achieve a practical test, however, the order of this process must be truncated, and tests are based on the least squares fit of

$$X_{1t} = \sum_{j=1}^{K} d_{1j} X_{1,t-j} + \sum_{j=1}^{K} d_{2j} X_{2,t-j} + \epsilon_{1t} \tag{8.5.1}$$

where ϵ_{1t} is taken to be white noise, and we have again omitted the intercept term, assuming for ease of exposition a zero-mean series. In (8.5.1), the order K of the approximating autoregression is often in practice set rather arbitrarily at some moderately high number: an alternative, as in Hsiao [1979], is to use some order estimation criterion such as AIC to fix this lag. The null hypothesis that X_2 does not cause X_1 then corresponds to $d_{2j} = 0$ ($j = 1, \ldots, K$), and the usual F-test can be employed.

An alternative test, due to Sims [1972], is based on the infinite-lags two-sided regression

$$X_{2t} = \sum_{j=-\infty}^{\infty} \beta_j X_{1,t-j} + V_t \tag{8.5.2}$$

Sims showed that X_{2t} does not cause X_{1t} if and only if $\beta_{-j} = 0$ ($j = 1, 2, \ldots$). Unfortunately, a practical test does not follow directly from this result, since the innovation series V_t in (8.5.2) is not necessarily white noise. Sims suggested that, for many economic time series this difficulty could often be satisfactorily resolved by first applying to each the filter $(1 - 0.75B)^2$. However, such an approach is rather arbitrary and will not invariably be satisfactory. As an alternative, a low-order autoregressive process might be postulated for this error term. Perhaps a more useful modification of the Sims test is employed by Geweke, Meese, and Dent [1983]. These authors propose the addition of lagged terms in X_2 to the right-hand side of (8.5.2), yielding

$$X_{2t} = \sum_{j=-\infty}^{\infty} \beta_j X_{1, t-j} + \sum_{j=1}^{\infty} \gamma_j X_{2, t-j} + \epsilon_t \qquad (8.5.3)$$

where now the ϵ_t series is white noise by construction. A practical test now follows by truncating the infinite sums in (8.5.3) and using the usual F-test of $\beta_{-j} = 0$ ($j = 1, 2, \ldots$).

A rather different test for causal direction is based on the work of Haugh [1976], Pierce [1977], and Pierce and Haugh [1977]. Suppose that X_{1t} and X_{2t} are generated by univariate ARIMA processes with white noise innovations ϵ_{1t} and ϵ_{2t}. Pierce and Haugh then note that X_2 does not cause X_1 if and only if the correlation is zero between ϵ_{1t} and $\epsilon_{2, t-j}$ for all positive j. They therefore propose the fitting of ARIMA models to each individual series, basing a test for causality on the sample cross correlations between the residual series.

The properties of variants of these three tests of causal direction have been studied by Geweke, Meese, and Dent [1983] and Nelson and Schwert [1982]. The simulation results reported by Nelson and Schwert suggest a strong preference for the Granger and Sims tests over the Haugh–Pierce test, while Geweke, Meese, and Dent indicate a preference for the Wald variants of either the Granger test or the Sims test. Specifically, then, their recommendation is to estimate (8.5.1) by least squares, denoting by $\hat{\sigma}_1^2$ the error variance estimate. Next, estimate by least squares

$$X_{1t} = \sum_{j=1}^{K} d_j X_{1, t-j} + \epsilon_t$$

If $\hat{\sigma}^2$ denotes the residual variance estimate for this regression, the test statistic is

$$T = n(\hat{\sigma}^2 - \hat{\sigma}_1^2)/\hat{\sigma}_1^2$$

which has an asymptotic χ^2 distribution with K degrees of freedom under the null hypothesis that X_2 does not cause X_1.

Nelson and Schwert further find in their simulations a serious loss of power in the tests when they are based on unnecessarily heavily parameterized models. This suggests the possibility of basing tests for causality on a parsimoniously parameterized vector ARMA model fitted to the data. This approach is followed by Newbold and Hotopp [1986]. Let (X_{1t}, X_{2t}) be a pair of time series generated by an ARMA(p, q) model, which we now write as

$$\begin{bmatrix} a_{11}(B) & a_{12}(B) \\ a_{21}(B) & a_{22}(B) \end{bmatrix} \begin{bmatrix} X_{1t} \\ X_{2t} \end{bmatrix} = \begin{bmatrix} b_{11}(B) & b_{12}(B) \\ b_{21}(B) & b_{22}(B) \end{bmatrix} \begin{bmatrix} \eta_{1t} \\ \eta_{2t} \end{bmatrix} \quad (8.5.4)$$

Following Kang [1981], we can write (8.5.4), exactly as in (8.3.12), as

$$|a(B)| \begin{bmatrix} X_{1t} \\ X_{2t} \end{bmatrix}$$

$$= \begin{bmatrix} a_{22}(B)b_{11}(B) - a_{21}(B)b_{21}(B) & -[a_{12}(B)b_{22}(B) - a_{22}(B)b_{12}(B)] \\ -[a_{21}(B)b_{11}(B) - a_{11}(B)b_{21}(B)] & a_{11}(B)b_{22}(B) - a_{21}(B)b_{12}(B) \end{bmatrix} \begin{bmatrix} \eta_{1t} \\ \eta_{2t} \end{bmatrix}$$

Now, the direction of causal relationship between X_{1t} and X_{2t} is the same as that between $|a(B)|X_{1t}$ and $|a(B)|X_{2t}$. Hence, it follows that X_2 does not cause X_1 if and only if

$$a_{12}(B)b_{22}(B) - a_{22}(B)b_{12}(B) = 0 \quad (8.5.5)$$

For an ARMA(p, q) process, then, noncausality imposes a set of $p + q$ constraints on the parameters of the model. These constraints can be tested directly from the fitted model. For example, for the ARMA(1, 1) model, the restriction (8.5.5) implies

$$(-a_{12}B)(1 + b_{22}B) - (1 - a_{22}B)(b_{12}B) = 0$$

so that

$$-(b_{12} + a_{12})B + (b_{12}a_{22} - a_{12}b_{22})B^2 = 0$$

Therefore X_2 does not cause X_1 if and only if

$$b_{12} + a_{12} = 0$$

and

$$b_{12}a_{22} - a_{12}b_{22} = 0 \quad (8.5.6)$$

The most direct procedure for testing this hypothesis is through a Wald test. Let $\boldsymbol{\beta}$ denote the vector of autoregressive and moving average parameters, and $\mathbf{f}(\boldsymbol{\beta}) = 0$ the set of constraints on these parameters implied by (8.5.5). Denote by $\hat{\boldsymbol{\beta}}$ the unconstrained estimators of $\boldsymbol{\beta}$, obtained through maximum likelihood, and by $\hat{\boldsymbol{\Sigma}}_{\boldsymbol{\beta}}$ their estimated covariance matrix. The Wald test is then based on the value of $\mathbf{f}(\hat{\boldsymbol{\beta}})$. It can be shown that, under the null hypothesis, $n^{-1/2}\mathbf{f}(\hat{\boldsymbol{\beta}})$ has an asymptotic normal distribution with mean zero and a covariance matrix that is consistently estimated by

$$\hat{\boldsymbol{\Sigma}}_{\mathbf{f}} = \left[\frac{\partial \mathbf{f}}{\partial \boldsymbol{\beta}'} \right] \hat{\boldsymbol{\Sigma}}_{\boldsymbol{\beta}} \left[\frac{\partial \mathbf{f}}{\partial \boldsymbol{\beta}'} \right]'$$

where $\partial \mathbf{f}/\partial \boldsymbol{\beta}'$ is the $(p + q) \times (p + q)$ matrix whose (i, j)th element is the partial derivative of the ith member of $\mathbf{f}$ with respect to the jth member of

β, evaluated at $\hat{\beta}$. Then, the Wald test statistic is

$$W = n\mathbf{f}(\hat{\beta})'\hat{\Sigma}_f^{-1}\mathbf{f}(\hat{\beta}) \tag{8.5.7}$$

Under the null hypothesis of noncausality, this statistic has an asymptotic χ^2 distribution with $p + q$ degrees of freedom. Returning to the ARMA(1, 1) example, X_2 not causing X_1 implies in (8.5.6) constraints involving just four of the parameters of the model, so that we need only be concerned about the part of $\hat{\Sigma}_\beta$ relating to those parameters. Then, if we write

$$\beta' = (a_{12}, a_{22}, b_{12}, b_{22})$$

it follows from (8.5.6) that

$$\frac{\partial \mathbf{f}}{\partial \beta'} = \begin{bmatrix} 1 & 0 & 1 & 0 \\ -\hat{b}_{22} & \hat{b}_{12} & \hat{a}_{22} & -\hat{a}_{12} \end{bmatrix}$$

The test statistic is then readily computed. The advantage of this approach is that it requires only the estimation of the unconstrained model. It is not necessary to re-estimate the model subject to the constraints (8.5.5) as would be required in order to carry out a likelihood ratio test.

This procedure was used to test for causality in two of the examples of Section 8.3. For the series on employment and wages, the fitted multivariate model was ARMA(1, 1), so that the appropriate test statistics are constructed as illustrated above. For the null hypothesis that wages do not cause employment, we obtained for the test statistic (8.5.7) the value 4.718. Comparison with tabulated values of the χ^2 distribution with two degrees of freedom reveals that this null hypothesis can be rejected at the 10% but not at the 5% level of significance. For testing the null hypothesis that employment does not cause wages, the calculated statistic was 7.204, so that this null hypothesis is rejected at the 5% level. We find, then, quite strong evidence of employment causing wages, with some suggestion of the possibility of feedback.

For the data on sales and advertising, we fit in Section 8.3 an ARMA(2, 1) model. In this case, then, noncausality imposes three constraints on the model parameters. For the null hypothesis that advertising does not cause sales, the calculated test statistic (8.5.7) was 4.846. Comparison with tabulated values of the χ^2 distribution with three degrees of freedom shows that the null hypothesis cannot be rejected at the 10% level. On the other hand, the null hypothesis that sales do not cause advertising can be rejected at very low significance levels: the test statistic was 35.63.

8.6 Testing for Co-Integration

The idea of co-integration was introduced in Section 7.4. If X_t and Y_t are both $I(1)$ series, they are said to be co-integrated if there exists a constant A such that $Z_t = X_t - AY_t$ is $I(0)$, so that Z_t is stationary with a positive, finite spectrum at zero frequency. Since the type of model that should be built and the kinds of forecasts produced will depend on whether the series are co-integrated, it will be of interest to test for co-integration. A two-stage testing procedure has been investigated by Granger and Engle. In the first stage, the coefficient A is estimated by least squares or maximum likelihood; in the second the resulting series $Z_t = X_t - \hat{A}Y_t$ is tested as $I(0)$ rather than $I(1)$. If the series are co-integrated, it is clear that a good estimate for A can be expected, since any linear combination, such as $Z_t(C) = X_t - CY_t$ will be $I(1)$ and thus have very large (theoretically infinite) variance, whereas, if C equals the true A value, then Z_t will be $I(0)$ and have finite variance. The plot of variance ($Z_t(C)$) against C will theoretically have a singularity at $C = A$, and a least squares estimate should find this. The regression $X_t = AY_t + u_t$ will be called the co-integrating regression. Stock [1985] has shown that the variance of $\hat{A}$ is almost $O(N^{-2})$ rather than the usual $O(N^{-1})$ for regression parameter estimates with stationary series having sample size N. This indicates that the spurious regression results discussed in Section 6.4 have to be completely reinterpreted when the two $I(1)$ series involved are co-integrated. In any case, if the series are co-integrated, a good estimate of A can be expected, and so Z_t will be well estimated by u_t. The second stage of the test procedure is then to test if $\hat{Z}_t$ is $I(0)$.

Granger and Engle [1985] have considered several different tests, but only the two that they recommend will be discussed here. The easiest to use is based on the Durbin–Watson statistic d of the co-integration regression. The standard tables for this statistic cannot be used, since one is not testing whether $d = 2$ but rather that d is significantly positive, if the null hypothesis is that Z_t is $I(0)$, i.e., that X_t and Y_t are co-integrated. If the sample size is 100, Granger and Engle found critical values by simulation for two cases. In the first case, X_t and Y_t are independent random walks. In the second case they are independent ARIMA(4, 1, 0) series, with $\Delta X_t = 0.8 \Delta X_{t-4} +$ white noise, and similarly for ΔY_t. The critical values found are shown in Table 8.8.

The second test, called the augmented Dickey–Fuller test, runs the regression

$$\Delta u_t = -\pi u_{t-1} + \sum_{j=1}^{P} b_j \Delta u_{t-j} + e_t$$

using u_t, the residual from the co-integrating regression. If $\pi = 0$, u_t will be $I(1)$, so the hypothesis of co-integration corresponds to π being significantly positive. The test-statistic is the t statistic for π, but the t distribution is not appropriate. Table 8.8 shows the critical values for this statistic, again derived from a simulation. It is seen that the second test has more stable critical values, but the Durbin–Watson test was found to be somewhat more powerful. The extent to which the critical values change with sample size has yet to be determined.

Table 8.8   *Critical Values of Co-Integration Test Statistics*

	Level		
Durbin–Watson Statistics[a]	1%	5%	10%
$q = 2$			
A	.511	.386	.322
B	.455	.282	.209
$q = 3$			
A	.488	.367	.308
Augmented Dickey–Fuller t-statistics[a]			
$q = 2$			
A	3.77	3.17	2.84
B	3.73	3.17	2.91
$q = 3$			
A	3.69	3.13	2.82

[a] Cases: A, all series random walk, B, all series ARIMA(4, 1, 0).
q = number of series. B is not available for $q = 3$

If more than two series are being considered as co-integrated (so that X_{it}, $i = 1, \ldots, q$ are all $I(1)$ but a co-integrating vector α may exist so that $Z_t = \alpha' X_t$ is $I(0)$), then under the hypothesis of co-integration the same test statistics can be used. The table shows the critical values for $q = 2$ and $q = 3$; they are not known for other q values. The vector α need not be unique for $q > 2$; a possible procedure is to run $q - 1$ separate regressions, each time dropping a different X_{it} series from the regression. Again, the effect on the critical values of the two test statistics is not known.

A: *"How is your wife?"*
B: *"Compared to what?"*

9.1 Typical Suboptimality of Economic Forecasts

Given a fairly limited information set, for example all past values of a time series, one might reasonably hope in practice to achieve a forecast that at least closely approximates the optimum. Indeed, the univariate Box–Jenkins procedure described in Chapters 3 and 5 might well be expected to achieve this goal frequently, given a sufficiently large sample. Even in this situation, however, further improvement may still be achievable through consideration of the possibilities of nonlinearity and nonstationarity, as will be seen in Chapter 10. More importantly, though, the forecaster in the real world is not, and should not be, constrained to employ an information set of this kind. The information considered by many macroeconomic forecasters is indeed vast. Insofar as forecasts from quantitative models are modified judgmentally, the information taken into account is often of a qualitative nature, being a sublimation of the practitioner's experience of the variable under study and its principal determinants. Indeed, in forming economic forecasts, it is often the case that noneconomic information could profitably be taken into account. Thus, the supply of grains to the market in any given year, and hence prices of food, is greatly affected by the weather. Again, the supply and price of oil in the past two or three years have been determined as much by political as economic factors. Thus, given a world in which the amount of potential information is vast and the number of potential ways of employing it enormous (partly because in many areas economic theory is ill structured, or insufficient data are available to distinguish with any high degree of confidence between competing theories), it makes very little sense to view forecast optimality as a useful working concept. Put another way, we doubt whether any economic forecaster would view his product as the best that could possibly be achieved given all the information in the universe.

Once it is recognized that the typical economic forecast cannot generally be thought of as in any sense optimal, two consequences follow. First, a forecast may well be able to be improved. One way to achieve this would be to consider two or more forecasts of the same quantity since it is often the case in macroeconomics that competing forecasts are available. Suppose one has several forecasts, then it is quite possible that any one of them contains useful information absent in the others, and so rather than discard all but one forecast, it could well be profitable to incorporate them all into an overall combined forecast. A particularly simple way to achieve this is to let the combined forecast be a weighted average, with appropriately chosen weights, of the individual forecasts. Since the economic forecaster will not be in the position to assert reasonably that his forecasts are the best possible, it is important that economic forecasts be critically evaluated. An evaluation exercise, as well as providing information about the relative worth of a set of forecasts, may well suggest directions in which the forecast-generating mechanism can be improved, and hence act as a stimulus to future productive research. With this in mind, it follows that the evaluation criteria employed should be as demanding as possible since the object ought to be self-criticism rather than self-congratulation.

In the remainder of this chapter methods that have been employed in the combination and evaluation of forecasts are discussed, and details of some actual evaluation exercises, applied to macroeconomic forecasts in the past few years, are given.

9.2 The Combination of Forecasts

As a simple example of the potential of combining forecasts, an examination of data given in Barnard [1963] is instructive. One-step ahead forecasts of world airline passenger miles per month over the period 1951–1960 are given for both a Box–Jenkins model and an exponential smoothing model. The former yielded an error variance of 148.6 and the latter 177.7. However, an alternative forecast, which is simply the average of the two individual forecasts, can be shown to have an error variance of 130.2. Thus, in this particular instance, a combined forecast that outperforms both individual forecasts can readily be found. One is led to ask the question as to whether more sophisticated combination rules might lead to further improvement and produce a procedure of wider applicability.

Following Bates and Granger [1969], consider first the case of combining two *unbiased* one-step ahead forecasts. Let $f_n^{(1)}$ and $f_n^{(2)}$ be forecasts of X_n with errors

$$e_n^{(j)} = X_n - f_n^{(j)}, \qquad j = 1, 2$$

such that

$$E(e_n^{(j)}) = 0, \qquad E(e_n^{(j)2}) = \sigma_j^2, \qquad j = 1, 2$$

and

$$E(e_n^{(1)}e_n^{(2)}) = \rho\sigma_1\sigma_2$$

Consider now a combined forecast, taken to be a weighted average of the two individual forecasts (since both are unbiased),

$$C_n = kf_n^{(1)} + (1 - k)f_n^{(2)}$$

The forecast error is

$$e_n^{(c)} = X_n - C_n = ke_n^{(1)} + (1 - k)e_n^{(2)}$$

Hence the error variance is

$$\sigma_c^2 = k^2\sigma_1^2 + (1 - k)^2\sigma_2^2 + 2k(1 - k)\rho\sigma_1\sigma_2 \qquad (9.2.1)$$

This expression is minimized for the value of k given by

$$k_0 = \frac{\sigma_2^2 - \rho\sigma_1\sigma_2}{\sigma_1^2 + \sigma_2^2 - 2\rho\sigma_1\sigma_2} \qquad (9.2.2)$$

and substitution into (9.2.1) yields the minimum achievable error variance as

$$\sigma_{c,0}^2 = \frac{\sigma_1^2\sigma_2^2(1 - \rho^2)}{\sigma_1^2 + \sigma_2^2 - 2\rho\sigma_1\sigma_2} \qquad (9.2.3)$$

Note $\sigma_{c,0}^2 < \min(\sigma_1^2, \sigma_2^2)$ unless either ρ is exactly equal to σ_1/σ_2 or to σ_2/σ_1. If either equality holds, then the variance of the combined forecast is equal to the smaller of the two error variances. Thus, a priori, it is reasonable to expect in most practical situations that the best available combined forecast will outperform the better individual forecast—it cannot, in any case, do worse.

Two results of passing interest can be derived from expressions (9.2.2) and (9.2.3). First it can be seen that

$$k_0 \gtreqless 0 \qquad \text{if and only if} \qquad \sigma_2/\sigma_1 \gtreqless \rho$$

It thus follows that, if $f_n^{(2)}$ is the optimal forecast based on a particular information set, any other forecast $f_n^{(1)}$ based on the same information set must be such that $\rho = \sigma_2/\sigma_1$, exactly. The situation $k_0 < 0$ is interesting. In much of our empirical work on combining we have constrained the weights to be nonnegative, it being rather difficult to justify on general grounds the assignment of a negative weight to a particular forecast. However, in light of the above conditions, it appears that an inferior forecast may still be worth including with negative weight on the grounds that its relatively high error variance is outweighed by a large ρ value—that is to say, the part of the variable of interest left unexplained by it is sufficiently strongly related to the part left unexplained by the better forecast. A second point concerns the behavior of (9.2.3) as ρ approaches -1 or 1. In the former case $\sigma_{c,0}^2$ tends to zero, implying a perfect forecast is obtainable. As ρ approaches 1, $\sigma_{c,0}^2$ also tends to zero except when $\sigma_1 = \sigma_2$, in which case its limit is σ_1^2. In interpreting the result for ρ tending to 1, which at first sight seems counter-intuitive, it should be borne in mind that ρ is the correlation between the two forecast errors, not between the forecasts themselves. It is simply explained, as follows. Consider two forecasts producing errors $e_n^{(1)}$ and $Ae_n^{(1)}$, where A is positive. Then

$$e_n^{(1)} = X_n - f_n^{(1)} \quad \text{and} \quad e_n^{(2)} = Ae_n^{(1)} = A(X_n - f_n^{(1)})$$

Hence, the second forecast is

$$f_n^{(2)} = X_n - e_n^{(2)} = (1 - A)X_n + Af_n^{(1)}$$

Thus, this forecast, for $A \neq 1$, involves the quantity to be forecast X_n and one has exactly

$$X_n = -\frac{A}{1 - A} f_n^{(1)} + \frac{1}{1 - A} f_n^{(2)}$$

Now, as it stands, formula (9.2.2) is of no operational value since in practice one would never know the values σ_1^2, σ_2^2, and ρ. However, suppose that the two forecasting procedures have been observed over the previous $n - 1$ time periods, yielding errors $e_t^{(j)}$, $t = 1, 2, \ldots, n - 1$, $j = 1, 2$. Denoting the combining weight to be employed at time n by $\hat{k}_n$, and replacing quantities in (9.2.2) by their sample estimates, a natural choice is

$$\hat{k}_n = \frac{\displaystyle\sum_{t=n-v}^{n-1} (e_t^{(2)2} - e_t^{(1)}e_t^{(2)})}{\displaystyle\sum_{t=n-v}^{n-1} (e_t^{(1)2} + e_t^{(2)2} - 2e_t^{(1)}e_t^{(2)})} \tag{9.2.4}$$

Given a sample $e_t^{(j)}$, $t = n - v, \ldots, n - 1$, $j = 1, 2$, from a bivariate normal distribution, the quantity (9.2.4) is the maximum likelihood estimator of k_0 of (9.2.2). Alternatively, it can be viewed as a least-squares estimator based on the same sample since the combined forecast at time t can be written

$$C_t - f_t^{(2)} = k(f_t^{(1)} - f_t^{(2)})$$

or alternatively

$$e_t^{(2)} = k(e_t^{(2)} - e_t^{(1)}) + e_t^{(c)}$$

where $e_t^{(c)}$ is the error of the combined forecast. Estimation of k by least squares then yields (9.2.4). Although this choice of combining weights is a very natural one, it is subject to two difficulties. First, population correlation coefficients are generally not well estimated in small samples; and second it may be that the relative performance of the two forecasting methods is nonstationary, suggesting the use of a system of weights that can adapt fairly quickly through time. With these considerations in mind, Bates and Granger were led to consider a number of alternative choices of weights, including the following:

$$\hat{k}_n = \frac{\sum\limits_{t=n-v}^{n-1} e_t^{(2)2}}{\sum\limits_{t=n-v}^{n-1} (e_t^{(1)2} + e_t^{(2)2})} \qquad (9.2.5)$$

$$\hat{k}_n = \alpha \hat{k}_{n-1} + \frac{(1-\alpha) \sum\limits_{t=n-v}^{n-1} e_t^{(2)2}}{\sum\limits_{t=n-v}^{n-1} (e_t^{(1)2} + e_t^{(2)2})}, \qquad 0 < \alpha < 1 \qquad (9.2.6)$$

$$\hat{k}_n = \frac{\sum\limits_{t=1}^{n-1} W^t (e_t^{(2)2} - e_t^{(1)} e_t^{(2)})}{\sum\limits_{t=1}^{n-1} W^t (e_t^{(1)2} + e_t^{(2)2} - 2e_t^{(1)} e_t^{(2)})}, \qquad W \geqslant 1 \qquad (9.2.7)$$

$$\hat{k}_n = \frac{\sum\limits_{t=1}^{n-1} W^t e_t^{(2)2}}{\sum\limits_{t=1}^{n-1} W^t (e_t^{(1)2} + e_t^{(2)2})}, \qquad W \geqslant 1 \qquad (9.2.8)$$

If one wishes to restrict the weights employed to lie between zero and one, then appropriate end points of this range can be substituted for any calculated values from (9.2.4) or (9.2.7) falling outside the range.

Bates and Granger.applied the various combining formulas to the world airline passenger data, looking at several pairs of univariate one-step ahead forecasts, with generally successful results. This prompted a wider study by Newbold and Granger [1974], who considered the combination of one-step ahead Box–Jenkins, Holt–Winters, and stepwise autoregressive forecasts for the 80 monthly series in the collection described in Section 5.6. Forecasts were combined in pairs, using (9.2.4) and (9.2.5) with $v = 1, 3, 6, 9,$ and 12; (9.2.6) for combinations of $\alpha = 0.5, 0.7,$ and 0.9 and $v = 1, 3, 6, 9, 12$; and (9.2.7) and (9.2.8) for $W = 1, 1.5, 2,$ and 2.5. The weights were constrained to lie between zero and unity. Table 9.1 shows the percentage of series for which the combination of a pair of forecasts yielded an overall forecast superior to *both* individual forecasts, employing here and throughout this section the criterion of mean squared error. It appears from this table that those procedures that ignore correlation between the forecast errors (for-

Table 9.1   *Combination of pairs of forecasts; percentage number of series for which the combined forecast outperforms both individual forecasts for: (A) Box-Jenkins combined with Holt–Winters, (B) Box–Jenkins combined with stepwise autoregressive, (C) Holt–Winters combined with stepwise autoregressive*

Formula (9.2.4)			ν	Formula (9.2.5)			ν	α	Formula (9.2.6)		
A	B	C		A	B	C			A	B	C
37.50	25.00	37.50	1	37.50	27.50	37.50	1	0.5	40.00	41.25	46.25
26.25	26.25	30.00	3	32.50	38.75	46.25	1	0.7	41.25	38.75	46.25
20.00	25.00	28.75	6	37.50	38.75	46.25	1	0.9	37.50	40.00	48.75
25.00	20.00	33.75	9	40.00	40.00	46.25	3	0.5	32.50	40.00	45.00
21.25	18.75	35.00	12	37.50	40.00	45.00	3	0.7	38.75	41.25	47.50
Formula (9.2.7)				Formula (9.2.8)			3	0.9	37.50	40.00	50.00
A	B	C	W	A	B	C	6	0.5	41.25	43.75	48.75
18.75	16.25	30.00	1.00	35.00	41.25	43.75	6	0.7	41.25	40.00	48.75
30.00	26.25	40.00	1.50	35.00	41.25	48.75	6	0.9	37.50	37.50	47.50
35.00	25.00	37.50	2.00	37.50	41.25	48.75	9	0.5	40.00	40.00	45.00
36.25	31.25	38.75	2.50	37.50	40.00	50.00	9	0.7	40.00	36.25	48.75
							9	0.9	36.25	37.50	48.75
							12	0.5	38.75	41.25	50.00
							12	0.7	37.50	38.75	48.75
							12	0.9	33.75	36.75	45.00

mulas (9.2.5), (9.2.6), and (9.2.8)) are considerably more successful than those that attempt to take account of it. It emerges from the table that when Box–Jenkins is combined with one of the fully automatic procedures, the resulting forecast outperforms both individual forecasts on about 40% of all occasions for the more successful combining methods. Table 9.2 compares these combined forecasts with the individual Box–Jenkins forecasts. It is seen that, for the combining methods that ignore correlation between the individual forecast errors, the combined forecasts outperform the individual Box–Jenkins forecasts on a slight majority of the series in the collection. The only exception is for formula (9.2.5) with $\nu = 1$. However, this approach would be employed only if one suspected extreme nonstationarity in the relative performance of the individual forecasting methods—a situation for which one could not make a strong a priori argument in the present context.

   In Section 5.5, the notion of a fully automatic predictor that would be a weighted average of a forecast obtained by stepwise autoregression and one derived from an exponential smoothing procedure was briefly introduced. To examine the potential usefulness of such a combined forecast, Table 9.3 gives results for the combination of Holt–Winters and stepwise autoregressive forecasts. The results of this table are much more conclusive than those of Table 9.2. In this situation, combining definitely appears to be worthwhile, and hence the resulting fully automatic forecast seems to be a potentially useful tool in those situations where for one reason or another a full Box–Jenkins analysis is not possible.

Table 9.2   *Percentage number of series for which Box–Jenkins is outperformed by (A) Box–Jenkins combined with Holt–Winters, (B) Box–Jenkins combined with stepwise autoregressive*

Formula (9.2.4)			Formula (9.2.5)			Formula (9.2.6)		
A	B	ν	A	B	ν	α	A	B
53.75	41.25	1	55.00	48.75	1	0.5	57.50	58.75
46.25	42.50	3	50.00	53.75	1	0.7	57.50	57.50
41.25	38.75	6	55.00	52.50	1	0.9	55.00	56.25
47.50	38.75	9	57.50	53.75	3	0.5	50.00	53.75
45.00	37.50	12	56.25	55.00	3	0.7	56.25	56.25
Formula (9.2.7)			Formula (9.2.8)		3	0.9	55.00	53.75
A	B	W	A	B	6	0.5	58.75	56.25
42.50	37.50	1.00	53.75	55.00	6	0.7	58.75	55.00
46.25	41.25	1.50	52.50	56.25	6	0.9	55.00	52.50
48.75	41.25	2.00	55.00	57.50	9	0.5	57.50	53.75
50.00	46.25	2.50	55.00	56.25	9	0.7	57.50	52.50
					9	0.9	53.75	53.75
					12	0.5	57.50	55.00
					12	0.7	56.25	53.75
					12	0.9	51.25	53.75

Table 9.3   *Percentage number of series for which the combined Holt–Winters and stepwise autoregressive forecast outperforms: (A) Holt–Winters, (B) stepwise autoregressive*

Formula (9.2.4)			Formula (9.2.5)			Formula (9.2.6)		
A	B	ν	A	B	ν	α	A	B
63.75	65.25	1	63.75	71.25	1	0.5	68.75	77.50
60.00	65.25	3	67.50	78.75	1	0.7	71.25	75.00
57.50	65.25	6	67.50	78.75	1	0.9	72.50	76.25
57.50	71.25	9	68.75	77.50	3	0.5	67.50	77.50
60.00	71.25	12	68.75	76.25	3	0.7	70.00	77.50
Formula (9.2.7)			Formula (9.2.8)		3	0.9	71.25	78.75
A	B	W	A	B	6	0.5	70.00	78.75
57.50	70.00	1.00	68.75	75.00	6	0.7	70.00	78.75
62.50	73.75	1.50	68.75	80.00	6	0.9	68.75	78.75
62.50	72.50	2.00	68.75	80.00	9	0.5	68.75	76.25
63.75	70.00	2.50	68.75	81.25	9	0.7	70.00	78.75
					9	0.9	70.00	78.75
					12	0.5	70.00	80.00
					12	0.7	70.00	78.75
					12	0.9	67.50	77.50

The evidence of Tables 9.1–9.3 points strongly in favor of the combining procedures that ignore correlation over those that attempt to take correlation into account. To confirm this indication, and to attempt to see if one particular procedure could be regarded as a "best bet," each method was ranked (giving rank 1 to the best and rank 33 to the worst) for each of the 240 pairwise combinations. Formula (9.2.5) with $v = 12$ had the lowest average rank, though there was remarkably little to choose between the best few methods. Average ranks for methods that attempted to account for correlation were a good deal higher than for those which did not. Full details of these results are given in Newbold and Granger [1974].

Using formula (9.2.5) with $v = 12$, the combined forecasts were compared in terms of ratios of average squared forecast errors with the Box–Jenkins forecasts. The combined Holt–Winters and stepwise autoregressive forecasts outperformed Box–Jenkins on 46.25% of series in the sample. The geometric means of the ratios of average squared forecast errors were

$$\frac{\text{average squared error Box–Jenkins and Holt–Winters combined}}{\text{average squared error Box–Jenkins}} = 0.94$$

$$\frac{\text{average squared error Box–Jenkins and stepwise autoregressive combined}}{\text{average squared error Box–Jenkins}}$$

$$= 0.98$$

$$\frac{\text{average squared error Box–Jenkins}}{\text{average squared error Holt–Winters and stepwise autoregressive combined}}$$

$$= 0.99$$

Thus, on the average, a slight improvement in accuracy is obtained when Box–Jenkins is combined with one or other of the fully automatic procedures. However, the most striking aspect of these calculations is the strong performance of the combined Holt–Winters and stepwise autoregressive forecast relative to that of Box–Jenkins. Clearly this combination produces a fully automatic forecast of considerable merit.

Now, the examples of combination given so far are not really designed to show the procedure in its best possible light. After all, it would be reasonable to expect combination to be most profitable when the individual forecasts are very dissimilar in nature. For example, combination of forecasts generated by an econometric model with those generated by an efficient time series analysis method ought to be potentially useful. Granger and Newbold [1975] give an example which uses 20 one-step ahead quarterly forecasts of real inventory investment generated by the Wharton–EFU econometric model. Forecasts of the same quantity were generated from a univariate Box–Jenkins procedure and combined with the model forecasts. The results are shown in Table 9.4. In this particular case, even though the Box–Jenkins forecast is on average considerably better than the econometric forecast, the latter apparently contains very useful information absent in the former. Thus, with

Table 9.4 *Sums of squared errors of forecasts of real inventory investment, except farm sector* (*U.S.A*)

S.S.E.
Box–Jenkins 64.4
Wharton–EFU 120.0
Combined Forecasts

Formula (9.2.4)		Formula (9.2.5)	Formula (9.2.6)		
SSE	v	SSE	v	α	SSE
73.0	1	58.4	1	0.5	45.1
49.7	3	49.4	1	0.7	41.7
46.6	6	46.8	1	0.9	39.0
43.6	9	43.5	3	0.5	44.2
45.1	12	45.0	3	0.7	41.0
Formula (9.2.7)		Formula (9.2.8)	3	0.9	38.8
SSE	W	SSE	6	0.5	42.2
44.1	1.00	44.0	6	0.7	40.3
44.4	1.50	46.3	6	0.9	38.6
45.1	2.00	47.5	9	0.5	40.2
47.2	2.50	48.4	9	0.7	39.4
			9	0.9	38.1
			12	0.5	41.6
			12	0.7	40.4
			12	0.9	38.2

the exception of formulas (9.2.4) and (9.2.5) with $v = 1$—extreme cases that will very rarely be appropriate in practice—all the procedures yield a combined forecast that considerably outperforms the better individual forecast. The examples given so far serve to emphasize the potential value of combination in situations where an optimal or near-optimal forecast is not available. It was seen that combination of Box–Jenkins with a univariate fully automatic forecast produced only a small improvement. This is to be expected since intelligent application of the principles of Box and Jenkins should very often lead to a forecast that is near-optimal, given the restricted information set consisting only of past values of the time series. However, examination of nonoptimal forecasts yields very different results, as was seen in the combination of Holt–Winters and stepwise autoregressive. In the wider context of macroeconomic forecasting, a much larger quantity of potentially valuable information is available. It is doubtful whether the concept of fully efficient use of this information is of much practical value. For example, the results of Table 9.4 indicate that, in forming the econometric forecast, information on past values of real inventory investment was almost certainly not efficiently employed. It is in this wider context that combination of forecasts is likely to prove most fruitful.

Many of the results discussed earlier in this section can be extended to the combination of more than two forecasts, as discussed by Reid [1969] and Newbold and Granger [1974]. Let $f_n^{(j)}$, $j = 1, 2, \ldots, M$, be a set of one-step ahead forecasts of X_n. Assume, as before, that these forecasts are unbiased. Now write $\mathbf{f}_n' = (f_n^{(1)}, f_n^{(2)}, \ldots, f_n^{(M)})$, and the individual forecast errors as $\mathbf{e}_n = X_n \mathbf{1} - \mathbf{f}_n$ with $E(\mathbf{e}_n \mathbf{e}_n') = \Sigma$ and where $\mathbf{1}' = (1, 1, \ldots, 1)$. Then the combined forecast can again be written as a weighted average of individual forecasts, so that

$$C_n = \mathbf{k}_n' \mathbf{f}_n, \qquad \mathbf{k}_n' \mathbf{1} = 1, \qquad 0 \leqslant k_n^{(j)} \leqslant 1 \qquad \text{for all } j$$

where $\mathbf{k}_n' = (k_n^{(1)}, k_n^{(2)}, \ldots, k_n^{(M)})$. It is straightforward to show that the variance of the combined forecast error is minimized by taking the value of $\mathbf{k}_n$ given by

$$\mathbf{k}_0 = (\Sigma^{-1} \mathbf{1})/(\mathbf{1}' \Sigma^{-1} \mathbf{1}),$$

an expression that simplifies to (9.2.2) when $M = 2$. Since the elements of Σ will not be known in practice, this expression cannot be used as it stands. However, formulas (9.2.4)–(9.2.8) can be generalized as follows

$$\hat{\mathbf{k}}_n = (\hat{\Sigma}^{-1} \mathbf{1})/(\mathbf{1}' \hat{\Sigma}^{-1} \mathbf{1}) \quad \text{where} \quad (\hat{\Sigma})_{i,j} = v^{-1} \sum_{t=n-v}^{n-1} e_t^{(i)} e_t^{(j)} \quad (9.2.9)$$

$$\hat{k}_n^{(i)} = \left(\sum_{t=n-v}^{n-1} e_t^{(i)2} \right)^{-1} \Bigg/ \left(\sum_{j=1}^{M} \left(\sum_{t=n-v}^{n-1} e_t^{(j)2} \right)^{-1} \right) \qquad (9.2.10)$$

$$\hat{k}_n^{(i)} = \alpha \hat{k}_{n-1}^{(i)} + (1 - \alpha) \left(\sum_{t=n-v}^{n-1} e_t^{(i)2} \right)^{-1} \Bigg/ \left(\sum_{j=1}^{M} \left(\sum_{t=n-v}^{n-1} e_t^{(j)2} \right)^{-1} \right),$$

$$0 < \alpha < 1 \quad (9.2.11)$$

$$\hat{\mathbf{k}}_n = (\hat{\Sigma}^{-1} \mathbf{1})/(\mathbf{1}' \hat{\Sigma}^{-1} \mathbf{1})$$

where

$$(\hat{\Sigma})_{i,j} = \left(\sum_{t=1}^{n-1} W^t e_t^{(i)} e_t^{(j)} \right) \Bigg/ \left(\sum_{t=1}^{n-1} W^t \right), \qquad W \geqslant 1 \quad (9.2.12)$$

$$\hat{k}_n^{(i)} = \left(\sum_{t=1}^{n-1} W^t e_t^{(i)2} \right)^{-1} \Bigg/ \left(\sum_{j=1}^{M} \left(\sum_{t=1}^{n-1} W^t e_t^{(j)2} \right)^{-1} \right), \qquad W \geqslant 1 \quad (9.2.13)$$

Newbold and Granger [1974] considered the combination of Box–Jenkins, Holt–Winters, and stepwise autoregressive one-step ahead forecasts for 80 time series using the above formulas, restricting weights to lie between zero and one. The results are summarized in Table 9.5.

The geometric mean for the ratio of the average squared error of the combined forecast to that of Box–Jenkins for formula (9.2.10) with $v = 12$ was 0.92. Two conclusions can be drawn from these results. First, the formulas that ignore correlation between the individual forecast error series

Table 9.5 *Percentage number of series for which the combined Box-Jenkins, Holt-Winters, and stepwise autoregressive forecast outperforms Box-Jenkins*

Formula (9.2.9)		Formula (9.2.10)	Formula (9.2.11)		
	ν		ν	α	
50.00	1	50.00	1	0.5	60.00
52.50	3	65.00	1	0.7	61.25
47.50	6	60.00	1	0.9	60.00
52.50	9	63.75	3	0.5	63.75
51.25	12	62.50	3	0.7	61.25
Formula (9.2.12)		Formula (9.2.13)	3	0.9	61.25
	W		6	0.5	62.50
48.75	1.00	61.25	6	0.7	61.25
47.50	1.50	65.00	6	0.9	60.00
47.50	2.00	63.75	9	0.5	65.00
48.75	2.50	63.75	9	0.7	62.50
			9	0.9	62.50
			12	0.5	62.50
			12	0.7	62.50
			12	0.9	62.50

continue to do considerably better than those that attempt to take it into account. Second, whatever combining method is employed, a further slight improvement in forecast accuracy results from the addition of the third forecast.

Winkler and Makridakis [1983] have applied the same combining rules to ten forecasting methods used on 1001 different time series. They found the techniques based on (9.2.10) and (9.2.11) to be superior to other combinations and that generally the combinations outperformed the individual forecasting methods. These results are thus consistent with those reported in detail above but based on a far bigger data set.

If it is a good idea to combine m forecasts, then it seems very likely that combining $m + 1$ forecasts will be even better, and there is often an extra forecast available that is underutilized. If the series being predicted is stationary, then the mean level of that series is a useful, but inefficient, forecast whose inclusion in the combination can yield an improvement, as shown by Granger and Ramanathan [1984]. If the series is integrated of order one, then the most recent value of the series provides an excellent additional forecast.

When the number of forecasts to be combined is very large, as for example when information from a survey of forecasters is available, the methods discussed above become computationally expensive and the combining weights are inclined to become unstable. A simpler technique, suggested by Figlewski [1983], regresses each individual forecast error series e_{it} onto a single factor z_t, so that

$$e_{it} = \alpha_i + \beta_i z_t + \epsilon_{it}$$

with z_t taken to be the mean deviation over all forecasters. Once the β_i and var(ϵ_{it}) have been estimated, a simple form for the combining formula in place of (8.2.9) emerges. Using some well-known inflation forecasts from the regular Livingston survey Figlewski obtains substantial improvements with this method of combination compared with simple averaging, even after the individual biases were removed.

In many cases the combined forecasts can be further improved by realizing that the various techniques discussed in this section do not necessarily produce white noise forecast errors even when each individual forecast error series is white noise.

9.3 The Evaluation of Forecasts

The problem of how to evaluate a set of economic forecasts or a forecasting model has received a good deal of attention in the past few years, and many extensive evaluation exercises have been carried out. In part this is a result of the multitude of large-scale macroeconomic models that have sprung up. All these models have their distinctive features, reflecting the multitude of fashions in which one can view macroeconomic behavior. Moreover, from the standpoint of economic theory, the specification of any one of these models is generally defensible–indeed, great care has been taken to ensure that it should be. However, from the same viewpoint, none is regarded as perfect–reality is far too complex, and in many areas theory too ill defined for this to be possible. Of course, practitioners can and do argue the merits of particular models on the basis of theoretical specification, but it is generally difficult to make out a case for one formulation over another, or even to argue the intrinsic worth of a complex model, on a priori grounds alone. Again, the inevitable suboptimality of any set of economic forecasts achieved through use of the methodology outlined in Section 6.3 argues strongly for their detailed evaluation.

An evaluation of forecast performance can, and probably should, be carried out at two levels. At the subjective level, one could look particularly closely at any large errors, or perhaps any failures to detect turning points, which have been made and try to determine the cause of these inadequacies. It may be, for example, that failure to allow for particular circumstances is responsible. If these circumstances could have been foreseen at the time forecasts were made, then the forecast-generating mechanism should be altered to preclude the possibility of making the same mistake again. The inherent danger in such an approach, and one of the reasons it is not of itself sufficient, lies in a natural tendency for the practitioner to explain away all his errors in terms of events (strikes, dramatic shifts in government policy, and so on) that could not possibly have been anticipated at the time forecasts were prepared. Such an attitude is hardly likely to lead to improved performance in the future. An objective evaluation of forecast performance is, in our opinion, of the utmost importance. This has been accepted for a number of years, and various criteria have been made available, principally by Theil [1958, 1966] and by Mincer and Zarnowitz [1969]. More recently, Granger and Newbold [1973] have argued that many of the evaluation criteria previously employed were insufficiently demanding, and have proposed a more stringent alternative.

An objective evaluation of a set of forecasts might seek to answer one or more of the following three questions:

(a) Is one set of forecasts better than its competitors?

(b) How "good," in some sense, is a particular set of forecasts?

(c) Can the forecast-generating mechanism be modified in some way so as to yield improved forecast performance?

Each of these points will be discussed in turn, but it is first necessary to have a criterion for forecast accuracy. The relevant concept in this connection is the cost of error function introduced in Chapter 4. It is assumed that for every forecast error e there is an associated cost $C(e)$. It is reasonable to assume that this function is such that

$$C(0) = 0$$

and

$$C(e_1) > C(e_2) \quad \text{if either} \quad e_1 > e_2 > 0 \quad \text{or} \quad e_1 < e_2 < 0$$

Furthermore, in many applications it may be quite reasonable to assume a symmetric cost function, but as noted in Section 4.2 this will not always be the case. Given these assumptions, there remains, of course, an infinity of functions from which to choose. In many instances—for example, macroeconomic forecasting by some independent agency—the costs of making a forecast error are typically notional rather than real since decisions are not generally made as a result of these forecasts. In situations where forecasts lead to decisions an accountant might be able to quantify the costs of particular errors. However, he may not be able to do so with any great precision since these costs themselves will not occur until sometime in the future, and hence must be predicted. The problem is therefore circular in nature. Given these difficulties, the practitioner is generally forced to choose a specific cost function, the most popular by far being

$$C(e) = ae^2, \qquad a > 0 \qquad (9.3.1)$$

Three factors argue for the choice of the quadratic cost of error function. It is often a priori not an unreasonable assumption, it is mathematically more tractable than any alternative, and it bears an obvious relationship to the least squares criterion generally used in estimating forecasting models. Thus forecasts will be judged here in terms of expected squared error.

In the remainder of this chapter only the cost function (9.3.1) will be employed, though, as noted in Section 4.2 and in Granger [1969a], some progress can be made with alternative functions. In fact, if one's primary interest is in comparing two forecasts, the choice of cost function within a very wide range may not be too critical. Granger and Newbold [1973] consider the very general case of two forecasting procedures producing zero-mean white noise errors $e^{(j)}$, $j = 1, 2$, which are identically distributed apart from a scaling constant, i.e., $e^{(j)}$ has cumulative distribution function $F(x/S_j)$, so that the larger is S_j the more spread is the distribution of $e^{(j)}$. Consider now a general cost function satisfying $C(0) = 0$ and that monotonically increases from $e = 0$, so that $C(e_1) > C(e_2)$ if either $e_1 > e_2 > 0$ or $e_1 < e_2 < 0$. It can be shown that for *any* such cost function, the predictor producing errors distributed with the lower scale factor S_j has smaller expected cost. Of course, in practice, expected cost must be estimated from sample values, and while this result holds for the population, it will not necessarily do so in a finite sample.

Let X_t, $t = 1, 2, \ldots, N$, be an observed time series and let f_t, $t = 1, 2, \ldots, N$, be a series of forecasts available at time $t - h$; that is, f_t is a forecast of X_t made h times periods previously. The forecast errors are then simply

$$e_t = X_t - f_t, \qquad t = 1, 2, \ldots, N$$

and the criterion following from (9.3.1), expected squared forecast error, is estimated by

$$D_N^2 = \frac{1}{N} \sum_{t=1}^{N} e_t^2 \qquad (9.3.2)$$

Consider now the first potential requirement of an evaluation exercise: the comparison of two or more sets of forecasts of the same quantity. Suppose two competing forecasting procedures produce errors $e_t^{(1)}$ and $e_t^{(2)}$, $t = 1, 2, \ldots, N$. Then, if expected squared error is to be the criterion, the procedure yielding the lower average squared error (9.3.2) over the sample period will be judged superior. One would like to determine, where possible, whether one procedure performed significantly better than the other under the usual criteria of statistical significance. It is tempting in this context to employ the usual variance ratio or F test. However, this would be inappropriate for two reasons. First, it is not reasonable to assume in general that the errors produced by one procedure will be uncorrelated with those produced by another. Second, for forecasts of more than one step ahead, the error series are not typically white noise even for optimal forecasts. In fact, for optimal forecasts, the h-step ahead forecast errors constitute in general a moving average process of order $h - 1$. A valid test of one-step ahead forecast errors, under assumptions that frequently may not be too unreasonable, can easily be derived. Suppose that $(e_t^{(1)}, e_t^{(2)})$, $t = 1, 2, \ldots, N$, constitutes a random sample from a bivariate normal distribution with means zero, variances σ_1^2 and σ_2^2, and correlation coefficient ρ. In particular, then, it is assumed that the individual forecasts are unbiased and the forecast errors not autocorrelated—properties that are certainly desirable, though not always attained, in one-step ahead forecasts. Consider, now, the pair of random variables $e^{(1)} + e^{(2)}$ and $e^{(1)} - e^{(2)}$. Now

$$E[(e^{(1)} + e^{(2)})(e^{(1)} - e^{(2)})] = \sigma_1^2 - \sigma_2^2$$

and so the two error variances, and hence, given the assumption of unbiasedness, the two expected squared errors, will be equal if and only if this pair of random variables is uncorrelated. Thus the usual test for zero correlation, based on the sample correlation coefficient

$$r = \frac{\displaystyle\sum_{t=1}^{N} (e_t^{(1)} + e_t^{(2)})(e_t^{(1)} - e_t^{(2)})}{\left[\displaystyle\sum_{t=1}^{N} (e_t^{(1)} + e_t^{(2)})^2 \sum_{t=1}^{N} (e_t^{(1)} - e_t^{(2)})^2 \right]^{1/2}}$$

can be employed, under the stated assumptions, to test equality of expected squared forecast errors. In fact (see, e.g., Lehmann [1959]) this test is uniformly most powerful unbiased.

Attempts to compare forecasts on the basis of criteria that are not monotonic functions of D_N^2 of (9.3.2) can lead to inconsistencies. For example, consider the "inequality coefficient"

$$U_1 = D_N \Big/ \left[\left(\frac{1}{N} \sum f_t^2 \right)^{1/2} + \left(\frac{1}{N} \sum X_t^2 \right)^{1/2} \right] \tag{9.3.3}$$

The numerator of this expression and the second quantity in the denominator (which will in any case be fixed in any comparisons) are harmless enough. Introduction of the first term in the denominator, simply an estimate of the standard deviation of the predictor series, adds into the expression a term that is irrelevant in judging forecast quality. It is this factor that gives the inequality coefficient the potential to produce misleading results, as the following simple example demonstrates. Suppose that a time series X_t is generated by the first-order autoregressive process $X_t = aX_{t-1} + \epsilon_t$. Let a be a fixed number with $0 \leqslant a < 1$, and consider the set of one-step ahead predictors of X_t given by

$$f_t = \beta X_{t-1}, \qquad 0 \leqslant \beta \leqslant 1$$

Let us examine the limiting case as sample size N tends to infinity, so that population values replace the corresponding sample quantities. Now,

$$\lim_{N \to \infty} D_N^2 = \left[(1 - a^2) + (\beta - a)^2 \right] \text{var}(X)$$

and

$$\lim_{N \to \infty} \left(\frac{1}{N} \sum f_t^2 \right) = \text{var}(f) = \beta^2 \, \text{var}(X)$$

It then follows that

$$\lim_{N \to \infty} U_1^2 = 1 - \left[2\beta(1 + a)/(1 + \beta)^2 \right]$$

But U_1^2, and hence U_1, is minimized, not by taking $\beta = a$, which is the optimal forecast, but by $\beta = 1$, whatever the value of a. The reason is that (9.3.3) gives great weight to the variance of the predictor series, which in this particular case is highest at $\beta = 1$. Needless to say, any evaluation criterion capable of yielding such misleading results is dangerous and its use should be avoided.

The second goal of an evaluation exercise—assessment of the worth, in some absolute sense, of a set of forecasts—is by far the most difficult of the three. Numerous possibilities, of varying degrees of utility, have been proposed and the following brief review is intended to point out which lines of attack are in our opinion most fruitful. The first and most obvious policy, when no competitor against which to judge a set of forecasts is available, is to construct one. It is becoming increasingly common for forecasters to compare their product with so-called "naïve" forecasts—that is, forecasts derived without the benefit of economic theory, and generally consisting of some function of past values of the series of interest. For example, the coefficient

$$U_2^2 = N^{-1} \sum (X_t - f_t)^2 / N^{-1} \sum X_t^2 \qquad (9.3.4)$$

proposed by Theil [1966] compares mean squared error of a forecast with that of the "no change rule" (future values forecast as last available observed value) if X is taken to denote actual change and f predicted change. More recently, the naïve competitors contemplated have become rather more sophisticated. For example, Cooper [1972] employs autoregressive models and Dhrymes et al. [1972] propose univariate Box–Jenkins models, which given the results of Section 5.6 would appear to concur with the suggestion of Mincer and Zarnowitz [1969] that the best available extrapolative univariate procedure be employed. Although, as will be seen in the next section, this kind of approach is frequently used, its value is by no means obvious. For example, why consider only univariate time series techniques as competitors when it may well be possible to produce superior forecasts through use of the multivariate time series procedures discussed in the previous chapter? If a sophisticated model fails to outperform a naïve extrapolation rule, then clearly something is seriously wrong; but suppose it does succeed in such an undemanding task; ought one really then to be wholly satisfied? We think not. A more demanding alternative is to consider the combination of a forecast with its competitor. If the variance of the combined forecast error is not significantly less than that of the forecast of interest, then the competing forecast would appear to possess no additional useful information. Granger and Newbold [1973] term this concept "conditional efficiency" and urge that model builders be dissatisfied with their products if they are not conditionally efficient with respect to univariate Box–Jenkins forecasts.

A similar idea is considered by Nelson [1972b]. Let $f_t^{(1)}$ denote a set of one-step ahead forecasts derived from a model and $f_t^{(2)}$ a corresponding set of univariate Box–Jenkins forecasts. Consider the regression

$$X_t = kf_t^{(1)} + (1 - k)f_t^{(2)} + \epsilon_t \quad \text{or} \quad (X_t - f_t^{(2)}) = k(f_t^{(1)} - f_t^{(2)}) + \epsilon_t$$

$$(9.3.5)$$

The weight k can be estimated by ordinary least squares and its difference from unity tested for significance. (Nelson also considers the generalization of (9.3.5) in which the weights are not constrained to sum to one and Hatanaka [1974] further generalizes to an equation with a constant term and several alternative forecasts.) Nelson's procedure is certainly a practical approach to computing conditional efficiency, although in some circumstances we may wish to allow for the possibility of changing weights through time. In fact, Nelson applied combination only to sample period fitted values, and employed the technique as a means of improving model forecasts, using weights derived over the period of fit to generate postsample forecasts. This may well be useful, but we would also regard the conditional efficiency criterion as being of great potential value in actual forecast evaluation.

An alternative line of attack is to seek some measure of forecast quality not dependent on the construction of an artificial set of competing forecasts. It was for this purpose that the inequality coefficient U_1 of (9.3.3) was designed. It satisfies $0 \leqslant U_1 \leqslant 1$, taking the value zero only if the forecasts are perfect, that is, $f_t = X_t$ for $t = 1, 2, \ldots, N$. It takes the value one when $f_t = -bX_t$, $t = 1, 2, \ldots, N$, for any $b \geqslant 0$. However, the objections we have raised concerning this coefficient rule out its profitable use in any evaluation exercise.

Mincer and Zarnowitz [1969] attempt a definition of forecast efficiency based on the regression

$$X_t = \alpha + \beta f_t + e_t \quad (9.3.6)$$

A forecast is deemed "efficient" if $\alpha = 0$ and $\beta = 1$ in this expression, and efficiency is tested by the application of ordinary least squares to the available sample. One can raise two practical objections to such an approach. First, in order to obtain consistent estimates it is necessary to assume f_t is uncorrelated with e_t—a requirement which will certainly hold for optimal forecasts, but which need not necessarily do so in practical applications of forecast evaluation. Second, one must assume, for the usual test procedures to be valid, that the error series e_t is white noise. This will not necessarily be so for suboptimal one-step ahead forecasts, and is not generally so even for optimal forecasts of more than one step ahead. However, a far more fundamental objection can be raised to this concept of efficiency, as can be seen from the following simple example. Suppose that X_t is generated by the random walk model

$$X_t = X_{t-1} + \epsilon_t$$

and consider the set of one-step ahead predictors

$$f_t^{(j)} = X_{t-j}, \qquad j = 1, 2, 3, \ldots$$

Now, for any j, (9.3.6) will in theory have $\alpha = 0$ and $\beta = 1$, and hence all these forecasts will be deemed "efficient" by the criterion of Mincer and Zarnowitz. Their criterion is certainly a desirable one for a forecast and hence constitutes a necessary condition for forecast efficiency, but according to any acceptable interpretation of that word it cannot be regarded as a *sufficient* condition. The best one can say of the Mincer–Zarnowitz condition is that any forecast f satisfying $\alpha = 0$ and $\beta = 1$ in (9.3.6) is, as noted by Hatanaka [1974], optimal in the class $c + df$ where c and d are any constants. It would seem to us that any acceptable definition of forecast efficiency must contemplate the existence of an optimal forecast based on the given information set. The efficiency of a particular forecast would then be the ratio of expected squared error (or some other criterion if a different cost function is employed) of the optimal forecast to that of the given forecast. Unfortunately, this concept is in general of very little operational worth since the optimal forecast error variance is typically unknown. An exception is the case where the information set is restricted to include only past values of the variable to be forecast and in addition only linear predictors are considered. If X_t has known spectrum $f(\omega)$, then Kolmogorov [1941b] shows that the minimum attainable forecast error variance is given by

$$I = \exp\left[\frac{1}{2\pi} \int_{-\pi}^{\pi} \log 2\pi f(\omega) \, d\omega \right]$$

The possibility of estimating this quantity from a given set of data is considered by Janacek [1975]. For general purposes, however, we feel that the only concept of efficiency of any practical value is that of conditional efficiency discussed earlier.

In the absence of a competing set of forecasts, attempts at evaluation have centered on comparisons of the forecast and actual time series. There are three difficulties with such an approach. First, the properties of an optimal predictor series typically differ from those of the actual series. For, let f_t be the optimal predictor of X_t, based on a particular information set, and let e_t be the forecast error so that

$$X_t = f_t + e_t \tag{9.3.7}$$

Now, for the forecast to be optimal in the expected squared error sense, the error series must have mean zero and be uncorrelated with the predictor series. The first of these requirements implies that $E(X_t) = E(f_t)$ and the second that $\text{var}(X_t) = \text{var}(f_t) + \text{var}(e_t)$. Thus, unless the error series takes on the value zero with probability one, the predictor series will have smaller variance than the real series. Second, many of the measures of forecast quality one might propose are not invariant to linear transformations of the variable to be forecasted. In particular, one gets different results when comparing predicted and actual values than when comparing predicted change and actual change. For example, perhaps the simplest form of presentation of a set of forecasts is to graph predicted and actual values simultaneously. For the levels of economic time series, such pictures almost invariably look extremely impressive. This is simply a result of the fact that most such series follow integrated processes, whose smooth graphs are rather easy to duplicate with a predictor series. Indeed, on this criterion, Box and Newbold [1971] demonstrated that a random walk can appear to give reasonable predictions of another *independent* random walk. However, if one graphs predicted change and actual change, the forecasts typically appear in a much less favorable light since changes in economic series are far less smooth than levels. Since the object of an evaluation exercise ought to be to examine forecast quality as critically as possible, we shall for the remainder of this section assume that X_t is a series of changes and f_t a corresponding series of predicted changes. The third problem is much more difficult to surmount and arises because in most practical situations one has no idea of the minimum attainable forecast error variance. This would not be too serious a problem if all the series one encountered were inherently equally difficult to forecast. However, this is by no means the case. For example, it is not too difficult to predict reasonably well (at least over relatively short horizons) changes in consumption. On the other hand, changes in stock market prices, as many can confirm from bitter experience, are considerably more difficult to anticipate. In the latter case, then, the forecaster ought to be satisfied with results that appear considerably less impressive than those obtained in the former. However, provided these difficulties are kept in mind, it is possible to find simple measures that do convey some idea of the quality of a set of forecasts.

To begin, assume that the series to be forecast has fixed mean and variance, given by

$$E(X_t) = \mu_x \quad \text{and} \quad E\left[(X_t - \mu_x)^2\right] = \sigma_x^2$$

One can consider three attributes of a predictor series f_t; its mean μ_f, its variance σ_f^2, and the degree of its correlation ρ with X_t. Now, expected squared forecast error can be written as

$$E\left[(X_t - f_t)^2\right] = (\mu_f - \mu_x)^2 + (\sigma_f - \rho\sigma_x)^2 + (1 - \rho^2)\sigma_x^2 \quad (9.3.8)$$

Taking μ_x and σ_x to be fixed numbers, it is clear that expected squared error is minimized by finding as large a ρ as possible—that is, a predictor series as strongly correlated with the actual series as possible—and simultaneously

$$\mu_f = \mu_x, \qquad \sigma_f = \rho\sigma_x \qquad (9.3.9)$$

The second of these conditions confirms the already stated conclusion that, for optimal forecasts, the variance of the predictor series is less than that of the actual. In fact, these requirements have already been met in different form, for provided f_t and e_t in (9.3.6) are uncorrelated, it is straightforward to verify that $\alpha = 0$ and $\beta = 1$ in that expression if and only if (9.3.9) holds. Thus, for one-step ahead forecasts, the conditions (9.3.9) can be tested in actual samples by the usual linear regression procedures. Further, provided (9.3.9) does hold for different forecasts of the same quantity, the best forecast will be the one most correlated with the actual values. Thus the population correlation coefficient, or in practice its sample estimate, can be used as a measure of forecast quality. If such a procedure is to be adopted, however, the conditions (9.3.9) should also be checked. We emphasize again that the correlation recommended is that between predicted and actual changes. It is trivially easy to obtain a predictor series that is apparently highly correlated with the level of any economic time series, making the correlation coefficient between the two series virtually meaningless.

An alternative measure, which is in fact equivalent if the forecast and error series are uncorrelated, follows naturally from (9.3.7). Define PM to be the ratio of error variance to variance of the series to be forecast, so that

$$PM = \sigma_e^2/\sigma_x^2 \qquad (9.3.10)$$

It is straightforward to verify that, if f_t and e_t are uncorrelated, $PM = 1 - \rho^2$. The square on the correlation coefficient in this expression is at first sight worrying, but in fact if ρ is negative f_t and e_t must be correlated. Now, given our assumption, PM lies between zero and one, taking the value zero if f is a perfect forecast—that is, the series X is purely deterministic—and the value one if f_t is the mean of X for all t. The measure (9.3.10), or its sample estimate, can be viewed as a criterion for judging forecast performance or, if f is an optimal forecast based on a particular information set, as a measure of the predictability of a time series. In the latter context, it is clear that PM increases as the forecast horizon is extended, and that it is nonincreasing as the information set considered is widened.

An interesting application of this measure involves the probability that the forecast and actual series will have the same sign if they have zero mean, or alternatively if their deviations from their common mean will have the same sign. On the assumption that these series are distributed as bivariate normal with correlation ρ, it follows from Kendall and Stuart [1963, p. 351] that this

Table 9.6   *Probability (p) that forecast and actual values have the same signs*

PM	0	0.1	0.3	0.5	0.7	0.9	1
ρ	1	0.949	0.837	0.707	0.548	0.316	0
p	1	0.968	0.903	0.833	0.753	0.644	0.5

probability is given by

$$p = \frac{1}{2} + \frac{1}{\pi} \arcsin \rho = \frac{1}{2} + \frac{1}{\pi} \arccos PM$$

Some specific values are shown in Table 9.6.

Finally, turning to the third requirement of an evaluation exercise, one can propose diagnostic checks on forecast performance. The object here is not simply to assess the quality of a set of forecasts, but rather to suggest possible strategies for improving the forecast generating mechanism. In this context, the measure of conditional efficiency with respect to univariate Box–Jenkins forecasts is relevant, for, should a set of forecasts be inefficient by this criterion, the implication is that the forecaster has not optimally taken account of information provided by past values of the time series. An examination of the specification of lag and error structure in the relevant equations of the model may well suggest remedies for this defect.

Theil [1958] has observed two decompositions of average squared forecast error (9.3.2); these were thought to provide insight into the causes of forecast error and are frequently calculated in actual evaluation exercises. They are given by

$$D_N^2 = \frac{1}{N} \sum (X_t - f_t)^2 = (\bar{f} - \bar{X})^2 + (s_f - s_x)^2 + 2(1 - r)s_f s_x \quad (9.3.11)$$

and

$$D_N^2 = (\bar{f} - \bar{X})^2 + (s_f - rs_x)^2 + (1 - r^2)s_x^2 \qquad (9.3.12)$$

where $\bar{f}$ and $\bar{X}$ are the sample means of the predictor and predicted series, s_f and s_x are the sample standard deviations, and r is the sample correlation between the two series. The equality (9.3.11) leads to the definition of the quantities

$$U^M = (\bar{f} - \bar{X})^2/D_N^2, \qquad U^s = (s_f - s_x)^2/D_N^2, \qquad U^c = 2(1 - r)s_f s_x/D_N^2$$

Clearly $U^M + U^s + U^c = 1$ and Theil suggests that these quantities, which are often calculated in actual evaluation exercises, have useful interpretations. We doubt that this is so, for consider the following simple example. Let X_t be generated by the first-order autoregressive process

$$X_t = aX_{t-1} + \epsilon_t, \qquad 0 \leqslant a \leqslant 1$$

The optimal forecast of X_t, based on the information set consisting of all past values of X, is given by $f_t = aX_{t-1}$ and, for this predictor, as sample size tends to infinity,

$$U^M = 0, \qquad U^s = \frac{1-a}{1+a}, \qquad U^c = \frac{2a}{1+a}$$

As a varies from 0 to 1, U^s and U^c can take on any values, subject only to the restrictions $0 \leqslant U^s$, $U^c \leqslant 1$ and $U^s + U^c = 1$. Thus interpretation of these quantities is impossible. In the more general forecasting context, the difficulty is that some series are inherently not easy to forecast. Thus, however wide the information set employed, a high correlation between predictor and predicted will not be achieved. In such situations, as is seen from (9.3.9), the standard deviation of the forecast series will be markedly less than that of the actual series for optimal forecasts, and consequently U^s can be expected to differ substantially from zero. On the other hand, for more predictable series, the value taken by U^s can be expected to be lower for optimal forecasts.

The decomposition (9.3.12) is the sample analogue of (9.3.8) and so as such is easier to interpret. It leads to the definition of the quantities

$$U^M = (\bar{f} - \bar{X})^2/D_N^2, \qquad U^R = (s_f - rs_x)^2/D_N^2, \qquad U^D = (1 - r^2)s_x^2/D_N^2$$

As already noted, for optimal forecasts U^M and U^R should not differ significantly from zero, and hence U^D should be close to unity. In fact these requirements are equivalent to those that the sample estimates of α and β in (9.3.6) not differ significantly from zero and unity, respectively. Such a test is worth performing in conjunction with the plotting of Theil's "prediction realization diagram"—a plot of predicted against actual values, yielding a spread of points around the line of perfect forecasts $f_t = X_t$, which could give useful information concerning inadequacies in forecast performance, provided it is handled carefully. A potential danger, however, is to leap to the conclusion that forecast changes tend to underestimate the magnitude of large absolute changes, and that some simple remedy is available for correcting this defect. This phenomenon, however, can simply result from the fact that optimally the standard deviation of the predictor series is less than that of the actual, and hence ought only to be corrected for if a predictor series more strongly correlated with the true series of interest can be found—a task that may be by no means simple.

It should now be clear that examination of the relationship between the forecast and actual series is fraught with danger. However, more clear-cut and frequently more useful, conclusions can often be drawn by looking at the error series e_t. This can, of course, be tested directly for zero mean, but more important is an examination of its time series properties. Optimal h-step ahead forecasts have errors with autocorrelations of order h and higher equal to zero, for otherwise the forecast error will be correlated with something that is known at the time the forecast is made, and hence the forecast could have been improved upon. Ideally, one would like to do a full correlogram or spectral analysis of the error series, but rarely will a sufficiently long set of data be available to make such an exercise worthwhile. As a minimum, one-step ahead forecast errors can be tested for randomness against the alternative of first-order autocorrelation by comparing the von Neumann ratio

$$Q = \frac{(N - 1)^{-1} \sum\limits_{t=2}^{N} (e_t - e_{t-1})^2}{N^{-1} \sum\limits_{t=1}^{N} (e_t - \bar{e})^2}$$

with tabulated values given by Hart [1942]. In fact, as will be seen in the following section, in many evaluation exercises involving large-scale econometric models, one-step ahead forecasts are "corrected" for autocorrelated errors. However, the point here is that if a procedure produces such errors, then the model itself should be corrected, not simply the forecasts it generates.

9.4 A Survey of the Performance of Macroeconomic Forecasts

The major source of macroeconomic forecasting is the proprietors of large-scale macroeconomic models. Though frequently revised and updated, many models have been in existence sufficiently long to have established a track record in forecasting. Of course, these models may also be used for purposes other than forecasting. For example, they may be viewed as vehicles for the explanation of, or testing of theories about, macroeconomic behavior. Also, models are frequently used to assess the potential consequences of various policy alternatives or to "simulate" the behavior of endogenous variables under particular assumed time-paths for the exogenous variables, following the work of Adelman and Adelman [1959]. (A number of exercises of this sort are reported in Hickman [1972].) However, our concern here is with forecasting and with the use of large-scale macroeconomic models as forecasting tools, though it must be added that we would be dubious about the value of a model for any of these other purposes if it were incapable of forecasting well.

At this time a great deal of empirical evidence has accumulated on the quality of macroeconomic forecasts and on the merits of the models as forecasting tools. However, it cannot be said that there is widespread agreement on how this empirical evidence should be interpreted or indeed on how an evaluation exercise should be properly carried out. Difficulties in assessing the information contained in the vast number of published studies arise for a number of reasons. First, many of the most widely regarded macroeconomic models have evolved over the years in response to perceived changes in the structure of economic behavior, new theoretical developments in macroeconomic theory, or obvious inadequacies in the performance of earlier model versions. Thus, the results of evaluation exercises published several years ago may say very little about the merits of current versions of the models. A further difficulty concerns the different historical periods over which forecasts have been evaluated. One approach to forecasting might be expected to fare relatively well in certain time periods but not in others. For example, it has often been argued that, while a simple univariate time series model might prove adequate, at least in the short run, for forecasting when economic activity is relatively stable, it must suffer in comparison with well-specified econometric models in an era of substantial exogenous shocks.

A third difficulty, which seems even harder to resolve, concerns the question of precisely what should be evaluated. We must distinguish between the ability of a model to forecast well and the ability of a team of experienced, knowledgeable, and skilled economists, aided to a greater or lesser extent by a model, to forecast well. It seems to us to be both valid and useful to ask both questions, though this view is not universally held. On the one hand McNees [1982] asserts that "very little" can be learned from *ex post* comparisons in which econometric models are mechanically projected forward to generate forecasts. On the other, Fair [1984, p. 263] asserts that *ex ante* comparisons, in which actual published forecasts are used are "of little interest from the point of view of examining the predictive accuracy of models," since they depend on judgmental forecasts of exogenous variables together with the other subjective modifications discussed in Section 6.3. The debate boils down to the question of whether the model and the team building and interpreting it are inextricably intertwined or can the model be usefully examined in isolation.

A common thread running through many published evaluations of the forecasting ability of econometric models is the use, as a benchmark for comparison, of "naïve" time series models, such as pure autoregressive or ARIMA processes. Much of the early work along these lines provided a good deal of amusement to time series analysts. Cooper [1972] examined seven previously specified quarterly models of the U.S. economy, designated Friend–Taubman, Fromm, Klein, Liu, OBE, Wharton–EFU, and Goldfeld. Each model was fitted to a sample of 48 quarterly observations. Also, for 33 endogenous variables, a univariate autoregressive model was fitted over the same sample period, the order of the autoregressions being determined as the process with smallest sample error variance up to a maximum permitted order of eight. The naïve forecasts obtained from the autoregressive models were compared with forecasts derived from the econometric models over a post-sample period of 20 quarters. Only one-quarter-ahead forecasts were computed. The econometric "forecasts" were obtained by solving the models after insertion of actual future values of exogenous variables. No mechanical or judgmental modification of the econometric forecasts was attempted.

Table 9.7 *Number of times, for 33 series, a particular forecasting method performed best, using mean-squared-error as a criterion, in Cooper's study*

Method	Number of times best
Fromm	7
Liu	1
Klein	1
OBE	2
Wharton–EFU	4
Friend–Taubman	0
Goldfeld	0
Naïve	18

Cooper's study, then, was an attempt at the evaluation of the unaided models as forecasting tools. Table 9.7 gives a broad summary of Cooper's results. It can be seen that, for these 33 series, the univariate time series procedure outperforms *all* the econometric models on the majority of occasions. (In fact, because of differences in their specifications, some models did not yield forecasts of all 33 variables.) These results are certainly quite startling, but more detailed examination of Cooper's findings reveals, if anything, a position even less complimentary to the econometric models. Every model examined was outperformed, under the mean-squared-error criterion, on a substantial majority of occasions by the autoregressive predictor. Moreover, very frequently the naive forecasts were better than the model forecasts by very substantial margins indeed.

Cooper's findings on the relatively poor performance of econometric models in the generation of short-term forecasts were reinforced by similar results in smaller studies by Naylor *et al.* [1972], Nelson [1972b], Cooper and Nelson [1975], and Ibrahim and Otsuki [1976]. It is of some interest to note the approach used by Nelson and by Cooper and Nelson, as it employs something close to the concept of conditional efficiency advocated in the previous section. Forecasts derived from quarterly econometric models were compared with those from univariate ARIMA models. Often the time series forecasts are superior. However, even when that is not the case it frequently emerges that their use in combination with the econometric forecasts yields some improvement over the latter.

It will not surprise the reader to learn that the findings discussed above did not pass without comment. In particular, various reservations are expressed by Goldfeld [1972], McCarthy [1972], Green *et al.* [1972b], and Howrey *et al.* [1974]. The debate was rather lengthy, and its details need not detain us here. However, three points are relevant to the later literature. First, no attempt was generally made to allow for autocorrelated errors in the equations of the econometric models or to modify the forecasts by factors allowing for autocorrelation in the errors. As far as model specification is concerned, this was faithful to the practice at that time. It is our view that these studies pointed to very serious inadequacies in the dynamic specification of the models. To a certain extent, this lesson has been learned, and far more attention is now paid to such considerations, a factor which we believe goes far towards explaining the better performance of econometric models in more recent evaluation exercises.

Second, it is often argued that forecasting just one quarter ahead is of relatively little interest. Forecasts one or two years into the future are generally thought to be of more value rather than the prediction of what may turn out to be transient phenomena. However, one must surely retain serious misgivings about the value of any model that is seriously outperformed by an autoregressive or ARIMA predictor, even in the very short run. One difficulty in extending Cooper's approach to prediction several steps ahead is that some stance must be taken on the future values of exogenous variables required to derive model forecasts. If the true values are simply inserted several quarters into the future the position becomes unrealistic in the sense that such information would not, in practice, be available and in such circumstances it would be no great achievement for an econometric model to perform very well in comparison with a time series model.

It is partly for this reason that it has been argued that the most worthwhile comparison is between actual *ex ante* forecasts. This view is further strengthened by the argument that it is not meaningful to separate the models from their proprietors—that the two must be evaluated in conjunction. There is certainly a good deal of evidence to suggest that forecasts produced by economists, in collaboration with their models, compare far more favorably with naive time series forecasts than do the model predictions reported by Cooper. (Indeed, it could hardly be otherwise, or surely these people would long since have been driven to seek alternative employment!) McNees [1982] summarizes the results of *ex ante* forecast comparisons in Hirsch *et al.* [1976], McNees [1979], Eckstein [1981], and McNees [1981], as well as providing some additional results. (These last are interesting because they compare econometric forecasts with predictions derived from a vector autoregressive model, rather than simply a single series model.) The picture that emerges from this collection of studies is that generally, though not invariably, the published model forecasts outperform their naïve time series competitors, the improvement being more pronounced four quarters ahead than one quarter ahead. McNees [1982] concludes, "I know of *no* convincing evidence that suggests unconditional time series macroeconomic forecasts have been more accurate than those issued by prominent forecasters." We cannot disagree. It is, however, rather a pity that these studies did not evaluate the conditional efficiency of the model-based forecasts with respect to the time series forecasts. It would be interesting to know whether "prominent forecasters" make efficient use of the information contained in the past history of the series being predicted.

The position at the present time appears to be that teams of economists, aided by models, can at least generally reckon to do better than simple extrapolative time series models. However, when we examine the performance of the unaided models, the picture is less clear. Certainly, findings such as those of Christ [1975] and Hirsch et al. [1976] are far less bleak than Cooper's. Nevertheless the performance of the models is often not encouraging. This leads us to two related questions: would the teams of economists fare just about as well in forecasting without their models, and is it possible to quantify in some way the impacts on forecast quality of the various stages of mechanical and judgmental adjustments that are employed in practice? On the first question we have no direct evidence. On the second question, Haitovsky and Treyz [1972], Evans et al. [1972], and Hirsch et al. [1976] have attempted to provide some answers. However, their results are made difficult to interpret by the counterintuitive finding that, more often than not, econometric forecasts are *worse* when actual future values of the exogenous variables are used in place of the analysts' predictions. Perhaps this is evidence of the indivisibility of the model–analyst combination. However, Fair [1970, 1974], using a small model that generally outperforms naïve time series models in *ex post* forecast comparisons, finds improved forecasts using actual future exogenous variables.

Our own position is that *ex post* evaluation studies can be very useful, though certainly not without interpretational difficulties. For example, it is difficult to compare in this way two econometric models in which certain variables are exogenous in one and endogenous in the other. Fair [1979, 1984] discusses and implements a rather complicated evaluation procedure, based on stochastic simulation, designed to get around this difficulty. A recent study by Longbottom and Holly [1985] exhibits an attitude that is close to our own. These authors evaluate the forecasting performance of the London Business School model of the United Kingdom economy and use time series forecasts as benchmarks. They find that for most, but not all, variables the model forecasts outperform the time series forecasts. Where the time series forecasts are better, this is regarded as evidence of model misspecification, suggesting parts of the model where specification can be improved. However, the authors note that, in the interim period, where experiments with model structure are being carried out, a combination of time series and model forecasts can provide a useful stopgap. Longbottom and Holly also find that, even when the model forecast performs better than the time series forecast, a composite predictor may still be superior to the former, providing further evidence of misspecification. These results suggest that, in spite of complacency in some quarters about *ex ante* model forecast performance, 13 years after the publication of Cooper's study, teams working with well-established and successful models still find it valuable to evaluate models in conjunction with simple time series predictors.

9.5 Econometric Forecasting and Time Series Analysis

We now attempt to draw together some material from previous chapters and from earlier sections of this chapter, in order to assess the current state of the art of economic forecasting and to anticipate possible future developments. The most common approach to economic forecasting is through the construction of an econometric model, the results of which, heavily modified by the economist's judgment, form the basis of the forecasting approach. The degree of judgmental modification varies from one economist to another and also depends on the state of the economy at the time the forecasts are made. Nevertheless, judgmental modification is widely accepted as inevitable, and relatively few published forecasts are strictly derived from a quantitative model.

It is interesting to compare developments in the last few years in time series analysis and econometric model building methodology. Much effort has been devoted by time series analysts to the development of procedures for relating a relatively small number of time series. A practical procedure for relating a pair of series when causality is unidirectional was given by Box and Jenkins [1970], and in Chapter 8 we discussed recent research on the more difficult problem of model building in the presence of feedback. The appropriate methodology is far from straightforward even in the case of just two or three related time series, and, although some progress has been made, it is far from clear how best to proceed in the case of, say, ten related series. While time series analysts have been engaged in such modest tasks, teams of macroeconomists have constructed forecasting models involving hundreds of simultaneous equations fitted to data that time series analysts would view as neither plentiful nor of especially high quality. It is true that more attention has been paid to the dynamic structure of econometric models. Nevertheless, this dichotomy suggests either that, in their anxiety to produce large systems that faithfully represent the interrelationships in a complex national economy, econometricians have failed to touch some very important bases on the way, or that, for practical purposes, time series analysts have devoted considerable energy to relatively trivial problems. It will not surprise the reader to learn that we favor the former explanation, in line with, for example, Jenkins [1979], who is particularly scathing about the non-parsimony of large models.

Of course, it can be argued that it is through appeal to economic theory that economists are able to build such large models. Certainly, in a trivial sense this is true, for we simply could not conceive of the possibility of building a model linking, say, a hundred time series without some appeal to theory to limit the dimensionality of the parameter surface that needs to be considered. However, we have serious doubts, for a number of reasons, about the ability of economic theory to handle satisfactorily this task within the context of very large-scale models. First, as persuasively argued by Sims [1980], many of the restrictions apparently implied by theory are, on closer inspection, "incredible." Moreover, there are many areas in which economic theory is not terribly well developed, with the existence either of no very convincing theory or of several competing theories. Given the time series data typically available, it may often be impossible to distinguish at any reasonable level of significance among alternative theories. Even where a satisfactory theory is available, we would claim that such theory is almost invariably insufficiently precise about dynamic specification in the sense that it is clear that one structure must be appropriate, to the exclusion of all other possibilities. More obviously, no theory provides a completely accurate description of the behavior of economic agents, so that any postulated equation necessarily includes a stochastic error term. Naturally, since the error terms of the model represent that part of behavior that is unexplained by subject matter theory, we cannot appeal to theory for a specification of the time series properties of these error terms. Therefore, even if all other reservations are left aside, a model with n behavioral equations will involve a set of n time series errors about whose autocorrelations and cross-correlations economic theory has nothing to say. We would claim then that, after appeal to economic theory, the result will be a construct in which considerable uncertainty remains about the appropriate dynamic specification and error structure. Often in these circumstances rather simple possibilities are assumed and subjected to insufficiently rigorous testing. Such an approach is dangerous. In Chapter 6 we saw how failure to attack adequately the problem of autocorrelated errors can lead to nonsense regressions and consequently inefficient forecasts. We believe that the often disappointing forecast performance of large-scale econometric models, unaided by human judgment, can be attributed in large part to a too casual attitude to the specification of dynamics and error structure.

It is our view, then, that even after appeal to economic theory has been made, substantial problems of model selection and checking, which are essential ingredients of any competent time series analysis, must necessarily remain. We do not, however, wish to imply that econometricians are unaware of these issues or that the models they build are invariably naïve from the point of view of the time series analyst. For example, Hendry [1974] and Wall *et al.* [1975] reported more sophisticated models. The former employs a vector autoregressive error structure in a small simultaneous equation system, whereas the latter employ sets of transfer function–noise models. Moreover, some of the most exciting developments in econometrics in the last few years, many of which are summarized in Hendry and Richard [1983] and Hendry [1984], have emphasized the value of data in model specification and the importance of a wide range of checks on model adequacy. Many of these developments have not, however, found their way into the mainstream of applied economic work, and, as Hendry and Richard note, it is still the case that "many economists...use data evidence primarily to determine the orders of magnitude of a small number of unknown coefficients relevant to their theories." It should also be added that the more sophisticated treatments of specification and checking that have been reported in the literature have been restricted to very small-scale models; indeed, the great majority involve just single equations, which returns us to our original dichotomy between recent research in time series analysis and large-scale macroeconomic model building.

The large-scale model builder is left with the element of judgement, a quality whose exercise still appears to be essential to remain in business. It is, we believe, fair to say that many analysts whose models have mediocre forecasting ability nevertheless achieve after judgmental adjustment a respectable forecasting record. This, however, reminds us of the man who, when asked for directions, replied "Well, you shouldn't start from here." It seems to us reasonable to believe that it is possible, through increased attention to specification of dynamics and error structure, to build quantitative economic models that are far better forecasting tools than many of those in current use. Judgmental adjustments, however, would probably still be desirable to account for the influence of unquantifiable factors, or indeed any factors that for one reason or another were not formally incorporated in the model structure. It would appear likely, in such circumstances, that, given a superior starting point, the model builder could produce, on the average, better forecasts.

9.6 Leading Indicators

One of the earliest systematic attempts to forecast an important component of the economy was the construction of a group of leading indicators by Wesley Mitchell and Arthur Burns of the National Bureau of Economic Research, at the suggestion of Henry Morganthau, Jr., Secretary of the Treasury. The basic objective of their analysis was to find a group of economic variables that lead the macroeconomy at the turning points of the business cycle. Using an economic theory of the cycle, a group of possible leading indicators, for which data were available, were identified and then tested visually by comparing the shapes of the possible leading indicator and a general measure of the economy. By this procedure, indicators were separated into three groups: leading, coincident, and lagging. Through the years, the actual contents of these groups has changed somewhat, but the basic procedure has changed little. To ease interpretation, three indices are formed, one for each group, by applying weights to the more reliable components and summing. The weights are chosen more subjectively rather than from a statistical analysis of the data. The idea is that the indices of leading indicators (ILI) will turn before the bulk of the economy and so will be helpful for forecasting and for decisions on investment and planning, the index of coincident indicators will turn at the same time as the economy but may be available earlier than a statistic such as GNP, and finally the index of lagging indicators will turn, confirming the turn in the economy.

The most recent figures for all of the individual indicators and for the indicators in the U.S. are published monthly in *Business Conditions Digest*. How successful the index of leading indicators is can be partly judged by comparing its performance in predicting turning points in recent depressions. The state of the general economy can be judged by using the index of industrial production. Table 9.8 shows the performance of the ILI from 1960 through 1982. The second column are the "official" turning points as determined by the National Bureau for Economic Research (NBER). The last column are subjective estimates based on the graph of the index of leading indicators and are dates that subsequently represent fairly clear turning points.

For fairly major depressions, the index of leading indicators does appear to provide useful information, having clearly turned before the macroeconomy turned. There are some problems, however, as the index does need to move consistently from a peak or trough for several months before a turn is visually obvious and it also takes a couple of months for the data to become available. For minor depressions, false turns may occur and thus be misleading. Another difficulty is that there is some inconsistency about the extent of the lead, as Table 9.8 indicates. Nevertheless, the index of leading indicators has become a widely quoted and generally trusted forecasting tool. However, it has been rather misinterpreted. The index is intended only to forecast the timing of turning points and not the size of the forthcoming downswing or upswing nor to be a general indicator of the economy at times other than near turning points. Because of this, evaluation of the ILI by standard statistical techniques is not easy. The attempts at evaluation by NBER, mostly by subjective means, can be found in a variety of reports such as

Table 9.8   *Performance of ILI from 1960 through 1980.*

Peak/Trough	Economy Turning	ILI Turned
P	April, 1960	May, 1959
T	February, 1961	February, 1961
P	December, 1969	May, 1968
T	November, 1970	October, 1970
P	November, 1973	February, 1973
T	March, 1975	March, 1975
P	January, 1980	May, 1979
T	July, 1980	May, 1980
P	July, 1981	May, 1981
T	November, 1982	April, 1982

Moore and Shiskin [1967] and Zarnowitz and Boschan [1975]. Hatanaka (in Granger and Hatanaka [1964]) and Hymans [1973] evaluated the index and a number of individual leading indicators using spectral techniques, particularly concentrating on the phase diagram around the business cycle frequencies. They generally did find noticeable leads, although not always as extensive or consistent as suggested by the National Bureau, and Hymans found evidence that the weights used in forming the index of leading indicators could be greatly improved. Both Neftci [1979] and Auerbach [1982] applied regression procedures, in the form of "causality" tests. Auberbach found for both the full period 1949–1977, used as an in-sample test, and the period 1949–1973 plus the 1974–1975 recession, used as a post-sample test, that the ILI helped fit and forecast an index of industrial production (IIP) more accurately than an AR model for IIP. Furthermore, the NBER weights proved to be superior for forecasting to weights chosen to maximize in-sample goodness of fit. Less clear-cut decisions were reached when the dependent variable was an unemployment rate.

The sum of the evidence so far available suggests that the index of leading indicators is a useful forecasting method if used within the situations for which it was designed.

One fortune teller to another:
No doubt about it, Zelda, the future isn't what it used to be

CARTOON, SUN NEWSPAPER
London, 29 February 1972

10.1 State-Space Representation, the Kalman Filter

Although the ARMA and vector ARMA representations for a time series are quite easily interpreted and are convenient for many forecasting purposes, there is an alternative representation, called the state-space form, which is also capable of useful interpretation and model generalization.

Let y_t be a vector time series with g components, which is to be modeled using a given information set I_t. Suppose that there is a finite-order vector of s components, denoted by x_t, that fully captures all of the information in I_t relevant to modeling $E[y_t|I_t]$, so that x_t is essentially a sufficient statistic. In this discussion, only linear models are considered. The vector x_t is called the state vector and represents the generalized location or state of the system at time t. The two basic equations of the state-space representation are

$$\underset{(g \times 1)}{y_t} = \underset{(g \times s)}{\beta_t} \; \underset{(s \times 1)}{x_t} + \underset{(g \times u)(u \times 1)}{\gamma_t z_t} + \underset{(g \times 1)}{v_t} \qquad (10.1.1)$$

and

$$\underset{(s \times 1)}{x_t} = \underset{(s \times s)(s \times 1)}{T_t x_{t-1}} + \underset{(s \times L)(L \times 1)}{\delta_t w_t} + \underset{(s \times m)(m \times 1)}{G_t u_t} \qquad (10.1.2)$$

Equation (10.1.1) relates y_t to the present value of the state vector x_t plus a vector of other explanatory (exogenous) variables z_t and an error term v_t. The dimensions of vectors and matrices are indicated under each term. The equation is seen to be linear, to have possibly time-varying parameters, and to be of a structural form. It is thus not directly useful for forecasting, since forecasts of the explanatory variables would have to be determined and inserted. Equation (10.1.2) shows how the forecasts of the state variable can be formed. If one conditions $\mathbf{x}_t$ on I_{t-1}, then since $\mathbf{x}_{t-1}$ is a sufficient statistic, assuming a linear form gets one the Markov system (10.1.2). Here, $\mathbf{w}_t$ is another set of exogenous variables (possibly overlapping with $\mathbf{z}_t$), and again time-varying parameters are allowed. With these equations I_t is assumed to be the information in the observed endogenous variables $\mathbf{y}_t$. It should be noted that the state vector $\mathbf{x}_t$ need not be observable either directly or from the observable series $\mathbf{y}_t$, $\mathbf{w}_t$, or $\mathbf{z}_t$.

To proceed further, a number of assumptions are required.

(A1)   The model given by (10.1.1) and (10.1.2) completely represents the system of interest. It is, in fact, a rather general (linear) representation and most linear, finite parameter models, possibly with time-varying parameters, including ARMA models, can be represented in this form.

(A2)   The errors $\mathbf{v}_t$ and $\mathbf{u}_t$ are jointly normally distributed, with zero means, independently of each other and with variance matrices $\mathbf{R}_t$ and $\mathbf{Q}_t$, respectively, so that

$$\begin{bmatrix} \mathbf{v}_t \\ \mathbf{u}_t \end{bmatrix} \sim IN\left[\mathbf{0}, \begin{bmatrix} \mathbf{R}_t & \mathbf{0} \\ \mathbf{0} & \mathbf{Q}_t \end{bmatrix}\right]$$

(A3)   The starting value $\mathbf{x}_t$ is drawn from some normal distribution and is independent of all $\mathbf{u}_t$ and $\mathbf{v}_t$.

(A4)   The variables $\mathbf{z}_t$ and $\mathbf{w}_t$ are exogenous in that there is no causality from $\mathbf{y}_t$ and $\mathbf{x}_t$ to $\mathbf{z}_t$ and $\mathbf{w}_t$, and $\mathbf{z}_t$ and $\mathbf{w}_t$ are independent of all $\mathbf{u}_t$ and $\mathbf{v}_t$.

(A5)   The parameters $\boldsymbol{\beta}_t$, $\boldsymbol{\gamma}_t$, $\mathbf{T}_t$, $\boldsymbol{\delta}_t$, and $\mathbf{G}_t$ are known completely.

If $I_t : \mathbf{y}_{t-j}$, $j \geqslant 0$, then, with the above assumptions, the joint distribution of $\mathbf{x}_t$, $\mathbf{y}_t$ conditional on I_{t-1} is

$$\begin{bmatrix} \mathbf{x}_t \\ \mathbf{y}_t \end{bmatrix}\bigg|I_{t-1} \sim N\left[\begin{bmatrix} \mathbf{x}_{t|t-1} \\ \mathbf{y}_{t|t-1} \end{bmatrix}, \begin{bmatrix} \mathbf{P}_{t|t-1} & \mathbf{P}_{t|t-1}\boldsymbol{\beta}_t' \\ \boldsymbol{\beta}_t\mathbf{P}_{t|t-1} & \mathbf{H}_t \end{bmatrix}\right] \qquad (10.1.3)$$

where

$$\mathbf{H}_t = \boldsymbol{\beta}_t\mathbf{P}_{t|t-1}\boldsymbol{\beta}_t' + \mathbf{R}_t \qquad (10.1.4)$$

$$\mathbf{x}_{t|t-1} = \mathbf{T}_t\mathbf{x}_{t-1|t-1} + \boldsymbol{\delta}_t\mathbf{w}_t \qquad (10.1.5)$$

$$\mathbf{y}_{t|t-1} = \boldsymbol{\beta}_t\mathbf{x}_{t|t-1} + \boldsymbol{\gamma}_t\mathbf{z}_t \qquad (10.1.6)$$

$$\mathbf{P}_{t|t-1} = \mathbf{T}_t\mathbf{P}_{t|t-1}\mathbf{T}_t' + \mathbf{G}_t\mathbf{Q}_t\mathbf{G}_t' \qquad (10.1.7)$$

Here $\mathbf{x}_{t|t-1} = E[\mathbf{x}_t|I_{t-1}]$, $\mathbf{x}_{t-1|t-1} = E[\mathbf{x}_{t-1}|I_{t-1}]$, etc. For these equations, it is assumed that $\mathbf{w}_t$ and $\mathbf{z}_t$ are given values from outside the system. There is a standard theorem concerning multivariate normal distributions that says that if x and y are jointly normally distributed

$$\begin{bmatrix} \mathbf{x} \\ \mathbf{y} \end{bmatrix} \sim N\left(\begin{bmatrix} \boldsymbol{\mu}_x \\ \boldsymbol{\mu}_y \end{bmatrix}, \begin{bmatrix} \Sigma_{xx} & \Sigma_{xy} \\ \Sigma_{yx} & \Sigma_{yy} \end{bmatrix} \right)$$

then the conditional distribution of x given y is

$$\mathbf{x}|\mathbf{y} \sim N\left(\boldsymbol{\mu}_x + \Sigma_{xy}\Sigma_{yy}^{-1}(\mathbf{y} - \boldsymbol{\mu}_y), \Sigma_{xx} - \Sigma_{xy}\Sigma_{yy}^{-1}\Sigma_{yx} \right)$$

Using this result, one gets the further equations

$$\mathbf{x}_{t|t} = \mathbf{x}_{t|t-1} + \mathbf{k}_t(\mathbf{y}_t - \mathbf{y}_{t|t-1}) \tag{10.1.8}$$

$$\mathbf{P}_{t|t} = \mathbf{P}_{t|t-1} - \mathbf{k}_t\boldsymbol{\beta}_t\mathbf{P}_{t|t-1} \tag{10.1.9}$$

$$\mathbf{k}_t = \mathbf{P}_{t|t-1}\boldsymbol{\beta}_t'\mathbf{H}_t^{-1} \tag{10.1.10}$$

Here $\mathbf{x}_{t|t} = E[\mathbf{x}_t|I_t]$ and is the estimate of the unobserved $\mathbf{x}_t$ value given information about the y's up to and including time t.

The system of equations (10.1.4)–(10.1.10) is called the Kalman filter and has been discussed in great detail by Anderson and Moore [1979].

Of these equations, (10.1.6) gives the one-step forecast of $\mathbf{y}_t$ in terms of $\mathbf{x}_{t|t-1}$, which is given by (10.1.5) in terms of $\mathbf{x}_{t-1|t-1}$, which is itself given by (10.1.8), replacing t by $t - 1$. The iterative nature of the procedure is clear from these equations. The other equations continually update the weighting in matrix $\mathbf{k}_t$ in (10.1.8), which operates on the previous forecast error. The filter is ideal for computer use, although there may be a start-up problem if $\mathbf{x}_t$ is not actually known, and, with this form, one would need to know all of the various parameters and matrices, such as $\boldsymbol{\beta}_t$, $\mathbf{R}_t$, and $\mathbf{Q}_t$, perfectly. In practice, it is usual to make assumptions about the way these parameters vary, if at all, and to estimate these parameters and $\mathbf{x}_t$ from the data. Once the estimates are available, the filter provides a fast and convenient way to produce forecasts of $\mathbf{y}_t$ and estimates of $\mathbf{x}_t$.

As a simple example of the state–space representation, suppose that y_t is generated by the ARMA(2, 1) model

$$y_t = \alpha_1 y_{t-1} + \alpha_2 y_{t-2} + \epsilon_t + b\epsilon_{t-1}$$

A representation is

$$y_t = 0 \cdot x_{1t} + x_{2t}$$

$$\begin{bmatrix} x_{1t} \\ x_{2t} \end{bmatrix} = \begin{bmatrix} 0 & \alpha_2 \\ 1 & \alpha_1 \end{bmatrix}\begin{bmatrix} x_{1,t-1} \\ x_{2,t-1} \end{bmatrix} + \begin{bmatrix} b \\ 1 \end{bmatrix}\epsilon_t$$

Unfortunately, the representation is not unique, as the same ARMA(2, 1) model is given from the state-space representation

$$y_t = [b, 1]\begin{bmatrix} x_{1t} \\ x_{2t} \end{bmatrix}$$

$$\begin{bmatrix} x_{1t} \\ x_{2t} \end{bmatrix} = \begin{bmatrix} 0 & 1 \\ \alpha_2 & \alpha_1 \end{bmatrix}\begin{bmatrix} x_{1,t-1} \\ x_{2,t-1} \end{bmatrix} + \begin{bmatrix} 0 \\ 1 \end{bmatrix}\epsilon_t$$

Details of how vector ARMA models can be put into state–space form can be found in Priestley [1981, Vol. 2].

There are a number of immediate uses for the Kalman filter. If one has identified an ARMA model, this model can be estimated and evaluated and forecasts can be produced from it by transforming the model into the state–space form. A particular way of doing this, due to Akaike, is discussed in the following paragraph. Another use of the Kalman filter is with unobserved component models. Many models in economics and in time series analysis may be thought of as including unobserved components, such as trends, seasonals, national and regional factors, or permanent income. If these components are equated with the unobserved state variables and models are assumed for them that capture what are believed to be their major temporal features, the model can be translated into the state–space form and analyzed using the Kalman filter. A general description of unobserved component models can be found in Nerlove, Grether, and Carvalho [1979]. An applied study by Engle and Watson [1981] makes extensive use of the Kalman filter to formulate a single (unobserved) factor model of a multivariate time series of wage rates. The third immediate use of Kalman filters is with time-varying parameter models, which are discussed in the next section. The state–space representation is also useful for the formulation of nonlinear models, as will be seen in Section 10.3.

Akaike [1976] has introduced a statistical vector model identification procedure that can be automatically conducted on a computer without intervention by a statistician as a decision maker, except possibly to difference the series to achieve stationarity. The procedure is based on the observation that, if the vector series y_t is generated by the vector ARMA(p, q) model

$$\Phi_p(B)y_t = \theta_q(B)\epsilon_t$$

where $\Phi_p(B) = 1 - \Phi_1 B - \cdots - \Phi_p B^p$ and $\theta_q(B)$ are matrix polynomials in B of orders p and q, respectively (it is assumed here that $p > q$ for expositional convenience), then a state vector x_t can be constructed from the vector $y_t, y_{t+1,t}, \ldots, y_{t+p,t}$ where $y_{t+k,t} = E[y_{t+k}|y_{t-j}, \ j \geq 0]$ are the conditional forecasts. He shows that a state–space model can be written in the form

$$x_{t+1} = Fx_t + G\epsilon_t, \qquad y_t = Hx_t$$

where

$$x'_t = [y_t, y_{t+1,t}, \ldots, y_{t+p,t}], \qquad F = \begin{bmatrix} 0 & I & 0 & 0 & \cdots & 0 \\ 0 & 0 & I & 0 & \cdots & 0 \\ \theta_p & \theta_{p-1} & \theta_{p-2} & 0 & \cdots & \theta_1 \end{bmatrix}$$

and G is a matrix such that $G' = [1, \psi_1, \ldots, \psi_{p-1}]$, where the corresponding

Wold representation to the ARMA(p, q) model is

$$y_t = \left(\sum_{j=0}^{\infty} \psi_j B^j \right) \epsilon_t$$

and **H** is essentially a matrix of ones. However, if investigation suggests that certain of the components of x_t are not contributing to the representation, then a zero will be placed in the appropriate location in **H**.

In practice one does not know the values of p and q, but these can be determined directly from the data by the use of canonical correlation analysis. The first stage is to fit a sequence of vector autoregressive models of increasing order and to select the best using the Akaike information criterion (AIC), defined by

$$AIC_k = N \log(D_k) + 2n^2 k$$

where N = sample size, n is the dimension of vector y_t, k is the order of the AR model estimated, and D_k is the determinant of the covariance matrix of the residuals of that model. As k increases, the first term will generally decrease but the second term will increase, being a penalty function for the fact that more parameters (k^2) are being used than in a lower-order model. Suppose that the model selected is of order m; then the corresponding ψ_j terms can be estimated from it by an iterative procedure.

The canonical correlations between a pair of random vectors $(x_1, \ldots, x_m)$, $(y_1, \ldots, y_n)$ consist of finding coefficients $(a_{11}, \ldots, a_{1m})$ and $(b_{11}, \ldots, b_{1n})$ such that the correlation r_1 between the two linear combinations

$$u_1 = \sum_{i=1}^{m} a_{1i} x_i \quad \text{and} \quad v_1 = \sum_{j=1}^{n} b_{1j} y_j$$

is maximized. Next, two further linear combinations are selected, $u_2 = \sum_i a_{2i} x_i$, $v_2 = \sum_j b_{2j} y_j$, such that u_2 and v_2 are orthogonal to u_1 and v_1 and also so that $r_2 = \text{corr}(u_2, v_2)$ is maximized. This process continues until $\min(m, n)$ canonical correlations $r_1, r_2, \ldots$ and their corresponding pairs of canonical variates $(u_1, v_1), (u_2, v_2), \ldots$ have been extracted.

For the time series modeling process, the two sets of vectors used are the past $y_t^p = (y_t, y_{t-1}, \ldots, y_{t-m})$, where m was selected as above, and the future

$$y_t^f = (y_t, y_{t+1}, y_{t+2}, \ldots, y_{t+m})$$

(In some computing procedures y_t is not used in y_t^f.) For each value of m, the canonical correlations are estimated and the smallest one of these tested for significance. Once this test correlation is not significant, the previous value of m is selected as being the p value needed for the state–space representation. The full vector ARMA model can then be estimated using the Kalman filter procedures. The technique is rather a "black-box" method and involves a considerable amount of computing. However, models can be quickly formed on computers such as the IBM PC using commercially available programs. More details about this method of modeling can be found in Akaike [1976] and Vinod and Hui [1983].

In a forecasting competition reported by Engle and Goodrich [1985] involving forecasts of macrodemand for electricity and many alternative forecasting procedures, these state–space models performed among the very best, particularly in the very short run. In the longer run they often did slightly less well than some time-varying parameter models of the form discussed in the next section.

A further important application of state–space models and the Kalman filter is to the development of computationally efficient algorithms for the likelihood function of time series models; see, for example, Ansley and Kohn [1983], who consider the vector ARMA process with missing or aggregated data.

10.2 Time-Varying Parameter Models

Consider a simple relationship between a pair of observed series x_t, y_t of the form

$$y_t = \beta_t x_t + v_t \tag{10.2.1}$$

where the coefficient β_t is allowed to change through time. Throughout economics, changes in relationships can be expected as tastes, behavior, rules, and technologies change. For example, y_t could be residential demand for electricity per household in some regions and x_t could be temperature. Over a period of several years appliance efficiencies and house insulation qualities would change, and behavior could change. Thus the relationship between demand and temperature would probably evolve. On some occasions, the reasons for changing parameters will be known and are due to changes in measurable quantities, but often the causes of the change are not observable, as the efficiency and insulation levels in the above example illustrate. If one believes that parameter changes are quite slow, then a possible strategy for modeling these parameter changes is to assume an AR(1) model with a coefficient near one, so that

$$\dot{\beta}_t = \alpha \dot{\beta}_{t-1} + u_t; \qquad \dot{\beta}_t = \beta_t - \bar{\beta} \tag{10.2.2}$$

with α near one, for example. Here β_t is not strictly observable, although it may be estimated from the observed series. Equations (10.2.1) and (10.2.2) are of exactly the same form as the first two equations of the previous section after some simplifications. In (10.1.1) and (10.1.2), x_t was unobserved and β_t was assumed known. Now these situations are reversed: x_t is observed but not β_t. Clearly, the Kalman filter can be applied directly to the new situation, and time-varying parameter models can be estimated, interpreted, and forecast. The model can be generalized to vector series with several lags and by the introduction of exogenous variables into both equations. Many of these generalizations are discussed in Chow [1984]. A class of models in which parameters do not change smoothly has been investigated by Nicholls and Quinn [1982].

Experience suggests that these models can lead to improved forecasts, as the experiment mentioned in the previous section indicated, but it is recommended that one first apply a test for time-varying parameters, such as that proposed by Watson [1982]. Unfortunately, it is easy to "estimate" a time-varying parameter by the Kalman filter even when the actual parameter is constant.

10.3 Nonlinear Models

Although most time series models considered in this book have been linear, there is no particular reason to believe that actual generating processes are linear. Certainly most microeconomic optimum decision rules do not lead to linear relationships between inputs and output of the decision, and aggregation to the macro level could still produce nonlinear models. If the specification of the model is known, then various questions can be asked about its stability, forecastability, and the closeness of linear approximations, but in practice the correct specification is rarely known before the start of data analysis. One obvious way to proceed is to specify a class of models that it is hoped will at least approximate the true generating process. Given the success of ARMA models, a fairly obvious starting point for such a class is an ARMA model with parameters depending on the previous path of the series. Let x_t be the series of interest, ϵ_t a white noise innovation process, and $\mathbf{X}_t = (\epsilon_t, \epsilon_{t-1}, \ldots, \epsilon_{t-L+1}, x_t, x_{t-1}, \ldots, x_{t-u+1})$ be a "state vector", which will approximate all the relevant past information in the series. Then a fairly general nonlinear class of models may be written

$$x_t = L(\mathbf{X}_t) + \sum_{i=1}^{k} a_i(\mathbf{X}_{t-1})x_{t-i} + \sum_{j=1}^{l} b_j(\mathbf{X}_{t-1})\epsilon_{t-j} + \epsilon_t \quad (10.3.1)$$

The process is assumed to have finite memory if k and l are finite and the innovations have zero mean and constant variance, although this latter assumption can easily be removed. Because of its form, Priestley [1980] points out that such a model has a state–space form

$$\begin{aligned} \mathbf{X}_{t+1} &= \mathbf{L}(\mathbf{X}_t) + [\mathbf{F}(\mathbf{X}_t)]\mathbf{X}_t + \epsilon_{t+1} \\ x_t &= \mathbf{H}\mathbf{X}_t \end{aligned} \quad (10.3.2)$$

As it stands this model is almost too general for practical use without putting some constraints on the way that the "parameters" evolve. One way would be to let the functions a_i and b_j be linear in the state vector, assuming that these functions are smooth; this could give a reasonable local approximation.

Priestley suggests a different approach. He first adds the constant one to the state vector $\mathbf{X}_t$, thereby removing the necessity of having the term $L(\mathbf{X}_t)$ explicitly in the model. He then assumes that

$$a_i(\mathbf{X}_{t+1}) = a_i(\mathbf{X}_t) + \Delta\mathbf{X}'_{t+1} \cdot \beta_i^{(t+1)}$$

and

$$b_j(\mathbf{X}_{t+1}) = b_j(\mathbf{X}_t) + \Delta\mathbf{X}'_{t+1} \cdot \gamma_j^{(t+1)}$$

so that the parameters essentially evolve as random walks driven by a linear combination of changes in the state vector with time-varying parameters. Finally, the updating equations for these parameters are again assumed to be random walks. The full model becomes, in state–space form,

$$\mathbf{x}_t = \mathbf{H}\mathbf{X}_t, \qquad\qquad \mathbf{X}_{t+1} = \mathbf{F}_t\mathbf{X}_t + \boldsymbol{\epsilon}_{t+1}$$
$$\mathbf{F}_{t+1} = \mathbf{F}_t + \Delta\mathbf{X}'_{t+1} \cdot \mathbf{B}_{t+1}, \qquad \mathbf{B}_{t+1} = \mathbf{B}_t + \mathbf{V}_{t+1}$$

where $\boldsymbol{\epsilon}_t$ and $\mathbf{V}_t$ are zero-mean, white noise innovations. These equations allow a form of the Kalman filter to be used to provide forecasts. Priestley [1980] discusses the details of this approach including specification and estimation. Cartwright and Newbold [1983] have applied the autoregressive form of the general model with just two states to North Sea oil discovery data. They found "extensive gains in forecast performance."

A number of specific nonlinear time series models fit into the above framework. These include

(i)   The nonlinear autoregressive AR(1) model,

$$x_t = f(x_{t-1}) + \epsilon_t$$

where for stability one needs

$$|f(x)| \leqslant |x| \qquad \text{for all} \quad |x| \geqslant |x_0|$$

A parametric form for $f(x)$ can be assumed, such as a rational function or a nonparametric form estimated, as discussed by Robinson [1984]. The plot of x_t against x_{t-1} may indicate the nonlinearity, depending on the relative importance of ϵ_t and the complexity of the path produced by the model.

(ii)   The threshold autoregressive models, investigated by Tong and Lim [1980]. In this case, one has an autoregressive model whose parameters switch according to the region in which the recent past of the series lies, for example,

$$x_t = 0.6x_{t-1} + 0.3x_{t-2} + \epsilon_t$$

if

$$x_{t-1}, x_{t-2} \geqslant 0 \qquad \text{and} \qquad x_t = 0.3x_{t-1} - 0.5x_{t-2} + \epsilon_t$$

if either x_{t-1} or x_{t-2} is negative. These models involve an interesting type of nonlinearity, with nonsmooth, possibly severe switches in parameter values and are applied by Tong and Lim to sunspot and river-flow data.

(iii) Exponentially autoregressive models (discussed by Haggan and Ozaki [1981]). Here each parameter of an AR model takes the form $a_i = \alpha_i + \theta_i \exp(-\Sigma_j \gamma_j X_{t-j})$. Thus, if the series takes a very large value, the next term will come from an AR model with generally small coefficients. The models can easily be made stable and can display limit cycle and other nonlinear behavior known from nonlinear vibration theory.

(iv) Bilinear models. An example of a bilinear model is

$$x_t = \alpha x_{t-1} + \beta x_{t-2}\epsilon_{t-1} + \epsilon_t$$

where cross products between lagged x_t and ϵ_t occur in the model. The properties of these series are briefly discussed in the next section.

These are just a sample of the many forms of nonlinear models that are possible. So far, these models can be classified as being interesting and promising, but their general ability to produce superior forecasts has not yet been established by a comprehensive study. These models represent time-domain techniques for studying possible nonlinearities. Frequency domain techniques have also been suggested, as mentioned in Section 2.9.

A specific type of nonlinearity that occurs frequently in practice is when an instantaneous nonlinear transformation is applied to a series. The effects of such transformations are discussed in Section 10.5.

10.4 Bilinear Models

The general bilinear autoregressive moving average model of order (p, q, r, k) takes the form

$$x_t = \sum_{j=1}^{p} \alpha_j x_{t-j} + \sum_{i=0}^{q} b_i \epsilon_{t-i} + \sum_{j=1}^{k} \sum_{i=1}^{r} \beta_{ij} x_{t-i}\epsilon_{t-j} \qquad (10.4.1)$$

where ϵ_t is a zero-mean white noise input series and $b_0 = 1$. The "completely bilinear" model has $p = q = 0$. These models allow a certain amount of nonlinearity but are not so general that analytical solutions are impossible. A few special models have been given particular names: if $\beta_{kl} = 0$ for all $k > l$, the model is called superdiagonal; if $\beta_{kl} = 0$ for all $l > k$, it is called subdiagonal; and if $\beta_{kl} = 0$ except when $k = l$, it is called diagonal. The model is stable if x_t does not explode from its starting value and invertible if, given the actual specification and parameter values, then asymptotically the ϵ_t values can be perfectly estimated from the observed x's and any set of starting values for the ϵ's. Brockett has proved that if x_t is stable and is generated by any univariate generating mechanism, then there exists a bilinear model that approximates arbitrarily well the true mechanism over any finite sample period. However, the approximate model need not be invertible and thus may not be useful for forecasting.

Specific results are available for the properties of a number of bilinear models, but the best results are for orders $(p, q, r, 1)$. Models of order $(1, 0, 1, 1)$ were considered by Granger and Andersen [1978b], of order $(p, 0, p, 1)$ by Suhba Rao [1981], and of order $(p, q, r, 1)$ by Liu and Liu [1985]. Equation (10.4.1) can be rewritten in a state–space form

$$x_t = \mathbf{C}'\mathbf{y}_t, \qquad \mathbf{y}_t = \mathbf{A}\mathbf{y}_{t-1} + \mathbf{B}\mathbf{y}_{t-1}\epsilon_{t-1} + \mathbf{C}\sum_{j=0}^{q}\theta_j\epsilon_{t-j}$$

where

$$\mathbf{y}_t' = (x_t, x_{t-1}, \ldots, x_{t-s+1})_{1\times s}, \qquad s = \max(p, r)$$

$$\mathbf{A} = \begin{pmatrix} \alpha_1 & \alpha_2 & \cdots & \alpha_{p-1} & \alpha_p & 0 & \cdots & 0 \\ 1 & 0 & \cdots & 0 & 0 & 0 & \cdots & 0 \\ 0 & 1 & \cdots & 0 & 0 & 0 & \cdots & 0 \\ 0 & 0 & \cdots & 1 & 0 & 0 & \cdots & 0 \end{pmatrix}_{s\times s}$$

$$\mathbf{B} = \begin{pmatrix} \beta_1 & \beta_2 & \cdots & \beta_r & 0 & \cdots & 0 \\ \mathbf{0} & & & \mathbf{0} & & & \mathbf{0} \end{pmatrix}_{s\times s}$$

$$\mathbf{C}' = (1, 0, 0, \ldots, 0)_{1\times s}$$

Define $\rho(\mathbf{D})$ for a matrix $\mathbf{D}$ to be the maximum of the absolute values of the eigenvalues of $\mathbf{D}$. It is known that x_t is first-order stationary if $\rho(\mathbf{A}) < 1$ and is second-order stationary if

$$\rho(\mathbf{A} \otimes \mathbf{A} + \mathbf{B} \otimes \mathbf{B}) < 1$$

where $\otimes$ denotes the Kronecker product operator. Furthermore, it can be shown that the autocorrelations of an order $(p, q, r, 1)$ model are the same as a particular ARMA(p, q) model. A sufficient condition for invertibility can be obtained for the order $(p, 1, r, 1)$ model.

The pure bilinear models of order $(0, 0, r, 1)$ can have autocorrelations similar to that of white noise, but the third-order moments, such as $E[x_t x_{t-1} x_{t-2}]$ and the autocorrelations of x_t^2 will not be zero. A simple two-stage procedure to investigate whether or not a bilinear model might be appropriate is to fit an ARMA model and then to consider the autocorrelations of the squared residuals. Maravall [1982] applied this approach to some Spanish monetary data, found evidence of bilinearity, and achieved a modest 10% or so improvement in mean squared forecast error.

10.5 Instantaneous Data Transformations

There is no completely convincing reason to analyze time series data in precisely the form in which they are provided by a company, government office, or whatever. It has already been seen that it is frequently advisable to consider the first difference of a series rather than the raw series. One possible change worth considering is the analysis of an instantaneously transformed series $Y_t = T(X_t)$ rather than the given series X_t, where $T(\ )$ is some well-behaved function. There are two main reasons that have been proposed for making such a transformation. The first is that Y_t may be a Gaussian series, with several consequent advantages, and the second is that the error from a linear model fitted to the transformed series may have a constant (homogeneous) variance, whereas a linear model fitted to the original series X_t may not have this property.

The main advantage of having a Gaussian series is that it is then known that the optimal single series, least-squares forecast will be a linear forecast, comprising a linear combination of past observed values. For non-Gaussian series it is possible that a nonlinear forecast will be superior, in a least-squares sense, to a linear one. That this possibility is not a necessity can be seen by considering the series generated by

$$X_t = aX_{t-1} + \epsilon_t \tag{10.5.1}$$

where ϵ_t is a zero mean white noise series having a nonnormal distribution, such as a rectangular or double exponential distribution. The optimal h-step forecast will be $f_{n,h} = a^h X_n$ and so is linear despite X_t not being a Gaussian process.

An example of a series with nonhomogeneous residual variances is that generated by

$$X_t = A(t)Z_t \tag{10.5.2}$$

where Z_t is a stationary series with mean μ and $A(t)$ is a positive smooth function of time. Differencing the X_t may produce a series that is stationary in mean but not in variance. If $Z_t > 0$, all t, the obvious transformation to consider is the logarithmic, so that

$$Y_t = \log X_t = \log A(t) + \log Z_t \tag{10.5.3}$$

and Y_t now has a trend only in mean, which could possibly be removed by differencing. In economics it is often observed that series have similar trends in mean and standard deviation, but for the logarithmic transformation to be appropriate, these quantities have to be proportional and there is no reason to suppose that actual series have such a property. To illustrate a different possibility, consider the following rather contrived model for X_t

$$X_t = a^2 X_{t-1} + \eta_t \tag{10.5.4}$$

where η_t is white noise but whose standard deviation is linearly related to X_{t-1} and so is not constant through time. This model can be derived from an AR(1) series Y_t given by

$$Y_t = aY_{t-1} + \epsilon_t \tag{10.5.5}$$

where ϵ_t is a zero-mean, Gaussian white noise series and then considering the model for $X_t = Y_t^2$, which is (10.5.4) with $\eta_t = \epsilon_t^2 + 2a\epsilon_t Y_{t-1}$. If one is given the series X_t to analyze, the proper transformation to apply is naturally $Y_t = X_t^{1/2}$ since Y_t is both Gaussian and has a constant variance error term.

In practice, the most popular instantaneous transformation is the logarithmic, although there has been an increased interest in the class of transformations introduced by Box and Cox [1964] (see Box and Jenkins [1973])

$$Y_t = \frac{\left[(X_t + m)^\theta - 1\right]}{\theta} \qquad (10.5.6)$$

which involves two parameters, m and θ, and which, for $\theta = 0$, corresponds to the logarithmic. The question of how to choose the parameters m and θ will be discussed later.

For whatever reason, instantaneous transformations are often used in practice, and it is important to study the time series properties of the resulting series and also the question of how to forecast X_{n+h} given that one only has available a model for $Y_t = T(X_t)$, where $T(\ )$ is the transformation used. These questions have been considered in some detail by Granger and Newbold [1976], and so only the main results will be presented here, largely without proof.

Let X_t be a stationary, Gaussian series with mean μ, variance σ^2 and autocorrelation sequence $\mathrm{corr}(X_t, X_{t-\tau}) = \rho_\tau$. Set $Z_t = (X_t - \mu)/\sigma$ so that $Z_t, Z_{t-\tau}$ will be jointly distributed as bivariate normal with zero means, unit variances and correlation ρ_τ. Consider an instantaneous transformation of the form $Y_t = T(Z_t)$ where $T(\ )$ can be expanded in terms of Hermite polynomials in the form

$$T(Z) = \sum_{j=0}^{m} \alpha_j H_j(Z) \qquad (10.5.7)$$

and where m can be infinite. The jth Hermite polynomial $H_j(Z)$ is a polynomial in Z of order j with, for example, $H_0(Z) = 1$, $H_1(Z) = Z$, $H_2(Z) = Z^2 - 1$, $H_3(Z) = Z^3 - 3Z$, and so forth. If X and Y are normally distributed random variables with zero means, unit variances, and correlation ρ, these polynomials have the important orthogonal properties

$$\begin{aligned} E[H_n(X)H_k(X)] &= 0, \qquad n \neq k \\ &= n!, \qquad n = k \end{aligned} \qquad (10.5.8)$$

and

$$\begin{aligned} E[H_n(X)H_k(Y)] &= 0, \qquad n \neq k \\ &= \rho^n n!, \qquad n = k \end{aligned} \qquad (10.5.9)$$

Using these properties, it is easy to show that $E(Y_t) = \alpha_0$ and

$$\mathrm{cov}(Y_t, Y_{t-\tau}) = \sum_{j=1}^{m} \alpha_j^2 j! \rho_\tau^j$$

Thus, the linear properties of the transformed series can be determined. It follows, for example, that if

$$Y_t = a + bX_t + cX_t^2 \qquad (10.5.10)$$

then

$$\text{cov}(Y_t, Y_{t-\tau}) = (b + 2c\mu)^2 \sigma^2 \rho_\tau + 2c^2 \sigma^2 \rho_\tau^2$$

and if $Y_t = \exp(X_t)$, then

$$\text{cov}(Y_t, Y_{t-\tau}) = \exp(2\mu + \sigma^2)(\exp(\sigma^2 \rho_\tau) - 1)$$

Further, if X_t is MA(q), Y_t has autocovariances appropriate for MA(q), but if X_t is AR(p) and Y_t is given by (10.5.10), then its autocovariances correspond to a mixed ARMA($\frac{1}{2}p(p + 3), \frac{1}{2}p(p + 1)$) process.

It may also be shown that if X_t is an integrated ARIMA($p, 1, q$) process, then Y_t will also be such that its first differences can be modeled as an ARMA process.

If X_t is Gaussian, or is at least assumed to have this property, and a model has been formed for it, then standing at time n an optimal forecast, $f_{n,h}$ of X_{n+h} can be easily formed by the methods discussed in Chapters 4 and 5, and it will be linear in X_{n-j}, $j \geq 0$. Suppose, however, that X_{n+h} is not the quantity for which a forecast is required, but rather

$$Y_{n+h} = T\left(\frac{X_{n+h} - \mu}{\sigma}\right)$$

needs to be forecast. An example would be an economist who has built a model for log price but actually wants to forecast price. Two forecasts of Y_{n+h} can be considered easily, the optimal forecast under a least squares criterion given by

$$g_{n,h}^{(1)} = E[Y_{n+h}|I_n] \qquad (10.5.11)$$

where I_n is the information set X_{n-j}, $j \geq 0$, and the naïve forecast

$$g_{n,h}^{(2)} = T\left[\frac{f_{n,h} - \mu}{\sigma}\right] \qquad (10.5.12)$$

Write $X_{n+h} = f_{n,h} + e_{n,h}^{(x)}$ so that $e_{n,h}^{(x)}$ is the h-step forecast error of X_{n+h} when the optimal forecast $f_{n,h}$ is used at time n, and denote

$$S^2(h) = \text{var}(e_{n,h}^{(x)}) \qquad (10.5.13)$$

Since Y_{n+h} is a function of a Gaussian variable, it can be shown that the optimal, generally nonlinear, forecast is given by

$$g_{n,h}^{(1)} = \sum_{j=0}^{m} \alpha_j A^j H_j(P) \qquad (10.5.14)$$

where

$$A = (1 - S^2(h)/\sigma^2)^{1/2}, \qquad P = (f_{n,h} - \mu)/(\sigma^2 - S^2(h))^{1/2} \quad (10.5.15)$$

A little algebra then yields the unconditional expected squared forecast error as

$$\text{var}(e_{n,h}^{(y)}) = \text{var}(Y_{n+h} - g_{n,h}^{(1)}) = \sum_{j=1}^{m} \alpha_j^2 j! (1 - A^{2j}) \quad (10.5.16)$$

In deriving this result it is necessary to use the facts that, under the conditions stated, $f_{n,h}$ is normally distributed and that

$$E[g_{n,h}^{(1)}] = E[Y_{n+h}] = \alpha_0 \quad (10.5.17)$$

Define as a measure of forecastability of a series Y_t, having finite variance, using a given information set, the quantity

$$R_{h,y}^2 = \frac{\text{var}(f_{n,h}^{(y)})}{\text{var}(Y_{n+h})} \quad (10.5.18)$$

where $f_{n,h}^{(y)}$ is the optimal forecast of Y_{n+h}, possibly a nonlinear forecast, based on the information set and using a least-squares criterion. Clearly, the nearer this quantity is to unity, the more forecastable is the series. If the series one is interested in does not have finite variance, an integrated process being an example, then the definition should be applied after the series has been differenced sufficiently often to produce a finite variance series, if this is possible. Since

$$\text{var}(Y_{n+h}) = \sum_{j=1}^{m} \alpha_j^2 j! \quad (10.5.19)$$

it follows from this and (10.5.16) that

$$R_{h,y}^2 = \frac{\sum_{j=1}^{m} \alpha_j^2 j! A^{2j}}{\sum_{j=1}^{m} \alpha_j^2 j!}$$

Assuming that X_t is nondeterministic, so that $S^2(h) > 0$, then

$$R_{h,x}^2 = A^2 \quad \text{and} \quad 0 \leqslant A^2 < 1$$

It thus follows that

$$R_{h,y}^2 < R_{h,x}^2, \quad m > 1 \quad \text{and} \quad A > 0.$$

This implies that any nonlinear instantaneous transformation of a Gaussian process X_t is always less forecastable than X_t, provided X_t is not simply a white noise series. We call this the *forecastability theorem*.

As an example, suppose that X_t has $\mu = 0$ and $\sigma = 1$ and is Gaussian, but that a forecast is required of $Y_{n+h} = \exp(X_{n+h})$. This would correspond to the example given earlier where X_t is log price and Y_t is price. Let, as before,

$f_{n,h}^{(x)}$ be the optimal forecast of X_{n+h} using I_n: X_{n-j}, $j \geq 0$, and $S^2(h)$ be the variance of the h-step forecast error of X_{n+h}. The optimal forecast of Y_{n+h} is then given by

$$g_{n,h}^{(1)} = \exp(f_{n,h} + \tfrac{1}{2}S^2(h))$$

and the naïve forecast is

$$g_{n,h}^{(2)} = \exp(f_{n,h})$$

which is seen to be biased and, naturally, to lead to a higher expected squared error. In this case it is fairly easily shown that

$$R_{h,y}^2 = \frac{\exp(1 - S^2(h)) - 1}{e - 1}$$

and of course

$$R_{h,x}^2 = 1 - S^2(h)$$

Some representative values for these quantities are:

$S^2(h)$	0.2	0.5	0.8
$R_{h,x}^2$	0.8	0.5	0.2
$R_{h,y}^2$	0.713	0.378	0.129

The results presented here are very general, although the normality assumption is rather a strong one and the formulas involved can be very complicated for some transformations, such as that in (10.5.6) with fractional θ. The first use of Hermite polynomials in tackling the problems just discussed was by Barrett and Lampard [1955].

In the above discussion, a Gaussian series was transformed into a nonnormal one and then the optimal nonlinear forecast found for the transformed series. If this sequence can be reversed, so that an instantaneous transformation can be found for the given series X_t of the form $Y_t = T(X_t)$ such that now Y_t is Gaussian, then this theory can be used to find a nonlinear forecast for X_t that should be superior to the best linear forecast, at least in theory. The obviously difficult part of this procedure is to find the proper transformation. Suppose that a specific class of transformations are to be considered, involving a vector of parameters θ, so that

$$Y_t(\theta) = T(X_t, \theta) \tag{10.5.20}$$

and that there exists a particular value for θ, denoted θ_0, such that $Y_t(\theta_0)$ is a Gaussian process, in the sense that an ARIMA model can be fitted to $Y_t(\theta_0)$ of the usual form

$$a(B)(1 - B)^d Y_t(\theta_0) = b(B)\epsilon_t \tag{10.5.21}$$

ignoring seasonal possibilities, and where ϵ_t is Gaussian white noise. The only question that now remains is how to find θ_0. There are at least two ways to approach this question and these do not necessarily give identical answers and could be thought of as having somewhat different objectives. The first approach is to write down the likelihood function for $Y_t(\theta)$. If it is supposed that an ARIMA model is fitted to $Y_t(\theta)$ for each θ, giving residuals $\epsilon_t(\theta)$ and the parameters of the model are chosen so that the estimate of the variance of $\epsilon_t(\theta)$ is minimized, giving $\hat{\sigma}_\epsilon^2(\theta)$, the log likelihood becomes

$$L(\theta) = -\tfrac{1}{2}n \log \hat{\sigma}_\epsilon^2(\theta) + \log J(X, \theta) \qquad (10.5.22)$$

where J is the Jacobian of the transformation. θ_0 is then chosen as the value of θ that maximizes $L(\theta)$. An alternative approach can be based on the forecastability theorem introduced above. This can be phrased as saying that, in terms of population values,

$$R^2(\theta) = 1 - \frac{\hat{\sigma}_\epsilon^2(\theta)}{\mathrm{var}(Y_t(\theta))} \qquad (10.5.23)$$

will have a maximum at $\theta = \theta_0$.

Both $L(\theta)$ and $R^2(\theta)$ depend on $\hat{\sigma}_\epsilon^2(\theta)$, and at first sight this is a difficult quantity to obtain as θ varies since the results of the previous section show that the ARIMA model may have to be reidentified for every θ value used. However, $\sigma_\epsilon^2(\theta)$ can be estimated without going through an actual model-building process by using result (4.5.7), which states that

$$\log \sigma_\epsilon^2(\theta) = \frac{1}{2\pi} \int_{-\pi}^{\pi} \log 2\pi s(\omega, \theta) \, d\omega \qquad (10.5.24)$$

where $s(\omega, \theta)$ is the spectrum of $Y_t(\theta)$. The use of this result to obtain a "nonparametric" estimate of $\log \sigma_\epsilon^2(\theta)$ was suggested by Brubacher and Wilson [1975]. The properties of this estimate have been studied by Janacek [1975], who found that the log of the periodogram, introduced in Section 1.4, provided an adequate estimate of the log-spectrum in these circumstances. Expressions for the bias, variance and distribution of the estimate of $\log \sigma_\epsilon^2(\theta)$ were also obtained. Thus, the suggested procedure is to form $Y_t(\theta)$ for various values of θ, to form estimates of $\log \sigma_\epsilon^2(\theta)$ from (10.5.24), and to use these estimates to find θ_0 using either (10.5.22) or (10.5.23).

10.6 Forecasting White Noise

Some time series analysts appear to believe that once a series has been filtered to produce a white noise residual, then modeling can stop since, as they believe, white noise cannot be forecast. As this belief is not necessarily true, further analysis may be worthwhile. As will be seen, there are a number of models that will produce "white noise" and yet produce series that are forecastable. Some of this section illustrates models introduced earlier in this chapter.

A white noise series is here defined as a series that has all theoretical autocorrelations zero, and an "empirical white noise series" is a series whose estimates of the autocorrelations all tend to zero as sample size becomes large. Pure white noise ϵ_t is a sequence of independent variables. It should be noted that these are linear and average properties. Of course, any stationary series forecast using an information set including the whole past of the series will produce one-step forecast errors that are white noise. However, it is always possible that there exists another series not used in the information set that if used would provide better forecasts, and so necessarily this extra series can help forecast the original forecast error.

Some examples of models that produce white noise and yet are potentially forecastable are

(i)   If $x_t \sim$ MA(1) so that

$$x_t = \epsilon_t + b\epsilon_{t-1}, \quad b < 0 \quad \text{and} \quad w_t = \alpha_1 x_t + \alpha_2(x_t^2 - 1)$$

$$\text{with} \quad \alpha_1^2/\alpha_2^2 = -2b/(1 + b^2)$$

then w_t has all autocorrelations zero. Thus, an instantaneous transformation can produce white noise from a series that is not white noise.

(ii)   Many bilinear models have theoretical autocorrelations that are zero. For example, if

$$x_t = \beta x_{t-2}\epsilon_{t-1} + \epsilon_t$$

with β var $\epsilon < 0.707$, then x_t is white noise, but since the model is invertible there exists a nonlinear forecast of x_{t+1} given x_{t-j}, $j \geqslant 0$.

(iii)   A nonlinear MA model, such as

$$x_t = \beta\epsilon_{t-1}\epsilon_{t-2} + \epsilon_t$$

where ϵ_t is Gaussian white noise, will look like a white noise but, even though it is not invertible, it can be forecast from regressions such as $x_t = \gamma x_{t-1}x_{t-2} + \epsilon_t$.

(iv)   A time-varying parameter MA(1) model, so that

$$x_t = \epsilon_t + b(t)\epsilon_{t-1}$$

where $b(t)$ is any process with (empirical) mean zero, will produce a series x_t that is empirical white noise.

These examples and others are proved in Granger [1983].

It is also possible to have deterministic processes that produce empirical white noise, as any pseudorandom variable generator illustrates. There are a number of simple deterministic models that have this property, for example,

$$x_t = 4x_{t-1}(1 - x_{t-1}) \quad \text{with} \quad 0 \leqslant x_0 \leqslant 1$$

or

$$x_t = 1 - 2|x_{t-1} - 1/2|$$

These so-called chaotic models have created a great deal of interest among physicists and mathematicians and increasingly so with economists. The existence of such models implies that any apparent white noise series "could" have been generated by a deterministic model and so, in principle, could be forecast perfectly. Such possibilities seem very unlikely in economics, given that economic variables arise from decisions by many individual economic agents. Nevertheless, tests will have to be devised for such chaotic series, using perhaps the suggestion by Wolf *et al.* [1985], but large amounts of data will be required and so such tests may be of little use in economics.

10.7 Predicting Variances: ARCH Models

If x_t is a time series, one is often interested in the conditional distribution of x_{t+1} given some information set I_t available at time t. Considering the first two moments of this distribution, the conditional mean

$$m_t = E[x_{t+1}|I_t] \qquad (10.7.1)$$

is the optimal one-stage forecast of x_{t+1} given I_t when using a least squares criterion, and the conditional variance is

$$h_t^2 = E\left[(x_{t+1} - m_t)^2|I_t\right] \qquad (10.7.2)$$

The majority of theoretical and applied work on modeling and forecasting concentrates on m_t as illustrated by the contents of most of this book. However, there is no reason to suppose that the variance h_t^2 cannot also be modeled using I_t. If a standard time-series model is constructed, it is quite common to find that the residuals are white noise but that squared residuals are not.

Denoting the one-step forecast errors by $\epsilon_t = x_t - m_{t-1}$, Engle [1982] has considered the specification

$$h_t^2 = \sum_{j=1}^{q} \gamma_j \epsilon_{t-j}^2 \qquad (10.7.3)$$

and called the resulting process autoregressive conditional heteroscedastic (ARCH). If the variance is changing through time in a predictable way, then the obvious advantage in modeling the variance is that by allowing for heteroscedasticity, better estimates of the parameters in m_t are achieved, and one should also obtain better estimates of the confidence intervals around the mean forecasts. Engle [1982] considers various forms for h_t, discusses their properties and estimation techniques, and uses a Lagrange multipler procedure to test for ARCH. He applied the technique to inflation data from the U.K. and found clear evidence of predictable variances: "the standard deviation of inflation increased from 0.6 percent to 1.5 percent over a few years, as the economy moved from the rather predictable sixties into the chaotic seventies."

A generalization to the bivariate ARCH model is presented by Engle, Granger, and Kraft [1984]. Two competing models of inflation—essentially a simple monetarist model and a mark-up model—have their forecasts combined using time-varying weights derived from bivariate ARCH equations and the results of Section 9.2.

The representation of h_t given in (10.7.3) can obviously be generalized to include observed driving variables. As an example, Granger, Robins, and Engle [1985] investigated the relationship between retail and wholesale prices, where the variances for each equation were given by (10.7.3) supplemented by squared lagged own and other prices and squared other forecast errors. Enriching the ARCH specification resulted in better models as measured by likelihood ratios and also gave a more interesting model interpretation. Wholesale prices were found to cause consumer prices both in mean and in variance. Squared consumer prices did not cause the variance in wholesale prices. If models were constructed ignoring ARCH, consumer prices appear to cause wholesale prices, but when ARCH was used, this causation becomes rather weak.

Because, in practice, variances do change through time in predictable ways, the use of ARCH models can be recommended, particularly when greater attention is paid to providing confidence intervals to forecasts than is currently the case. Further areas of clear importance for this development are those parts of economics, such as finance, that use variance as a measure of risk.

It might be noted that both simple ARCH and bilinear models have the property that an ARMA model fitted to such data will have residuals whose squares are not white noise. To differentiate between these two types of model, Weiss [1986] has combined them and considers a bilinear model with ARCH errors.

10.8 Forecasting Unobserved Components

Let X_t be a seasonal time series, generated by a member of the class of multiplicative seasonal ARIMA models, discussed in Sections 1.14 and 3.7. Much recent interest has been concentrated on the exploitation of the fitted ARIMA model in the development of a seasonal adjustment procedure, as discussed in Burman [1980] and Hillmer and Tiao [1982]. The given series is viewed as the sum of unobserved trend, seasonal, and irregular components, which, given the fitted model, can be estimated over the observation period. For example, suppose that X_t is generated by the model

$$(1 - B)(1 - B^{12})X_t = (1 + bB)(1 + b_s B^{12})\epsilon_t, \qquad (10.8.1)$$

for monthly data. Then the process can be decomposed as the sum

$$X_t = T_t + S_t + I_t \qquad (10.8.2)$$

In (10.8.2), the trend term T_t is such that its second difference is second-order moving average, the irregular component I_t is white noise, and the seasonal component is such that $\sum_{j=0}^{11} S_{t-j}$ is moving average of order eleven. Unfortunately, if such a decomposition exists, it is typically not unique. Rather, there will be an infinite number of possibilities, from which one must be chosen before a seasonally adjusted series can be found.

However, it is interesting to note, as shown by Box, Pierce, and Newbold [1986], that while the component processes are not unique, their optimal linear forecasts given X_{n-j} ($j \geq 0$) are unique. This result is quite general. For the model (10.8.1) with decomposition (10.8.2) it is straightforward to show that the optimal forecasts of the irregular component are

$$I_{n,h} = 0, \qquad \text{for all} \quad h$$

while those for the other components are

$$T_{n,h} = \alpha + \beta h, \qquad h = 1, 2, \ldots$$

and

$$S_{n,h} = \gamma_m; \qquad \sum_{m=1}^{12} \gamma_m = 0, \quad h = 1, 2, \ldots$$

where the γ_m are dummy variables, with $m = 1, \ldots, 12$ indexing the month of the year in which the observation X_{n+h} falls. These forecasts, then, take a particularly simple form, a simple linear trend, and the familiar seasonal dummy variables. Moreover, the parameters α, β, γ_m are independent of the choice of decomposition. Indeed, these parameters are easily found. Let $f_{n,h}$ be the optimal linear forecasts of X_{n+h}, given X_{n-j} ($j \geq 0$) and the model (10.8.1). Then, we can simply solve

$$f_{n,h} = T_{n,h} + S_{n,h}; \qquad h = 1, 2, \ldots, 13$$

to obtain these parameters. This yields

$$\beta = (f_{n,13} - f_{n,1})/12, \qquad \alpha = \sum_{h=1}^{12} f_{n,h} - 78\beta$$

and

$$\gamma_m = f_{n,m} - \alpha - \beta m; \qquad m = 1, 2, \ldots, 12$$

This same approach can be applied to many models in the seasonal ARIMA class.

Notice that this development suggests an alternative that is preferable to the common practice of working with seasonally adjusted data. Even if interest is exclusively in the nonseasonal component of a time series, that component is easily and efficiently predicted from a model fitted to the original data, rather than from one built for an adjusted series.

REFERENCES

ADAMS, F. G., and V. G. DUGGAL [1974], Anticipations variables in an econometric model: performance of the anticipations version of Wharton Mark III, *Int. Econ. Rev.* **15**, 267–284.

ADELMAN, I., and F. L. ADELMAN [1959], The dynamic properties of the Klein–Goldberger model, *Econometrica* **27**, 596–625.

AKAIKE, H. [1969], Fitting autoregressive models for prediction, *Ann. Inst. Stat. Math.* **21**, 243–247.

AKAIKE, H. [1974], Markovian representation of stochastic processes and its application to the analysis of autoregressive moving average processes, *Ann. Inst. Stat. Math.* **26**, 363–387.

AKAIKE, H. [1976], Canonical correlation analysis of time series and the use of an information criterion. *In* "Advances and Case Studies in System Identification" (R. Mehra and D. C. Lainiotis, eds.). New York: Academic Press.

ANDERSEN, L. C., and K. M. CARLSON [1974], St. Louis model revisited, *Int. Econ. Rev.* **15**, 305–327.

ANDERSON, B. D. O., and J. B. MOORE [1979], "Optimal Filtering," Englewood Cliffs, N.J.: Prentice-Hall.

ANDERSON, R. L. [1942], Distribution of the serial correlation coefficient, *Ann. Math. Stat.* **13**, 1–13.

ANDERSON, T. W. [1982], Some recent developments on the distribution of single equation estimators. *In* "Advances in Econometrics" (W. Hildenbrand, ed.). London and New York: Cambridge University Press.

ANDERSON, T. W., and T. SAWA [1973], Distributions of estimates of coefficients of a single equation in a simultaneous system and their asymptotic expansions, *Econometrica* **41**, 683–714.

ANDERSON, T. W., and T. SAWA [1979], Evaluation of the distribution function of the two stage least squares estimate, *Econometrica* **47**, 163–182.

ANSLEY, C. F. [1979], An algorithm for the exact likelihood of a mixed autoregressive–moving average process, *Biometrika* **66**, 59–65.

ANSLEY, C. F., and R. KOHN [1983], Exact likelihood of vector autoregressive–moving average process with missing or aggregated data, *Biometrika* **70**, 275–278.

ANSLEY, C. F., and P. NEWBOLD [1979a], On the finite sample distribution of residual autocorrelations in autoregressive–moving average models, *Biometrika* **66**, 547–553.

ANSLEY, C. F., and P. NEWBOLD [1979b], Multivariate partial autocorrelations, *Proc. Bus. Econ. Stat.*, *Am. Stat. Assoc.*, 349–353.

ANSLEY, C. F., and P. NEWBOLD [1980], Finite sample properties of estimators for autoregressive–moving average models, *J. Econometrics* **13**, 159–183.

ANSLEY, C. F., and P. NEWBOLD [1981], On the bias in estimates of forecast mean squared error, *J. Am. Stat. Assoc.* **76**, 569–578.

ANSLEY, C. F., W. A. SPIVEY, and W. J. WROBLESKI [1977], A class of transformations for Box–Jenkins seasonal models, *Appl. Stat.* **26**, 173–178.

AUERBACH, A. J. [1982], The index of leading indicators: "Measurement without theory," thirty-five years later, *Rev. Econ. Stat.* **64**, 589–595.

BACHELIER, L. [1900], Théorie de la spéculation, *Ann. Sci. Ecole. Norm. Sup., Paris, Ser. 3* **17**, 21–86.

BALL, R. J. (ed.) [1973], "The International Linkage of National Economic Models," Amsterdam: North Holland Publ. Co.

BARNARD, G. A. [1963], New methods of quality control, *J. Roy. Stat. Soc. A* **126**, 255–259.

BARRETT, J. F., and D. G. LAMPARD [1955], An expansion for some second order probability distributions and its application to noise problems, *I.R.E. Trans. PGIT*, **IT-1**, 10–15.

BARTLETT, M. S. [1946], On the theoretical specification of sampling properties of autocorrelated time series, *J. Roy. Stat. Soc. B* **8**, 27–41.

BATES, J. M., and C. W. J. GRANGER [1969], The combination of forecasts, *Oper. Res. Q.* **20**, 451–468.

BATTY, M. [1969], Monitoring an exponential smoothing forecasting system, *Oper. Res. Q.* **20**, 319–325.

BEGG, D. K. B. [1982], "The Rational Expectations Revolution in Macroeconomics: Theories and Evidence," Oxford: Philip Allan.

BEGUIN, J. M., C. GOURIEROUX, and A. MONFORT [1980], Identification of a mixed autoregressive–moving average process: the corner method, *In* "Time Series" (O. D. Anderson, ed.). Amsterdam: North Holland.

BELL, W. R., and S. C. HILLMER [1984], Issues involved with the seasonal adjustment of economic time series, *J. Bus. Econ. Stat.* **2**, 291–319.

BHATTACHARYYA, M. N., and A. P. ANDERSEN [1974], A post-sample diagnostic test for a time series model, Working paper, Dep. of Economics, Univ. of Queensland, Australia.

BLANC-LAPIERRE, A., and R. FORTET [1965], "Theory of Random Functions," New York: Gordon & Breach.

BOX, G. E. P., and D. R. COX [1964], An analysis of transformations, *J. Roy. Stat. Soc. B* **26**, 211–243.

BOX, G. E. P., and G. M. JENKINS [1962], Some statistical aspects of adaptive optimization and control, *J. Roy. Stat. Soc. B* **24**, 297–343.

BOX, G. E. P., and G. M. JENKINS [1970], "Time Series Analysis, Forecasting and Control," San Francisco: Holden Day.

BOX, G. E. P., and G. M. JENKINS [1973], Some comments on a paper by Chatfield and Prothero and on a review by Kendall, *J. Roy. Stat. Soc. A* **136**, 337–345.

BOX, G. E. P., G. M. JENKINS, and D. W. BACON [1967], Models for forecasting seasonal and non-seasonal time series. *In* "Spectral Analysis of Time Series" (B. Harris, ed.). New York: Wiley.

BOX, G. E. P., and P. NEWBOLD [1971], Some comments on a paper of Coen, Gomme, and Kendall, *J. Roy. Stat. Soc. A* **134**, 229–240.

BOX, G. E. P., and D. A. PIERCE [1970], Distribution of residual autocorrelations in autoregressive integrated moving average time series models, *J. Am. Stat. Assoc.* **65**, 1509–1526.

BOX, G. E. P., D. A. PIERCE, and P. NEWBOLD [1986], Estimating current trend and growth rates in seasonal time series, Working paper, Federal Reserve Board.

BOX, G. E. P., and G. C. TIAO [1975], Intervention analysis with applications to economic and environmental problems, *J. Am. Stat. Assoc.* **70**, 70–79.

BOX, G. E. P., and G. C. TIAO [1976], Comparison of forecast and actuality, *Appl. Stat.* **25**, 195–200.

BOX, G. E. P., and G. C. TIAO [1977], A canonical analysis of multiple time series, *Biometrika* **64**, 355–365.

BRILLINGER, D. R. [1981], "Time Series: Data Analysis and Theory," San Francisco: Holden Day.

BRILLINGER, D. R., and M. ROSENBLATT [1967a], Asymptotic theory of *k*-th order spectra,

In "Spectral Analysis of Time Series" (B. Harris, ed.). New York: Wiley.

BRILLINGER, D. R., and M. ROSENBLATT [1967b], Computation and interpretation of k th order spectra, *In* "Spectral Analysis of Time Series" (B. Harris, ed.). New York: Wiley.

BROWN, R. G. [1962], "Smoothing, Forecasting and Prediction of Discrete Time Series," Englewood Cliffs, New Jersey: Prentice Hall.

BRUBACHER, S. R., and G. T. WILSON [1975], Selecting data transformations for time series, Dept. of Mathematics, Univ. of Lancaster.

BURMAN, J. P. [1980], Seasonal adjustment by signal extraction, *J. Roy. Stat. Soc. A* **143**, 321–337.

CARTWRIGHT, P. A., and P. NEWBOLD [1983], A time series approach to the prediction of oil discoveries, *In* "Time Series Analysis: Theory and Practice 4" (O. D. Anderson, ed.). Amsterdam: North Holland.

CHAMBERLAIN, G. [1982], The general equivalence of Granger and Sims causality, *Econometrica* **50**, 569–582.

CHAN, W. Y. T., and K. F. WALLIS [1978], Multiple time series modelling: another look at the mink–muskrat interaction, *Appl. Stat.* **27**, 168–175.

CHATFIELD, C. [1979], Inverse autocorrelations, *J. Roy. Stat. Soc. A* **142**, 363–377.

CHATFIELD, C., and D. L. PROTHERO [1973], Box–Jenkins seasonal forecasting: problems in a case study, *J. Roy. Stat. Soc. A* **136**, 295–336.

CHOW, G. [1984], Random and changing coefficient models, *In* "Handbook of Econometrics, Vol. 2" (Z. Grilliches and M. D. Intriligator, eds.). Amsterdam: North Holland.

CHRIST, C. F. [1975], Judging the performance of econometric models of the U.S. economy, *Int. Econ. Rev.* **16**, 54–74.

CLEVELAND, W. S. [1972], The inverse autocorrelations of a time series and their applications, *Technometrics* **14**, 277–293.

COCHRANE, D., and G. H. ORCUTT [1949], Application of least squares regression to relationships containing autocorrelated error terms, *J. Am. Stat. Assoc.* **44**, 32–61.

COGGER, K. O. [1974], The optimality of general order exponential smoothing, *Oper. Res.* **22**, 858–867.

COOPER, D. M., and E. F. WOOD [1982], Identifying multivariate time series models, *J. Time Series Anal.* **3**, 153–164.

COOPER, J. P., and C. R. NELSON [1975], The *ex ante* prediction performance of the St. Louis and F.R.B.–M.I.T.–Penn. econometric models and some results on composite predictors, *J. Money, Credit, Banking* **7**, 1–32.

COOPER, R. L. [1972], The predictive performance of quarterly econometric models of the United States. *In* "Econometric Models of Cyclical Behavior" (B. G. Hickman, ed.). New York: Columbia Univ. Press.

CRAMER, H. [1961], On some classes of non-stationary stochastic processes. *In* "Proceedings of 4th Berkeley Symposium on Mathematical Statistics and Probability: Vol. 2, Contributions to Probability Theory," (J. Neyman, ed.). Berkeley: Univ. of California Press.

CROXTON, F. E., and D. J. COWDEN [1955], "Applied General Statistics," 2nd ed. Englewood Cliffs, New Jersey: Prentice Hall.

CURRIE, D. [1981], Some long run features of dynamic time series models, *Econ. J.* **91**, 704–715.

DAVIDSON, J. E. H., D. F. HENDRY, F. SRBA, and S. YEO [1978], Econometric modelling of the aggregate time series relationship between consumers' expenditure and income in the United Kingdom, *Econ. J.* **88**, 661–692.

DAVIES, N., and P. NEWBOLD [1979], Some power studies of a portmanteau test of time series model specification, *Biometrika* **66**, 153–155.

DAVIES, N., and P. NEWBOLD [1980a], Sample moments of the autocorrelations of moving average processes and a modification to Bartlett's asymptotic variance formula, *Comm. Stat. A* **9**, 1473–1481.

DAVIES, N., and P. NEWBOLD [1980b], Forecasting with misspecified models, *Appl. Stat.* **29**, 87–92.

DAVIES, N., M. B. PATE, and M. G. FROST [1974], Maximum autocorrelations for moving average processes, *Biometrika* 61, 199–200.

DAVIES, N., C. M. TRIGGS, and P. NEWBOLD [1977], Significance levels of the Box–Pierce portmanteau statistic in finite samples, *Biometrika* 64, 517–522.

DENT, W. [1977], Computation of the exact likelihood function of an ARIMA process, *J. Stat. Comp. and Simul.* 5, 193–206.

DHRYMES, P. J. [1971], "Distributed Lags: Problems of Formulation and Estimation," San Francisco: Holden Day.

DHRYMES, P. J. *et al.* [1972], Criteria for evaluation of econometric models, *Ann. Econ. Soc. Meas.* 1, 291–324.

DOAN, T., R. B. LITTERMAN, and C. A. SIMS [1984], Forecasting and conditional projection using realistic prior distributions, *Econometric Reviews* 3, 1–100.

DRAPER, N. R., and H. SMITH [1981], "Applied Regression Analysis," 2nd ed., New York: Wiley.

DURBIN, J. [1960], The fitting of time series models, *Rev. Inst. Int. Stat.* 28, 233–244.

DURBIN, J. [1970], Testing for serial correlation in least squares regression when some of the regressors are lagged dependent variables, *Econometrica* 38, 410–421.

DURBIN, J., and G. S. WATSON [1950], Testing for serial correlation in least squares regression I, *Biometrika* 37, 409–428.

DURBIN, J., and G. S. WATSON [1951], Testing for serial correlation in least squares regression II, *Biometrika* 38, 159–178.

DURBIN, J., and G. S. WATSON [1971], Testing for serial correlation in least squares regression III, *Biometrika* 58, 1–19.

ECKSTEIN, O. [1981], Econometric models for forecasting and policy analysis: the present state of the art. *In* "DRI Readings in Econometrics" (A. R. Sanderson, ed.), New York: McGraw Hill.

ECKSTEIN, O., E. W. GREEN, and A. SINAI [1974], The Data Resources model: uses, structure and analysis of the U.S. economy, *Int. Econ. Rev.* 15, 595–615.

ENGEL, E. M. R. A. [1984], A unified approach to the study of sums, products, time-aggregation and other functions of ARMA processes, *J. Time Series Anal.* 5, 159–171.

ENGLE, R. F. [1974], Band spectrum regression, *Int. Econ. Rev.* 15, 1–11.

ENGLE, R. F. [1978], Testing price equations for stability across spectral frequency bands, *Econometrica* 46, 869–882.

ENGLE, R. F. [1980], Exact maximum likelihood methods for dynamic regressions and band spectrum regressions, *Int. Econ. Rev.* 21, 391–407.

ENGLE, R. F. [1982], Autoregressive conditional heteroscedasticity with estimates of the variance of United Kingdom inflation, *Econometrica* 50, 987–1007.

ENGLE, R. F. [1985], Wald, likelihood ratio and Lagrange multiplier tests in econometrics. *In* "Handbook of Econometrics" (Z. Grilliches and M. D. Intriligator, eds.). Amsterdam: North Holland.

ENGLE, R. F., and R. L. GOODRICH [1985], Forecasting electricity demand: a comparison of methodologies, Project report, Electric Power Research Institute, Palo Alto, California.

ENGLE, R. F., C. W. J. GRANGER, and D. KRAFT [1984], Combining competing forecasts of inflation using a bivariate ARCH model, *J. Econ. Dynam. Control* 8, 151–165.

ENGLE, R. F., D. F. HENDRY, and J. F. RICHARD [1983]. Exogeneity, *Econometrica* 51, 277–304.

ENGLE, R. F., and M. WATSON [1981], A one-factor multivariate time series model of metropolitan wage rates, *J. Am. Stat. Assoc.* 76, 774–781.

ERICKSON, G. M. [1981], Using ridge regression to directly estimate lagged effects in marketing, *J. Am. Stat. Assoc.* 76, 766–773.

EVANS, M. K., Y. HAITOVSKY, and G. I. TREYZ [1972], An analysis of the forecasting properties of U.S. econometric models. *In* "Econometric Models of Cyclical Behavior" (B. G. Hickman, ed.). New York: Columbia Univ. Press.

EWAN, W. D., and K. W. KEMP [1960], Sampling inspection of continuous processes with no autocorrelation between successive results, *Biometrika* 47, 239–271.

FAIR, R. C. [1970], "A Short-Run Forecasting Model of the United States Economy," Lexington, Massachusetts: D. C. Heath.

FAIR, R. C. [1974], An evaluation of a short-run forecasting model, *Int. Econ. Rev.* 15, 285–303.

FAIR, R. C. [1979], An analysis of the accuracy of four macroeconometric models, *J. Polit. Econ.* 87, 701–718.

FAIR, R. C. [1984], "Specification, Evaluation and Analysis of Macroeconometric Models," Cambridge: Harvard University Press.

FIGLEWSKI, S. [1983], Optimal price forecasting using survey data, *Rev. Econ. Stat.* 65, 13–21.

FISHER, F. M. [1966], "The Identification Problem," New York: McGraw-Hill.

FROMM, G., L. R. KLEIN, and G. R. SCHINK [1972], Short- and long-term simulations with the Brookings model. *In* "Econometric Models of Cyclical Behavior" (B. G. Hickman, ed.). New York: Columbia Univ. Press.

GARDNER, E. S. [1985], Exponential smoothing: the state of the art, *J. Forecasting* 4, 1–28.

GARDNER, G., A. C. HARVEY, and G. D. A. PHILLIPS [1980], An algorithm for exact maximum likelihood estimation of autoregressive–moving average models by means of Kalman filtering, *Appl. Stat.* 29, 311–322.

GEWEKE, J. F. [1977], The dynamic factor analysis of economic time series models. *In* "Latent Variables in Socio-economic Models" (D. J. Aigner and A. S. Goldberger, eds.). Amsterdam: North Holland.

GEWEKE, J. [1982], Measurement of linear dependence and feedback between multiple time series, *J. Am. Stat. Assoc.* 77, 304–313.

GEWEKE, J., R. MEESE, and W. DENT [1983], Comparing alternative tests of causality in temporal systems, *J. Econometrics* 21, 161–194.

GLASBEY, C. A. [1982], A generalization of partial autocorrelations useful in identifying ARMA models, *Technometrics* 24, 223–228.

GODFREY, L. G. [1979], Testing the adequacy of a time series model, *Biometrika* 66, 67–72.

GODFREY, M. D., and H. KARREMAN [1967], A spectrum analysis of seasonal adjustment. *In* "Essays in Mathematical Economics in Honor of Oskar Morgenstern" (M. Shubik, ed.). New Jersey: Princeton Univ. Press.

GODOLPHIN, E. J., and J. M. UNWIN [1983], Evaluation of the covariance matrix for the maximum likelihood estimator of a Gaussian autoregressive moving average process, *Biometrika* 70, 279–284.

GOLDBERGER, A. S. [1962], Best linear unbiased prediction in the generalized linear regression model, *J. Am. Stat. Assoc.* 57, 369–375.

GOLDBERGER, A. S. [1964], "Econometric Theory," New York: Wiley.

GOLDFELD, S. M. [1972], Discussion of paper by R. L. Cooper. *In* "Econometric Models of Cyclical Behavior" (B. G. Hickman, ed.). New York: Columbia Univ. Press.

GRANGER, C. W. J. [1966], The typical spectral shape of an economic variable, *Econometrica* 34, 150–161.

GRANGER, C. W. J. [1969a], Prediction with a generalized cost of error function, *Oper. Res. Q* 20, 199–207.

GRANGER, C. W. J. [1969b], Investigating casual relations by econometric models and cross-spectral models, *Econometrica* 37, 424–438.

GRANGER, C. W. J. [1975], Some consequences of the valuation model when expectations are taken to be optimum forecasts, *J. Finance* 30, 135–145.

GRANGER, C. W. J. [1980], Testing for causality: a personal viewpoint, *J. Econ. Dynam. Control* 2, 329–352.

GRANGER, C. W. J. [1983], Forecasting white noise. *In* "Applied Time Series Analysis of Economic Data" (A. Zellner, ed.). Washington, D. C.: U.S. Department of Commerce, Bureau of the Census.

GRANGER, C. W. J. [1984], Co-integrated variables and error correction models, Working paper, Department of Economics, University of California, San Diego.

GRANGER, C. W. J. [1985a], Testing for causation in a decision science, Working paper, Department of Economics, University of California, San Diego.

GRANGER, C. W. J. [1985b], Implications of aggregation with common factors, Working paper, Department of Economics, University of California, San Diego.

GRANGER, C. W. J., and A. P. ANDERSEN [1978a], On the invertibility of time series models, *Stochastic Processes Applic.* **8**, 87–92.

GRANGER, C. W. J., and A. P. ANDERSEN [1978b], "An Introduction to Bilinear Time Series Models," Gottingen: Vandenhock and Ruprecht.

GRANGER, C. W. J., and R. F. ENGLE [1984], Applications of spectral analysis in econometrics. *In* "Handbook of Statistics, Vol. 5" (D. R. Brillinger and P. R. Krishnaiah, eds.). Amsterdam: Elsevier Science Publishers.

GRANGER, C. W. J., and R. F. ENGLE [1985], Dynamic model specification with equilibrium constraints: co-integration and error correction, Working paper, Department of Economics, University of California, San Diego.

GRANGER, C. W. J., and M. HATANAKA [1964], "Spectral Analysis of Economic Time Series," New Jersey: Princeton Univ. Press.

GRANGER, C. W. J., and A. O. HUGHES [1968], Spectral analysis of short series—a simulation study, *J. Roy. Stat. Soc. A* **131**, 83–99.

GRANGER, C. W. J., and A. O. HUGHES [1971], A new look at some old data: the Beveridge wheat price series, *J. Roy. Stat. Soc. A* **134**, 413–428.

GRANGER, C. W. J., and O. MORGENSTERN [1970], "Predictability of Stock Market Prices," Lexington, Massachusetts: D. C. Heath.

GRANGER, C. W. J., and M. MORRIS [1976], Time series modeling and interpretation, *J. Roy. Stat. Soc. A* **38**, 246–257.

GRANGER, C. W. J., and P. NEWBOLD [1973], Some comments on the evaluation of economic forecasts, *Appl. Econ.* **5**, 35–47.

GRANGER, C. W. J., and P. NEWBOLD [1974], Spurious regressions in econometrics, *J. Econometrics* **2**, 111–120.

GRANGER, C. W. J., and P. NEWBOLD [1975], Economic forecasting: the atheist's viewpoint, *In* "Modelling the Economy" (G. A. Renton, ed.). London: Heinemann Educational Books.

GRANGER, C. W. J., and P. NEWBOLD [1976], Forecasting transformed series, *J. Roy. Stat. Soc. B* **38**, 189–203.

GRANGER, C. W. J., and R. RAMANATHAN, [1984], Improved methods of combining forecasts, *J. Forecasting* **3**, 197–204.

GRANGER, C. W. J., R. P. ROBINS, and R. F. ENGLE [1985] Wholesale and retail prices: bivariate time series modeling with forecastable error variances, *In* "Model Reliability" (E. Kuh and R. Belsley, eds.). Cambridge: MIT Press.

GRANGER, C. W. J., and A. A. WEISS [1983], Time series analysis of error-correction models. *In* "Studies in Econometrics, Time Series and Multivariate Statistics" (S. Karlin, T. Amemiya and L. A. Goodman, eds.). New York: Academic Press.

GRAY, H. L., G. D. KELLEY, and D. D. MCINTIRE [1978], A new approach to ARMA modeling, *Comm. Stat. B* **7**, 1–77.

GREEN, G. R., M. LIEBENBERG, and A. A. HIRSCH [1972a], Short- and long-term simulations with the O.B.E. econometric model. *In* "Econometric Models of Cyclical Behavior" (B. G. Hickman, ed.). New York: Columbia Univ. Press.

GREEN, G. R., M. LIEBENBERG, and A. A. HIRSCH [1972b], Comment on paper by R. L. Cooper. *In* "Econometric Models of Cyclical Behavior" (B. G. Hickman, ed.). New York: Columbia Univ. Press.

HAGGAN, V., and T. OZAKI [1981], Modelling nonlinear vibrations using an amplitude-dependent autoregressive time series model, *Biometrika* **68**, 189–196.

HAITOVSKY, Y., and G. I. TREYZ [1972], Forecasts with quarterly macro-economic models, equation adjustments and benchmark predictions: the U.S. experience, *Rev. Econ. Stat.* **54**, 317–325.

HALLIN, M. [1980], Invertibility and generalized invertibility of time series models, *J. Roy. Stat. Soc. B* **42**, 210–212. Addendum [1981], **43**, 103.

HAMILTON, D. C., and D. G. WATTS [1978], Interpreting partial autocorrelation functions of seasonal time series models, *Biometrika* **65**, 135–140.

HANNAN, E. J. [1969], The identification of vector mixed autoregressive moving average systems, *Biometrika* **56**, 223–225.

HANNAN, E. J. [1970], "Multiple Time Series," New York: Wiley.

HANNAN, E. J. [1982], The estimation of the order of an ARMA process, *Ann. Statist.* **10**, 1071–1081.

HANNAN, E. J., and L. KAVALIERIS [1984], A method for autoregressive–moving average estimation, *Biometrika* **72**, 273–280.

HANNAN, E. J., and J. RISSANEN [1982], Recursive estimation of mixed autoregressive–moving average order, *Biometrika* **69**, 81–94. Correction [1983] **70**, 303.

HARRISON, P. J. [1965], Short-term sales forecasting, *Appl. Stat.* **14**, 102–139.

HARRISON, P. J. [1967], Exponential smoothing and short-term sales forecasting, *Manage. Sci.* **13**, 821–842.

HARRISON, P. J., and O. L. DAVIES [1964], The use of cumulative sum (Cusum) techniques for the control of routine forecasts of product demand, *Oper. Res.* **12**, 325–333.

HARRISON, P. J., and C. F. STEVENS [1971], A Bayesian approach to short term forecasting, *Oper. Res. Q.* **22** 341–362.

HART, B. L. [1942], Significance levels for the ratio of the mean square successive difference to the variance, *Ann. Math. Stat.* **13**, 445–447.

HATANAKA, M. [1974], A simple suggestion to improve the Mincer–Zarnowitz criterion for the evaluation of forecasts, *Ann. Econ. Soc. Meas.* 3, 521–524.

HAUGH, L. D. [1976], Checking the independence of two covariance-stationary time series: a univariate residual cross correlation approach, *J. Am. Stat. Assoc.* **71**, 378–385.

HENDRY, D. F. [1974], Stochastic specification in an aggregate demand model of the United Kingdom, *Econometrica* **42**, 559–578.

HENDRY, D. F. [1976], The structure of simultaneous equations estimators, *J. Econometrics* **4**, 51–88.

HENDRY, D. F. [1984], Present position and potential developments: some personal views. Time-series econometrics, *J. Roy. Statist. Soc. A* **147**, 327–339.

HENDRY, D. F., and G. E. MIZON [1978], Serial correlation as a convenient simplification, not a nuisance: a comment on a study of the demand for money by the Bank of England, *Econ. J.* **88**, 549–563.

HENDRY, D. F., and J. F. RICHARD [1983], The econometric analysis of economic time series, *Int. Stat. Rev.* **51**, 111–163.

HENDRY, D. F., and T. VON UNGERN-STERNBERG [1981], Liquidity and inflation effects on consumers' expenditure. *In* "Essays in the Theory and Measurement of Consumers' Behavior" (A. S. Deaton, ed.)., London and New York: Cambridge Univ. Press.

HICKMAN, B. G. (ed.) [1972], "Econometric Models of Cyclical Behavior," New York: Columbia Univ. Press.

HICKMAN, B. G. [1975], Project LINK in 1972: retrospect and prospect. *In* "Modelling the Economy" (G. A. Renton, ed.). London: Heinemann Educational Books.

HILLMER, S. C., and G. C. TIAO [1979], Likelihood function of stationary multiple autoregressive moving average models, *J. Am. Stat. Assoc.* **74**, 652–660.

HILLMER, S. C., and G. C. TIAO [1982], An ARIMA model-based approach to seasonal adjustment, *J. Am. Stat. Assoc.* **77**, 63–70.

HIRSCH, A. A., B. T. GRIMM, and G. V. L. NARASIMHAM [1976], Some multiplier and error characteristics of the BEA quarterly model. *In* "Econometric Model Performance" (L. R. Klein and E. Burmeister, eds.). Philadelphia: University of Pennsylvania Press.

HOLT, C. C. [1957], "Forecasting seasonals and trends by exponentially weighted moving averages," Carnegie Institute of Technology, Pittsburgh, Pennsylvania.

HOPWOOD, W. S., J. C. McKEOWN, and P. NEWBOLD [1981], Power transformations in time series models of quarterly earnings per share, *Accounting Rev.* **56**, 927–933.

HOPWOOD, W. S., J. C. McKEOWN, and P. NEWBOLD [1984], Time series forecasting models involving power transformations, *J. Forecasting* **3**, 57–61.

HOSKING, J. R. M. [1980a], Lagrange multiplier tests of time series models, *J. Roy. Stat. Soc. B* **42**, 170–181.

HOSKING, J. R. M. [1980b], The multivariate portmanteau statistic, *J. Am. Stat. Assoc.* **75**, 602–608.

HOSKING, J. R. M. [1981a], Lagrange multiplier tests of multivariate time series models, *J. Roy. Stat. Soc. B* **43**, 219–230.

HOSKING, J. R. M. [1981b], Equivalent forms of the multivariate portmanteau statistic, *J. Roy. Stat. Soc. B* **43**, 261–262.

HOTOPP, S. M. [1985], "Practical Methods in Multivariate Time Series Analysis," Ph.D. Thesis, University of Illinois, Department of Economics.

HOUTHAKKER, H. S., and L. D. TAYLOR [1966], "Consumer Demand in the United States," Cambridge: Harvard Univ. Press.

HOWREY, E. P. [1968], A spectrum analysis of the long-swing hypothesis, *Int. Econ. Rev.* **9**, 228–252.

HOWREY, E. P., L. R. KLEIN, and M. D. McCARTHY [1974], Notes on testing the predictive performance of econometric models, *Int. Econ. Rev.* **15**, 366–383.

HSIAO, C. [1979], Autoregressive modeling of Canadian money and income data, *J. Am. Stat. Assoc.* **74**, 553–560.

HYMANS, S. [1973], On the use of leading indicators to predict cyclical turning points, *Brookings Papers on Economic Activity* **2**, 339–384.

IBRAHIM, I. B., and T. OTSUKI [1976], Forecasting G. N. P. components using the method of Box and Jenkins, *Southern Econ. J.* **42**, 461–470.

JANACEK, G. [1975], Estimation of the minimum mean squared error of prediction, *Biometrika* **62**, 175–180.

JENKINS, G. M. [1979], "Practical Experiences with Modelling and Forecasting Time Series," Lancaster: Gwilym Jenkins and Partners.

JENKINS, G. M. and A. S. ALAVI [1981], Some aspects of modelling and forecasting multivariate time series, *J. Time Series Anal.* **2**, 1–47.

JOYEUX, R. [1979], "Harmonic Processes in Economics," Ph.D. Thesis, University of California, San Diego, Department of Economics.

JUDGE, G. G., W. E. GRIFFITHS, R. C. HILL, H. LUTKEPOHL, and T. C. LEE [1985], "The Theory and Practice of Econometrics," 2nd Ed., New York: Wiley.

KALMAN, R. E. [1960], A new approach to linear filtering and prediction problems, *J. Basic Eng.* **82**, 35–45.

KALMAN, R. E. [1963], New methods in Wiener filtering theory. *In* "Proceeding of First Symposium on Engineering Application of Random Function Theory and Probability" (J. L. Bogdanoff and F. Kozin, eds.). New York: Wiley.

KANG, H. [1981], Necessary and sufficient conditions for causality testing in multivariate ARMA models, *J. Time Series Anal.* **2**, 95–101.

KENDALL, M. G. [1954], "Exercises in Theoretical Statistics," London: Griffin.

KENDALL, M. G., and A. STUART [1963], "The Advanced Theory of Statistics," Vol. I, London: Griffin.

KLEIN, L. R. [1960], The efficiency of estimation in econometric models, Cowles Foundation Paper 157, Yale Univ., New Haven, Connecticut.

KLEIN, L. R. [1971a], "An Essay on the Theory of Economic Prediction," Chicago: Markham.

KLEIN, L. R. [1971b], Forecasting and policy evaluation using large scale econometric models: the state of the art. *In* "Frontiers of Quantitative Economics" (M. D. Intriligator, ed.). Amsterdam: North Holland Publ. Co.

KLEIN, L. R., and A. S. GOLDBERGER [1955], "An Econometric Model of the United States 1929–1952," Amsterdam: North Holland.

KOHN, R. [1982], When is an aggregate of a time series efficiently forecast by its past?, *J. Econometrics* **18**, 337–349.

KOLMOGOROV, A. [1939], Sur l'interpolation et l'extrapolation des suites stationnaires, *C. R. Acad. Sci. Paris* **208**, 2043–2045.

KOLMOGOROV, A. [1941a], Interpolation und Extrapolation von stationaren zufalligen Folgen, *Bull. Acad. Sci. (Nauk) U.R.S.S. Ser. Math.* **5**, 3–14.

KOLMOGOROV, A. [1941b], Stationary sequences in Hilbert space (in Russian), *Bull. Math. Univ. Moscow* **2** (6), 1–40.

KOOPMANS, L. H. [1974], "The Spectral Analysis of Time Series," New York: Academic Press.

LABYS, W. C., and C. W. J. GRANGER [1970], "Speculation, Hedging and Forecasts of Commodity Prices," Lexington, Massachusetts: D. C. Heath.

LEDOLTER, J. [1978], The analysis of multivariate time series applied to problems in hydrology, *J. Hydrol.* **36**, 327–352.

LEDOLTER, J., and G. E. P. BOX [1978], Conditions for the optimality of exponential smoothing forecast procedures, *Metrika* **25**, 77–93.

LEHMANN, E. L. [1959], "Testing Statistical Hypotheses," New York: Wiley.

L'ESPERANCE, W. D., and D. TAYLOR [1975], The power of four tests of autocorrelation in the linear regression model, *J. Econometrics* **3**, 1–21.

LEWIS, P. A. W. (ed.) [1972], "Stochastic Point Processes," New York: Wiley.

LI, W. K., and A. I. MCLEOD [1981], Distribution of the residual autocorrelations in multivariate ARMA time series models, *J. Roy. Stat. Soc. B* **43**, 231–239.

LIU, S. I., and L. LIU [1985], Theory of bilinear time series models, *Comm. Stat. A* **14**,

LJUNG, G. M., and G. E. P. BOX [1978], On a measure of lack of fit in time series models, *Biometrika* **65**, 297–303.

LJUNG, G. M., and G. E. P. BOX [1979], The likelihood function of stationary auto-regressive–moving average models, *Biometrika* **66**, 265–270.

LOEVE, M. [1963], "Probability Theory," Princeton: Van Nostrand.

LONGBOTTOM, J. A., and S. HOLLY [1985], The role of time series analysis in the evaluation of econometric models, *J. Forecasting* **4**, 75–87.

LUCAS, R. E., and T. J. SARGENT [1981], "Rational Expectations and Econometric Practice," Minneapolis: University of Minnesota Press.

LUTKEPOHL, H. [1985], Comparison of predictors for temporally and contemporaneously aggregated multivariate time series, Working paper, Department of Economics, University of California, San Diego.

MAKRIDAKIS, S., A. ANDERSEN, R. CARBONE, R. FILDES, M. HIBON, R. LEWANDOWSKI, J. NEWTON, E. PARZEN, and R. WINKLER [1982], The accuracy of extrapolation (time series) methods: results of a forecasting competition, *J. Forecasting* **1**, 111–153.

MAKRIDAKIS, S., and M. HIBON [1979], Accuracy of forecasting: an empirical investigation, *J. Roy. Stat. Soc. A* **142**, 97–145.

MALINVAUD, E. [1966], "Statistical Methods of Econometrics," Amsterdam: North Holland.

MANN, H. B., and A. WALD [1943], On the statistical treatment of linear stochastic difference equations, *Econometrica* **11**, 173–220.

MARAVALL, A. [1983], An application of nonlinear time series forecasting, *J. Bus. Econ. Stat.* **1**, 66–74.

MARIANO, R. S. [1982], Analytical small sample distribution theory in econometrics: the simultaneous equations case, *Int. Econ. Rev.* **23**, 503–534.

MARIANO, R. S., and T. SAWA [1972], The exact finite-sample distribution of the limited information maximum likelihood estimator in the case of two included exogenous variables, *J. Am. Stat. Assoc.* **67**, 159–163

MARQUARDT, D. W. [1963], An algorithm for least squares estimation of nonlinear parameters, *J. Soc. Ind. Appl. Math.* **2**, 431–441.

MARTIN, R. S., and J. H. WILKINSON [1965], Symmetric decomposition of positive definite band matrices, *Numer. Math.* **7**, 355–361.

McCARTHY, M. D. [1972], Discussion of paper by R. L. Cooper. *In* "Econometric Models of Cyclical Behavior" (B. G. Hickman, ed.). New York: Columbia Univ. Press.

McLEOD, A. I. [1975], Derivation of the theoretical autocovariance function of autoregressive moving average time series, *Appl. Stat.* **24**, 255–256. Correction [1977], **26**, 194.

McLEOD, A. I. [1978], On the distribution and application of residual autocorrelations in Box–Jenkins models, *J. Roy. Stat. Soc. B* **40**, 296–302.

McNEES, S. K. [1979], The accuracy of macroeconometric models and forecasts of the U.S. economy. *In* "Economic Modelling" (P. Ormerod, ed.). London: Heinemann Educational Books.

McNEES, S. K. [1981], The recent record of thirteen forecasters, *New England Econ. Rev.* Sept./Oct., 5–21.

McNEES, S. K. [1982], The role of macroeconometric models in forecasting and policy analysis in the United States, *J. Forecasting* **1**, 37–48.

MEISELMAN, D. [1962], "The Term Structure of Interest Rates," Englewood Cliffs, New Jersey: Prentice Hall.

MINCER, J., and V. ZARNOWITZ [1969], The evaluation of economic forecasts. *In* "Economic Forecasts and Expectations" (J. Mincer, ed.). New York: National Bureau of Economic Research.

MOORE, G. H., and J. SHISKIN [1967], "Indicators of Business Expansions and Contractions," New York: National Bureau of Economic Research.

MUTH, J. F. [1960], Optimal properties of exponentially weighted forecasts, *J. Am. Stat. Assoc.* **55**, 299–306.

MUTH, J. F. [1961], Rational expectations and the theory of price movements, *Econometrica* **29**, 315–335.

NAYLOR, T. H., T. G. SEAKS, and D. W. WICHERN [1972], Box–Jenkins methods: an alternative to econometric models, *Rev. Inst. Int. Stat.* **40**, 123–137.

NEAVE, H. R. [1970], An improved formula for the asymptotic variance of spectrum estimates, *Ann. Math. Stat.* **41**, 70–77.

NEAVE, H. R. [1972], Observations on "Spectral analysis of short series—a simulation study" by Granger and Hughes, *J. Roy. Stat. Soc. A* **135**, 393–405.

NEFTCI, S. [1979], Lead–lag relations, exogeneity and prediction of economic time series, *Econometrica* **47**, 104–113.

NELSON, C. R. [1972a], "The Term Structure of Interest Rates," New York: Basic Books.

NELSON, C. R. [1972b], The prediction performance of the F.R.B.–M.I.T.–PENN model of the U.S. economy, *Am. Econ. Rev.* **62**, 902–917.

NELSON, C. R., and G. W. SCHWERT [1982], Tests for predictive relationships between time series variables: a Monte Carlo investigation, *J. Am. Stat. Assoc.* **77**, 11–18.

NELSON, H. L., and C. W. J. GRANGER [1979], Experience with using the Box–Cox transformation when forecasting economic time series, *J. Econometrics* **10**, 57–69.

NERLOVE, M. [1964], Spectral analysis of seasonal adjustment procedures, *Econometrica* **32**, 241–286.

NERLOVE, M., D. M. GRETHER, and J. L. CARVALHO [1979], "Analysis of Economic Time Series," New York: Academic Press.

NERLOVE, M., and S. WAGE [1964], On the optimality of adaptive forecasting, *Manage. Sci.* **10**, 207–229.

NERLOVE, M., and K. F. WALLIS [1966], The use of the Durbin–Watson statistic in inappropriate situations, *Econometrica* **34**, 235–238.

NEWBOLD, P. [1973a], Forecasting Methods, Civil Service College Occasional Papers 18, London: H.M.S.O.

NEWBOLD, P. [1973b], Bayesian estimation of Box–Jenkins transfer function–noise models, *J. Roy. Stat. Soc.* B **35**, 323–336.

NEWBOLD, P. [1974], The exact likelihood function for a mixed autoregressive–moving average process, *Biometrika* **61**, 423–426.

NEWBOLD, P. [1978], Feedback induced by measurement errors, *Int. Econ. Rev.* **19**, 787–791.

NEWBOLD, P. [1980], The equivalence of two tests of time series model adequacy, *Biometrika* **67**, 463–465.

NEWBOLD, P. [1982], Causality testing in economics. *In* "Time Series Analysis: Theory and Practice 1" (O. D. Anderson, ed.), Amsterdam: North Holland.

NEWBOLD, P. [1983], Model checking in time series analysis. *In* "Applied Time Series Analysis of Economic Data" (A. Zellner, ed.). Washington D.C.: U.S. Department of Commerce, Bureau of the Census.

NEWBOLD, P., and T. BOS [1982], On the use of the Hannan–Rissanen criterion in time series model selection, Department of Economics, University of Illinois.

NEWBOLD, P., and N. DAVIES [1978], Error mis-specification and spurious regressions, *Int. Econ. Review* **19**, 513–519.

NEWBOLD, P., and C. W. J. GRANGER [1974], Experience with forecasting univariate time series and the combination of forecasts, *J. Roy. Stat. Soc.* A **137**, 131–146.

NEWBOLD, P., and S. M. HOTOPP [1986], Testing causality using efficiently parameterized vector ARMA models, *Appl. Math. Comput.*

NEWTON, H. J., and M. PAGANO [1983], The finite memory prediction of covariance–stationary time series, *SIAM J. Sci. Stat. Comput.* **4**, 330–339.

NICHOLLS, D. F., and A. D. HALL [1979], The exact likelihood function of multivariate autoregressive–moving average models, *Biometrika* **66**, 259–264.

NICHOLLS, D. F., and B. G. QUINN [1982], "Random Coefficient Autoregressive Models," Berlin: Springer-Verlag.

PARZEN, E. [1961], Mathematical considerations in the estimation of spectra, *Technometrics* **3**, 167–190.

PARZEN, E. [1967], "Time Series Analysis Papers," San Francisco: Holden Day.

PAYNE, D. J. [1973], "The determination of regression relationships using stepwise regression techniques," Ph.D. Thesis, Dept. of Mathematics, Univ. of Nottingham.

PHILLIPS, P. C. B. [1985], Understanding spurious regressions in econometrics, Cowles Foundation Discussion Paper 757, Yale University.

PIERCE, D. A. [1972], Residual correlations and diagnostic checking in dynamic disturbance time series models, *J. Am. Stat. Assoc.* **67**, 636–640.

PIERCE, D. A. [1977], Relationships—and the lack thereof—between economic time series, with special reference to money and interest rates, *J. Am. Stat. Assoc.* **72**, 11–22.

PIERCE, D. A., and L. D. HAUGH [1977], Causality in temporal systems: characterizations and a survey, *J. Econometrics* **5**, 265–294.

POSKITT, D. S., and A. R. TREMAYNE [1980], Testing the specification of a fitted ARMA model, *Biometrika* **67**, 359–363.

POSKITT, D. S., and A. R. TREMAYNE [1981a], An approach to testing linear time series models, *Ann. Statist.* **9**, 974–986.

POSKITT, D. S., and A. R. TREMAYNE [1981b], A time series application of the use of Monte Carlo methods to compare statistical tests, *J. Time Series Anal.* **2**, 263–277.

POSKITT, D. S., and A. R. TREMAYNE [1982], Diagnostic tests for multiple time series models, *Ann. Statist.* **10**, 114–120.

PRIESTLEY, M. B. [1965], Evolutionary spectra and non-stationary processes, *J. Roy. Stat. Soc. B* **27**, 204–237.

PRIESTLEY, M. B. [1980], State dependent models: a general approach to non-linear time series analysis, *J. Time Series Anal.* **1**, 47–72.

PRIESTLEY, M. B. [1981], "Spectral Analysis and Time Series," New York: Academic Press.

QUENOUILLE, M. H. [1949], Approximate tests of correlation in time series, *J. Roy. Stat. Soc. B* **11**, 68–84.

QUENOUILLE, M. H. [1957], "The Analysis of Multiple Time Series," London: Griffin.

RAO, C. R. [1948], Large sample tests of statistical hypotheses concerning several parameters with applications to problems of estimation, *Proc. Cambridge Philos. Soc.* **44**, 50–59.

REID, D. J. [1969], "A comparative study of time series prediction techniques on economic data," Ph.D. Thesis, Dept. of Mathematics, Univ. of Nottingham.

REINSEL, G. [1983], Some results on multivariate autoregressive index models, *Biometrika* **70**, 145–156.

RENTON, G. A. (ed.). [1975], "Modelling the Economy," London: Heinemann Educational Books.

RICHARDSON, D. H. [1968], The exact distribution of a structural coefficient, *J. Am. Stat. Assoc.* **63**, 1214–1226.

ROBINSON, P. M. [1984], Robust nonparametric autoregression. *In* "Robust and Non-linear Time Series Analysis" (J. Franke *et al.*, eds.), Berlin and New York: Springer-Verlag.

ROSENBLATT, M. [1957], Some purely deterministic processes, *J. Math. Mech.* **6**, 801–810.

SALMON, M. [1982], Error correction mechanisms, *Econ. J.*, **92**, 615–629.

SARGAN, J. D. [1964], Wages and prices in the United Kingdom: a study in econometric methodology, *In* "Econometric Analysis in National Economic Planning" (P. E. Hart, G. Mills, and J. N. Whittaker, eds.). London: Butterworth.

SARGAN, J. D. [1980], Some tests of dynamic specification for a single equation, *Econometrica* **48**, 879–897.

SARGENT, T. J., and C. A. SIMS [1977], Business cycle modeling without pretending to have too much a priori economic theory. *In* "New Methods in Business Cycle Research" (C. A. Sims, ed.). Minneapolis: Federal Reserve Bank.

SAWA, T. [1969], The exact distribution of a structural coefficient, *J. Am. Stat. Assoc.* **64**, 923–937.

SCHUSTER, A. [1898], On the investigation of hidden periodicities, *Terr. Magn. Atmos. Electr.* **3**, 13–41.

SHEPP, L. A., D. SLEPIAN, and A. O. WYNER [1980], On prediction of moving average processes, *Bell. Syst. Tech. J.* **59**, 367–415.

SHEPPARD, D. K. [1971], "The Growth and Role of U.K. Financial Institutions 1880–1962," London: Methuen.

SHIBATA, R. [1976], Selection of the order of an autoregressive model by Akaike's information criterion, *Biometrika* **63**, 117–126.

SILVEY, S. D. [1959], The Lagrangian multiplier test, *Ann. Math. Stat.* **30**, 389–407.

SIMS, C. A. [1972], Money, income and causality, *Am. Econ. Rev.* **62**, 540–552.

SIMS, C. A. [1980], Macroeconomics and reality, *Econometrica* **48**, 1–48.

SIMS, C. A. [1981], An autoregressive index model for the U.S., 1948–1975. *In* "Large-scale Macroeconometric Models" (J. Kmenta and J. B. Ramsey, eds.). Amsterdam: North Holland.

SINGLETON, K. J. [1980], Real and nominal factors in the cyclical behavior of interest rates, output and money, Working paper, Carnegie-Mellon University.

SNORRASON, A., P. NEWBOLD, and W. H. C. MAXWELL [1984], Multiple input transfer function–noise modeling of river flow. *In* "Frontiers in Hydrology" (W. H. C. Maxwell and L. R. Beard, eds.). Littleton, Colorado: Water Resources Publications.

SPOHN, W. [1983], Probabilistic causality: from Hume via Suppes to Granger. *In* "Causalita e Modelli Probabilistici" (M. C. Galavotti and G. Gambetta, eds.). Bologna: CLUEB Editrice.

STEIN, C. M. [1974], Multiple regressions. *In* "Contributions to Probability and Statistics: Essays in Honor of Harold Hotelling" (I. Oklin, ed.). Palo Alto, California: Stanford Univ. Press.

STOCK, J. H. [1985], Asymptotic properties of least squares estimators of co-integrating vectors, Working paper, Harvard University.

SUBBA RAO, T. [1981], On the theory of bilinear time series models, *J. Roy. Stat. Soc. B* **43**, 244–255.

SUBBA RAO, T., and M. M. GABR [1980], A test for linearity of stationary time series, *J. Time Series Anal.* **1**, 145–158.

SUITS, D. B. [1962], Forecasting and analysis with an econometric model, *Am. Econ. Rev.* **52**, 104–132.

TAYLOR, W. E. [1983], On the relevance of finite sample distribution theory, *Econometric Rev.* **2**, 1–139.

THEIL, H. [1958], "Economic Forecasts and Policy," Amsterdam: North Holland.

THEIL, H. [1966], "Applied Economic Forecasting," Amsterdam: North Holland.

THEIL, H., and S. WAGE [1964], Some observations on adaptive forecasting, *Manage. Sci.* **10**, 198–206.

TIAO, G. C., and G. E. P. BOX [1981], Modeling multiple time series with applications, *J. Am. Stat. Assoc.* **76**, 802–816.

TIAO, G. C., and R. S. TSAY [1983], Multiple time series modeling and extended sample cross-correlations, *J. Bus. Econ. Stat.* **1**, 43–56.

TINBERGEN, J. [1939], "Statistical Testing of Business Cycle Theories," Vol. II, Business Cycles in the United States of America 1919–1932. Geneva: League of Nations.

TONG, H., and K. S. LIM [1980], Threshold autoregression, limit cycles and cyclical data, *J. Roy. Stat. Soc. B* **42**, 245–292.

TRIGG, D. W. [1964], Monitoring a forecasting system, *Oper. Res. Q* **15**, 271–274.

TRIGG, D. W., and A. D. LEACH [1967], Exponential smoothing with an adaptive response rate, *Oper. Res. Q* **18**, 53–59.

TSAY, R. S., and G. C. TIAO [1984], Consistent estimates of autoregressive parameters and extended sample autocorrelation function for stationary and nonstationary ARMA models, *J. Am. Stat. Assoc.* **79**, 84–96.

VAN HORNE, J. C. [1971], "Financial Management and Policy," 2nd ed. Englewood Cliffs, New Jersey: Prentice Hall.

VELU, R. P., G. C. REINSEL, and D. W. WICHERN [1986], Reduced rank models for multiple time series, *Biometrika* **73**, 105–118.

VINOD, H. D., and B. S. HUI [1983], A canonical correlations approach to state vector analysis of capital appropriations and expenditures. *In* "Time Series Analysis: Theory and Practice 4" (O. D. Anderson, ed.). Amsterdam: North Holland.

WAGLE, B., J. Q. G. H. RAPPOPORT, and V. A. DOWNES [1968], A program for short-term sales forecasting, *The Statistician* **18**, 141–147.

WALKER, G. [1931], On periodicity in series of related terms, *Proc. Roy. Soc. London A* **131**, 518–532.

WALL, K. D., A. J. PRESTON, J. W. BRAY, and M. H. PESTON [1975], Estimates of a simple control model of the U.K. economy. *In* "Modelling the Economy" (G. A. Renton, ed.). London: Heinemann Educational Books.

WALLIS, K. F. [1972], Testing for fourth order autocorrelation in quarterly regression equations, *Econometrica* **40**, 617–636.

WALLIS, K. F. [1977], Multiple time series analysis and the final form of econometric models, *Econometrica* **45**, 1481–1497.

WALLIS, K. F. [1980], Econometric implications of the rational expectations hypothesis, *Econometrica* **48**, 49–73.

WATSON, M. W. [1982], A test for regression coefficient stability when a parameter is identified only under the alternative, Discussion Paper 906, Harvard Institute of Economic Research.

WEISS, A. A. [1986], ARCH and bilinear time series models: comparison and combination, *J. Bus. Econ. Stat.* **4**, 59–70.

WHITTLE, P. [1953], Estimation and information in stationary time series, *Ark. Mat. Astron. Fys.* **2**, 423–434.

WHITTLE, P. [1963], "Prediction and Regulation," London: English Universities Press.

WICHERN, D. W. [1973], The behavior of the sample autocorrelation function for an integrated moving average process, *Biometrika* **60**, 235–239.

WILKS, S. S. [1962], "Mathematical Statistics." New York: Wiley.

WILSON, G. T. [1969], Factorization of the generating function of a pure moving average process, *SIAM J. Num. Anal.* **6**, 1–7.

WILSON, G. T. [1973], The estimation of parameters in multivariate time series models, *J. Roy. Stat. Soc. B* **35**, 76–85.

WINKLER, R. L., and S. MAKRIDAKIS [1983], The combination of forecasts, *J. Roy. Stat. Soc. A* **146**, 150–157.

WINTERS, P. R. [1960], Forecasting sales by exponentially weighted moving averages, *Manage. Sci.* **6**, 324–342.

WOLD, H. [1954], "A Study in the Analysis of Stationary Time Series," 2nd ed. Uppsala: Almquist and Wicksell.

WOLF, A., J. B. SWIFT, H. L. SWINNEY, and J. D. VASTRANO [1985], Determining Lyapunov exponents from a time series, *Physica D* **16**, 285–317.

WOODWARD, W. A., and H. L. GRAY [1981], On the relationship between the S array and the Box–Jenkins method of ARMA model identification, *J. Am. Stat. Assoc.* **76**, 579–587.

YOO, S. [1986], Multi-cointegrated time series and generalized error correction models, Working paper, Department of Economics, University of California, San Diego.

YULE, G. U. [1926], Why do we sometimes get nonsense correlations between time series?—a study in sampling and the nature of time series, *J. Roy. Stat. Soc.* **89**, 1–64.

YULE, G. U. [1927], On a method for investigating periodicities in disturbed series with special reference to Wolfer's sunspot numbers, *Phil. Trans. Roy. Soc. London A* **226**, 267–298.

ZARNOWITZ, V. and C. BOSCHAN [1975], Cyclical indicators: an evaluation and new leading indexes, Business Conditions Digest, U.S. Department of Commerce, Bureau of Economic Analysis.

ZELLNER, A. (ed.) [1978], "Seasonal Analysis of Economic Time Series," Washington, D.C.: U.S. Department of Commerce, Bureau of the Census.

ZELLNER, A., and F. PALM [1974], Time series analysis and simultaneous equation econometric models, *J. Econometrics* **2**, 17–54.

AUTHOR INDEX

SUBJECT INDEX

A

Accumulated series, 2
Advertising expenditures, 253, 254
Aggregates, forecasting, 230
AIC criterion, 82, 86, 118, 256, 259, 301
Aitken's estimator, 191
Aliasing, 57
Anticipations variables, 205
ARCH models, 314, 315
ARIMA, 52, 57, 66, 76
ARMA, 55, 57, 67
AR(p), 17
Autocorrelations, 5, 10, 16, 20, 23, 78
Autocorrelation generating function, 89
Autocovariance, 5, 7, 14
Autoregressive conditional heteroscedastic model, 314
Autoregressive model, 13

B

Backward operator, 6
Band spectrum regression, 72
Bayesian AR model, 259
Bayes' theorem, 201
Best linear unbiased predictor, 190
BIC criterion, 118
Bilinear model, 305, 315
Bispectrum, 73
Bivariate models, 235
Black box, 33
Box–Cox transformation, 118, 308
Box–Jenkins models, 226
Box–Jenkins method, 163, 164, 182, 184–186, 265, 266, 269, 270–275, 280

Bureau of the Census, 70
Business Conditions Digest, 295
Business cycle, 294

C

Canonical correlation analysis, 301
Causality, 219, 220, 236, 298
Causality, tests, 259, 296
Change in model structure, 103
Chaotic models, 314
Cholesky decomposition, 92
Cochrane–Orcut procedure, 214
Coherence, 59, 60
Co-integration, 224, 225
Co-integration, tests, 262
Combination of forecasts, 152, 181, 266, 281
COMFAC analysis, 194, 195
Common factor, 91, 218, 231
Conditional prediction, 191
Continuous time series, 2
Convolution, 7
Correlogram, 5, 6, 42
Cost function, 121, 124, 277, 278
Covariance, 3
Cramer's representation, 51, 53, 59
Cross-correlations, 246
Cross-spectrum, 58, 66
Cusum techniques, 175
Cycles, 10

D

Data transformation, 306
Decomposition of squared error, 285, 286
Demand for electricity, 302